THE KEY

STUDENT STUDY GUIDE

Mathematics 10 Combined

S0-AWM-401

THE KEY student study guide is designed to help students achieve success in school. The content in each study guide is 100% curriculum aligned and serves as an excellent source of material for review and practice. To create this book, teachers, curriculum specialists, and assessment experts have worked closely to develop the instructional pieces that explain each of the key concepts for the course. The practice questions and sample tests have detailed solutions that show problem-solving methods, highlight concepts that are likely to be tested, and point out potential sources of errors. **THE KEY** is a complete guide to be used by students throughout the school year for reviewing and understanding course content, and to prepare for assessments.

Rao,Gautam,1961 –
THE KEY – Math 10 Combined Alberta
ISBN: 978-1-77044-423-2

1. Mathematics – Juvenile Literature. I. Title

Printed by
Castle Rock Research Corporation
2000 First & Jasper
10065 Jasper Avenue
Edmonton, AB T5J 3B1

10 9 8 7 6 5

Publisher
Gautam Rao

Contributors
Ron Zukowski

Reviewers
Kevin Barabash

Dedicated to the memory of Dr. V. S. Rao

Not for Reproduction

THE KEY

THE KEY consists of the following sections:

KEY Tips for Being Successful at School gives examples of study and review strategies. It includes information about learning styles, study schedules, and note taking for test preparation.

Class Focus includes a unit on each area of the curriculum. Units are divided into sections, each focusing on one of the specific expectations, or main ideas, that students must learn about in that unit. Examples, definitions, and visuals help to explain each main idea. Practice questions on the main ideas are also included. At the end of each unit is a test on the important ideas covered. The practice questions and unit tests help students identify areas they know and those they need to study more. They can also be used as preparation for tests and quizzes. Most questions are of average difficulty, though some are easy and some are hard—the harder questions are called *Challenger Questions*. Each unit is prefaced by a **Table of Correlations**, which correlates questions in the unit to the specific curriculum expectations. Answers and solutions are found at the end of each unit.

KEY Strategies for Success on Tests helps students get ready for tests. It shows students different types of questions they might see, word clues to look for when reading them, and hints for answering them.

Practice Tests includes one to three tests based on the entire course. They are very similar to the format and level of difficulty that students may encounter on final tests. In some regions, these tests may be reprinted versions of official tests, or reflect the same difficulty levels and formats as official versions. This gives students the chance to practice using real-world examples. Answers and complete solutions are provided at the end of the section.

For the complete curriculum document (including specific expectations along with examples and sample problems), visit https://education.alberta.ca/teachers/program.aspx.

THE KEY Study Guides are available for many courses. Check www.castlerockresearch.com for a complete listing of books available for your area.

For information about any of our resources or services, please call Castle Rock Research at 1.800.840.6224 or visit our website at http://www.castlerockresearch.com.

At Castle Rock Research, we strive to produce an error-free resource. If you should find an error, please contact us so that future editions can be corrected.

CONTENTS

KEY Tips for being Successful at School

KEY TIPS FOR BEING SUCCESSFUL AT SCHOOL

KEY FACTORS CONTRIBUTING TO SCHOOL SUCCESS

In addition to learning the content of your courses, there are some other things that you can do to help you do your best at school. You can try some of the following strategies:

- **Keep a positive attitude**: Always reflect on what you can already do and what you already know.

- **Be prepared to learn**: Have the necessary pencils, pens, notebooks, and other required materials for participating in class ready.

- **Complete all of your assignments**: Do your best to finish all of your assignments. Even if you know the material well, practice will reinforce your knowledge. If an assignment or question is difficult for you, work through it as far as you can so that your teacher can see exactly where you are having difficulty.

- **Set small goals for yourself when you are learning new material**: For example, when learning the parts of speech, do not try to learn everything in one night. Work on only one part or section each study session. When you have memorized one particular part of speech and understand it, move on to another one. Continue this process until you have memorized and learned all the parts of speech.

- **Review your classroom work regularly at home**: Review to make sure you understand the material you learned in class.

- **Ask your teacher for help**: Your teacher will help you if you do not understand something or if you are having a difficult time completing your assignments.

- **Get plenty of rest and exercise**: Concentrating in class is hard work. It is important to be well-rested and have time to relax and socialize with your friends. This helps you keep a positive attitude about your schoolwork.

- **Eat healthy meals**: A balanced diet keeps you healthy and gives you the energy you need for studying at school and at home.

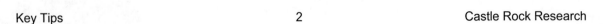

How to Find Your Learning Style

Every student learns differently. The manner in which you learn best is called your learning style. By knowing your learning style, you can increase your success at school. Most students use a combination of learning styles. Do you know what type of learner you are? Read the following descriptions. Which of these common learning styles do you use most often?

- **Linguistic Learner:** You may learn best by saying, hearing, and seeing words. You are probably really good at memorizing things such as dates, places, names, and facts. You may need to write down the steps in a process, a formula, or the actions that lead up to a significant event, and then say them out loud.

- **Spatial Learner:** You may learn best by looking at and working with pictures. You are probably really good at puzzles, imagining things, and reading maps and charts. You may need to use strategies like mind mapping and webbing to organize your information and study notes.

- **Kinesthetic Learner:** You may learn best by touching, moving, and figuring things out using manipulatives. You are probably really good at physical activities and learning through movement. You may need to draw your finger over a diagram to remember it, tap out the steps needed to solve a problem, or feel yourself writing or typing a formula.

SCHEDULING STUDY TIME

You should review your class notes regularly to ensure that you have a clear understanding of all the new material you learned. Reviewing your lessons on a regular basis helps you to learn and remember ideas and concepts. It also reduces the quantity of material that you need to study prior to a test. Establishing a study schedule will help you to make the best use of your time.

Regardless of the type of study schedule you use, you may want to consider the following suggestions to maximize your study time and effort:

- Organize your work so that you begin with the most challenging material first.

- Divide the subject's content into small, manageable chunks.

- Alternate regularly between your different subjects and types of study activities in order to maintain your interest and motivation.

- Make a daily list with headings like "Must Do," "Should Do," and "Could Do."

- Begin each study session by quickly reviewing what you studied the day before.

- Maintain your usual routine of eating, sleeping, and exercising to help you concentrate better for extended periods of time.

CREATING STUDY NOTES

MIND-MAPPING OR WEBBING

Use the key words, ideas, or concepts from your reading or class notes to create a mind map or web (a diagram or visual representation of the given information). A mind map or web is sometimes referred to as a knowledge map. Use the following steps to create a mind map or web:

1. Write the key word, concept, theory, or formula in the centre of your page.

2. Write down related facts, ideas, events, and information, and link them to the central concept with lines.

3. Use coloured markers, underlining, or symbols to emphasize things such as relationships, timelines, and important information.

The following examples of a Frayer Model illustrate how this technique can be used to study scientific vocabulary.

Definition	Notes
• Perimeter is the distance around the outside of a polygon.	• Perimeter is measured in linear units (e.g., metres, centimetres, and so on).

Perimeter

Examples	Non-Examples
• The length of a fence around a yard • The distance around a circle (circumference)	• The area of grass covering a lawn • The size of a rug lying on a floor

Definition	Notes
• A cube is a solid 3-D object with six faces.	• A cube is different from other shapes because it has six equally-sized square faces, eight vertices, and twelve equal edges.

Cube

Examples	Non-Examples

INDEX CARDS

To use index cards while studying, follow these steps:

1. Write a key word or question on one side of an index card.

2. On the reverse side, write the definition of the word, answer to the question, or any other important information that you want to remember.

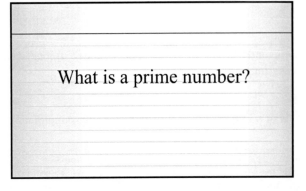

SYMBOLS AND STICKY NOTES—IDENTIFYING IMPORTANT INFORMATION

Use symbols to mark your class notes. For example, an exclamation mark (!) might be used to point out something that must be learned well because it is a very important idea. A question mark (?) may highlight something you are not certain about, and a diamond (◊) or asterisk (*) could highlight interesting information that you want to remember. Sticky notes are useful in the following situations:

- Use sticky notes when you are not allowed to put marks in books.

- Use sticky notes to mark a page in a book that contains an important diagram, formula, explanation, or other information.

- Use sticky notes to mark important facts in research books.

MEMORIZATION TECHNIQUES

- **Association** relates new learning to something you already know. For example, to remember the spelling difference between dessert and desert, recall that the word *sand* has only one *s*. So, because there is sand in a desert, the word *desert* has only one *s*.

- **Mnemonic** devices are sentences that you create to remember a list or group of items. For example, the first letter of each word in the phrase "Every Good Boy Deserves Fudge" helps you to remember the names of the lines on the treble-clef staff (E, G, B, D, and F) in music.

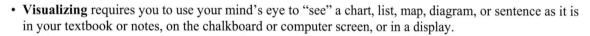

- **Acronyms** are words that are formed from the first letters or parts of the words in a group.
  For example, RADAR is actually an acronym for Radio Detecting and Ranging, and MASH is an acronym for Mobile Army Surgical Hospital. HOMES helps you to remember the names of the five Great Lakes (Huron, Ontario, Michigan, Erie, and Superior).

- **Visualizing** requires you to use your mind's eye to "see" a chart, list, map, diagram, or sentence as it is in your textbook or notes, on the chalkboard or computer screen, or in a display.

- **Initialisms** are abbreviations that are formed from the first letters or parts of the words in a group. Unlike acronyms, an initialism cannot be pronounced as a word itself. For example, BEDMAS is an initialism for the order of operations in math (Brackets, Exponents, Divide, Multiply, Add, Subtract).

KEY STRATEGIES FOR REVIEWING

Reviewing textbook material, class notes, and handouts should be an ongoing activity. Spending time reviewing becomes more critical when you are preparing for a test. You may find some of the following review strategies useful when studying during your scheduled study time:

- Before reading a selection, preview it by noting the headings, charts, graphs, and chapter questions.

- Before reviewing a unit, note the headings, charts, graphs, and chapter questions.

- Highlight key concepts, vocabulary, definitions, and formulas.

- Skim the paragraph, and note the key words, phrases, and information.

- Carefully read over each step in a procedure.

- Draw a picture or diagram to help make the concept clearer.

KEY STRATEGIES FOR SUCCESS: A CHECKLIST

Reviewing is a huge part of doing well at school and preparing for tests. Here is a checklist for you to keep track of how many suggested strategies for success you are using. Read each question, and put a check mark (✓) in the correct column. Look at the questions where you have checked the "No" column. Think about how you might try using some of these strategies to help you do your best at school.

KEY Strategies for Success	Yes	No
Do you attend school regularly?		
Do you know your personal learning style—how you learn best?		
Do you spend 15 to 30 minutes a day reviewing your notes?		
Do you study in a quiet place at home?		
Do you clearly mark the most important ideas in your study notes?		
Do you use sticky notes to mark texts and research books?		
Do you practise answering multiple-choice and written-response questions?		
Do you ask your teacher for help when you need it?		
Are you maintaining a healthy diet and sleep routine?		
Are you participating in regular physical activity?		

MEASUREMENT

Table of Correlations				
Outcome	**Practice Questions**	**Unit Test Questions**	**Practice Test 1**	**Practice Test 2**
By the end of this course, students will:				
10M *Develop spatial sense and proportional reasoning.*				
10M1.1 *solve problems that involve linear measurement.*	1, 2	1	13	13
10M1.2 *apply proportional reasoning to problems that involve conversions between SI and imperial units of measure.*	3, 4, 5	2, 3, 4	14	14
10M1.3 *solve problems, using SI and imperial units, that involve the surface area and volume of 3-D objects.*	6, 7, 8, 9, 10, 11, 12, 13, 14, 15, 16a, 16b	5, 6, 7, 8, 9, 10, 19a, 19b, 19c, 21, 22, 23, 24	15, 16, 17, 18	15, 16, 17, 18
10M1.4 *Develop and apply the primary trigonometric ratios to solve problems that involve right triangles*	17, 18, 19, 20, 21, 22, 23, 24a, 24b, 25	11, 12, 13, 14, 15, 16, 17, 18, 20a, 20b	19, 20, 21, 42a, 42b, 42c	19, 20, 21, 22

10M1.1 solve problems that involve linear measurement.

SOLVING LINEAR MEASUREMENT PROBLEMS

To estimate a linear measure, it is important to select the most appropriate **imperial** or SI unit of measure. A personal **referent** can then be used to approximate the length of an object or the distance between two points.

Example

To estimate the length of her car, Fiona could use the length of her thumb to the first joint or her stride length.

Which referent and corresponding imperial unit would be the **most appropriate** choice?

Solution

Using the thumb as a referent would be far too tedious, impractical, and prone to measurement error. Therefore, the stride, corresponding approximately to the imperial unit of 1 yd, would be the most appropriate referent to use in order to estimate the length of a car.

When solving problems involving linear measurement, use an appropriate instrument (ruler, tape measure, etc.), use necessary formulas, and use an effective problem-solving strategy.

Example

Conrad wanted to buy enough border material for his circular garden plot. Since he had no measuring instrument, he used his shoe to estimate the diameter of the garden plot to be 9.5 shoe lengths. When he got to the store, he measured his shoe with a tape measure, and determined its length to be $10\frac{3}{8}$ in.

To the nearest inch, what is the approximate length of the border material required?

Solution

Step 1
Calculate the diameter, d, of the garden plot.
d = shoe length × # of shoe lengths
$d = 10\frac{3}{8} \times 9.5$
$ = 10.375 \times 9.5$
$ = 98.5625$ in

Step 2
Determine the length of the border material by calculating the circumference, C, of the garden plot.
$C = \pi d$
$ = \pi \times 98.5625$
$ \approx 309.6432$ in

The approximate length of the border material required is 310 in.

1. Which of the following SI units would be **most appropriate** to use when estimating the height of a trophy?
   A. Metre
   B. Kilometre
   C. Millimetre
   D. Centimetre

Use the following information to answer the next question.

Anjuli wanted to determine the perimeter of the given shape. Anjuli estimated the perimeter to be 72 yd. She used her stride as a referent, and each stride was about 1 yd.

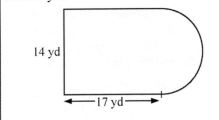

14 yd

17 yd

2. Based on the actual perimeter of the shape, what was the error of Anjuli's estimation, in terms of stride lengths?

    A. 1 stride   **B.** 2 strides

    C. 3 strides   **D.** 4 strides

10M1.2 apply proportional reasoning to problems that involve conversions between SI and imperial units of measure.

CONVERTING WITHIN OR BETWEEN IMPERIAL AND METRIC UNITS

Measurement conversions can be made within or between SI (metric) and imperial systems by setting up **proportions** that represent the relationship between the units. These conversions can also be verified using **unit analysis**.

The following table shows some of the relationships between common imperial and common metric units of length.

Imperial System	Metric System
1 mi = 1 760 yd = 5 280 ft	1 km = 1 000 m
1 yd = 3 ft = 36 in	1 m = 100 cm
1 ft = 12 in	1 cm = 10 mm

Note: An expanded table illustrating relationships between other common metric units can be found on a formula sheet.

Example

    Convert 32 560 yd to miles, and verify the result using unit analysis.

Solution

    Step 1
    Set up the appropriate proportion, in which x represents the number of miles.

$$\frac{\text{yd}}{\text{mi}} \rightarrow \frac{1\ 760}{1} = \frac{32\ 560}{x}$$

    Step 2
    Solve for x using cross products.

$$1\ 760x = 32\ 560$$
$$\frac{1\ 760x}{1\ 760} = \frac{32\ 560}{1\ 760}$$
$$x = 18.5$$

    Thus, 32 560 yd is equivalent to 18.5 mi.

    Step 3
    Verify the result using unit analysis.

$$32\ 560\ \text{yd} \times \frac{1\ \text{mi}}{1\ 760\ \text{yd}} = 18.5\ \text{mi}$$

The following table shows the exact conversions between some imperial and metric units of length.

Exact Conversions
1 in = 2.54 cm
1 ft = 0.3048 m
1 yd = 0.9144 m
1 mi = 1.609 344 km

Example

    Enzo wants to put baseboards around the perimeter of his room.

    If he measures the perimeter to be 40 ft 10 in and baseboards cost $4.24 /m, what is the total cost of the baseboards for his room, to the nearest cent?

Solution

    Step 1
    Write 40 ft 10 in in terms of feet.

$$40\ \text{ft}\ 10\ \text{in} = 40\frac{10}{12}\ \text{ft}$$

Step 2
Set up the appropriate proportion, in which x represents the number of metres.

$$\dfrac{\text{ft}}{\text{m}} \rightarrow \dfrac{1}{0.3048} = \dfrac{40\frac{10}{12}}{x}$$

Step 3
Solve for x using cross products.

$$x = (0.3048)\left(40\frac{10}{12}\right)$$
$$= (0.3048)(40.8333\ldots)$$
$$\approx 12.446 \text{ m}$$

Step 4
Determine the total cost, C, to the nearest cent.
$$C = 12.446 \text{ m} \times \$4.24/\text{m}$$
$$\approx \$52.771\ 04$$

Therefore, the total cost of the baseboards is $52.77.

Use the following information to answer the next question.

A map of Alberta has a scale of 1:4 590 000. The distance on the map between Edmonton and Calgary is $2\frac{3}{8}$ in.

3. What is the actual distance between Edmonton and Calgary, rounded to the nearest kilometre?

A. 268 km   **B.** 277 km

C. 300 km   **D.** 321 km

Use the following information to answer the next question.

A hall measures 40 yd long and 15 yd wide. The hall is to be completely covered with rugs that each measure 6 ft × 5 ft. Each rug costs $35.

4. Assuming none of the rugs overlap, what is the cost of covering the floor of the hall?

A. $700   **B.** $2 100

C. $4 500   **D.** $6 300

Numerical Response

5. Rounded to the nearest whole centimetre, 5 ft10 in is equivalent to _____ cm.

10M1.3 solve problems, using SI and imperial units, that involve the surface area and volume of 3-D objects.

SURFACE AREAS AND VOLUMES OF THREE-DIMENSIONAL OBJECTS

The **surface area** (*SA*) of any three-dimensional object is the sum of the areas (*A*) of all the object's faces. The **volume** (*V*) of a three-dimensional object is the amount of space the object takes up.

RIGHT PRISMS AND RIGHT CYLINDERS

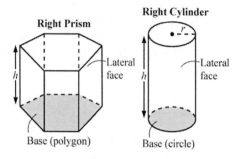

The surface area of a right prism or right cylinder can be determined by adding the surface area of the two bases and the **lateral faces**. The surface area of the lateral faces can be found by multiplying the height by the **perimeter** or **circumference** of the base.

$SA = 2(A_{\text{base}}) + h(P_{\text{base}})$, where

P = perimeter or circumference

The volume of a right prism or right cylinder is equal to the area of the base times the height.

$V = A_{\text{base}} \times h$

Since the base of a right cylinder is a circle in which $A_{\text{circle}} = \pi r^2$ and $C_{\text{circle}} = 2\pi r$, the surface area and volume of a right cylinder can also be defined in terms of its radius, r.

$SA_{\text{cylinder}} = 2\pi r^2 + 2\pi rh$

$V_{\text{cylinder}} = \pi r^2 h$

Right Pyramids and Right Cones

Right Pyramid

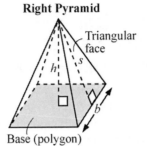

Triangular face

Base (polygon)

The surface area of a right pyramid can be determined by adding the area of the base and the area of the triangular faces that meet at the **apex**. The area of each triangular face can be found by multiplying the **slant height** by the base and dividing by 2.

$$SA = A_{\text{base}} + A_{\text{triangular faces}}$$
$$= A_{\text{base}} + n\left(\frac{bs}{2}\right)$$

The variable n equals the number of faces.

The volume of a right pyramid is equal to one-third of the area of the base times the height.

$$V = \frac{(A_{\text{base}})h}{3}$$

Right Cone

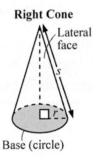

Lateral face

Base (circle)

The surface area of a right cone can be determined by adding the area of the base and the area of the lateral face. The area of the lateral face can be found by multiplying the circumference of the base by the slant height of the cone and dividing by 2.

$$SA = A_{\text{base}} + A_{\text{lateral face}}$$
$$= \pi r^2 + \pi r s$$

The volume of a right cone is equal to one-third of the area of the base times the height.

$$V = \frac{(A_{\text{base}})h}{3}$$
$$= \frac{\pi r^2 h}{3}$$

Spheres

Sphere

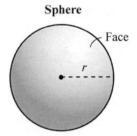

Face

The surface area and volume of a sphere can be determined using the given formulas.

$$SA = A_{\text{face}}$$
$$= 4\pi r^2$$
$$V = \frac{4\pi r^3}{3}$$

Determining Surface Area

To find the surface area of any three-dimensional object, sketch a **net** (a two-dimensional representation of all the object's faces), and then calculate the sum of all the areas of the faces.

Example

Find the surface area, *SA*, of the given right square pyramid.

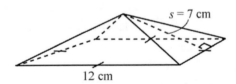

$s = 7$ cm

12 cm

Solution

Step 1

Begin by sketching a net diagram.

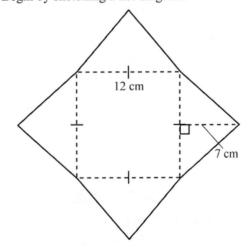

12 cm

7 cm

Step 2

Since the net diagram consists of one square and four congruent triangles, calculate their areas.

$$A_{\text{bottom square}} = l \times w$$
$$= 12 \times 12$$
$$= 144 \text{ cm}^2$$

$$A_{\text{triangle}} = \frac{b \times h}{2}$$
$$= \frac{12 \times 7}{2}$$
$$= 42 \text{ cm}^2$$

$$A_{\text{four triangles}} = 42 \times 4$$
$$= 168 \text{ cm}^2$$

Step 3

Calculate the total surface area of the right square pyramid.

$$SA_{\text{pyramid}} = 144 + 168$$
$$= 312 \text{ cm}^2$$

The surface area of the right square pyramid is 312 cm².

DETERMINING VOLUME

The volume of a three-dimensional object can be determined using the appropriate formula.

Example

A cylindrical-shaped tank has a diameter of 8 ft and a height of 10 ft, as shown in the given diagram.

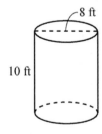

Determine the volume of the tank, to the nearest cubic foot.

Solution

Step 1

Find the radius, r, of the cylinder.

$$r = \frac{1}{2}d$$
$$= \frac{1}{2}(8)$$
$$= 4 \text{ ft}$$

Step 2

Determine the volume of the cylinder using the appropriate formula.

$$V_{\text{cylinder}} = \pi r^2 h$$
$$= \pi(4)^2(10)$$
$$= \pi(16)(10)$$
$$\approx 502.6548 \text{ ft}^3$$

The volume of the tank, to the nearest cubic foot, is 503 ft³.

RELATIONSHIPS BETWEEN VOLUMES OF THREE-DIMENSIONAL OBJECTS WITH THE SAME BASE AND HEIGHT

There is a unique relationship between the volume of a right cylinder and the volume of a right cone with the same base and height.

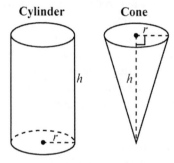

If you were to fill the cone in the given diagram to the top with sand or water and then pour it into the given cylinder, you would find that the cylinder would be one-third full. In other words, it would take three cones of sand or water to fill the cylinder.

The volume of a right cylinder is three times the volume of a right cone with the same base and height.

$$3 \times V_{\text{cone}} = V_{\text{cylinder}} \text{ or } V_{\text{cone}} = \frac{1}{3}V_{\text{cylinder}}$$

Similarly, there is a unique relationship between the volume of a right prism and the volume of a right pyramid with the same base and height.

Prism   **Pyramid**

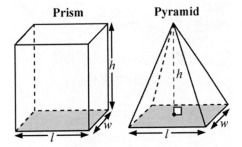

The volume of a right prism is three times the volume of a right pyramid with the same base and height.

$$3 \times V_{\text{pyramid}} = V_{\text{prism}} \text{ or } V_{\text{pyramid}} = \frac{1}{3}V_{\text{prism}}$$

DETERMINING AN UNKNOWN DIMENSION OF A THREE-DIMENSIONAL OBJECT

An unknown dimension of a three-dimensional object can be determined when given the surface area or volume and the remaining dimensions. These types of problems can be solved by rearranging the formulas to isolate the unknown variable or by substituting in known values before solving for the unknown variable.

Example

Consider a right cone that has a volume of 230 cm³ and a radius of 7 cm.

What is the height of the cone, to the nearest tenth of a centimetre?

Solution

The volume of a right cone is given by the formula $V = \dfrac{\pi r^2 h}{3}$. To determine the height of the cone, isolate the variable h. This can be done using one of two methods.

Method 1

Isolate the variable, and then substitute in the given values.

1. $V = \dfrac{\pi r^2 h}{3}$

   Divide both sides by $\dfrac{\pi r^2}{3}$.

   $$\frac{V}{\frac{\pi r^2}{3}} = h$$

   or

   $$h = \frac{V}{\frac{\pi r^2}{3}}$$

2. Substitute 230 for V and 7 for r into the equation, and solve for h.

   $$h = \frac{(230)}{\frac{\pi(7)^2}{3}}$$

   $$= \frac{230}{\frac{49\pi}{3}}$$

   $$\approx \frac{230}{51.313}$$

   $$\approx 4.48 \text{ cm}$$

The height of the right cone, to the nearest tenth of a centimetre, is 4.5 cm.

Method 2

Substitute in the given values, and then isolate the variable.

1. $V = \dfrac{\pi r^2 h}{3}$

    Substitute 230 for V, and 7 for r into the equation.

    $(230) = \dfrac{\pi (7)^2 h}{3}$

    $230 = \dfrac{\pi 49 h}{3}$

    $230 = \dfrac{49}{3} \pi h$

2. Divide both sides by $\dfrac{49}{3} \pi$.

    $\dfrac{230}{\dfrac{49}{3}\pi} = \dfrac{\dfrac{49}{3}\pi h}{\dfrac{49}{3}\pi}$

    $\dfrac{230}{\dfrac{49}{3}\pi} = h$

    $h = \dfrac{230}{\dfrac{49}{3}\pi}$

    $\approx \dfrac{230}{51.313}$

    ≈ 4.48

The height of the right cone, to the nearest tenth of a centimetre, is 4.5 cm.

SOLVING PROBLEMS INVOLVING THREE-DIMENSIONAL COMPOSITE SHAPES

You can solve problems involving the surface area or volume of three-dimensional **composite** shapes by breaking down the shapes into smaller recognizable components. Calculate the areas or volumes of each of the components, and then add or subtract them to determine the required measurement.

Example

A rectangular piece of solid metal has a hole drilled through it in the shape of a cylinder.

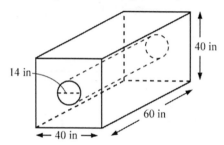

Calculate the volume of the remaining metal, to the nearest cubic inch.

Solution

Step 1

Determine the radius of the cylinder.

$r = \dfrac{d}{2}$

$ = \dfrac{14}{2}$

$ = 7 \text{ in}$

Step 2

Determine the volume of the remaining metal by subtracting the volume of the right cylinder from the volume of the right square prism.

$V_{\text{metal}} = V_{\text{square prisim}} - V_{\text{cylinder}}$

$\phantom{V_{\text{metal}}} = A_{\text{base}} \times h - A_{\text{base}} \times h$

$\phantom{V_{\text{metal}}} = (l \times w) \times h - (\pi r^2) \times h$

$\phantom{V_{\text{metal}}} = (40 \times 40) \times 60 - (\pi \times 7^2) \times 60$

$\phantom{V_{\text{metal}}} \approx 96\ 000 - 9\ 236.282\ 402$

$\phantom{V_{\text{metal}}} \approx 86\ 763.7176 \text{ in}^3$

The volume of the remaining metal, to the nearest cubic inch, is $86\ 764 \text{ in}^3$

---

6. A necklace contains 24 spherical beads of silver, each having a radius of 0.5 cm. The beads are to be coated, and the cost of coating is $10 per cm^2. What is the approximate total cost, to the nearest dollar, for coating the beads?

   A. $31.00   B. $75.00

   C. $126.00   D. $754.00

Use the following information to answer the next question.

Cindy makes a tent in the shape of a square pyramid. The net of the tent is given in the following figure, along with its corresponding dimensions.

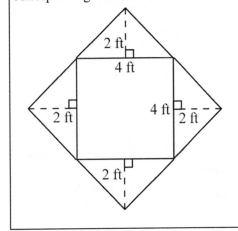

7. What is the total surface area of the tent?

   A. 32 square feet   B. 40 square feet

   C. 70 square feet   D. 90 square feet

Use the following information to answer the next question.

This snow cone has a diameter of 5.5 cm and a height of 13 cm.

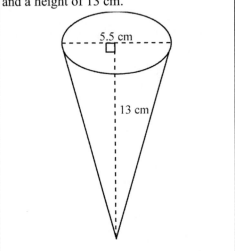

8. How much ice is needed to fill the snow cone to the brim?

   A. 92 cm^3 B. 103 cm^3

   C. 309 cm^3 D. 412 cm^3

Two water tanks, one prism-shaped and one pyramid-shaped, with particular dimensions are shown.

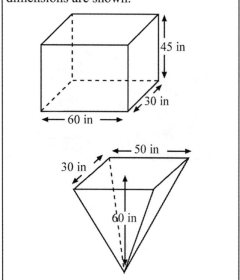

9. How much more water can the prism-shaped water tank hold than the pyramid-shaped water tank?

A. 9 000 in³   **B.** 30 000 in³

C. 51 000 in³   **D.** 81 000 in³

A small cereal box, as shown in the given diagram, holds 350 g of cereal.

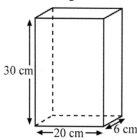

The same cereal is also available in a large box with dimensions of
40 cm × 24 cm × 18 cm.

10. What is the maximum amount of cereal the large box could hold?

A. 2 728 g   **B.** 1 680 g

C. 1 200 g   **D.** 480 g

Use the following information to answer the next question.

A cylinder has a diameter of 12 cm and a height of h cm. A cone has the same base diameter and height as the given cylinder.

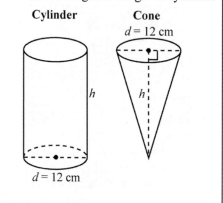

11. Which of the following equations can be used to determine the volume of the cone?

A. $V_{cone} = 12\pi h$

B. $V_{cone} = 36\pi h$

C. $V_{cone} = 48\pi h$

D. $V_{cone} = 144\pi h$

Use the following information to answer the next question.

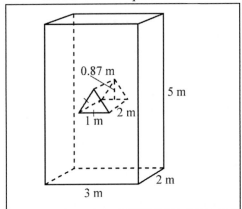

12. Determine the surface area of the composite figure shown.

    A. 62.00 m^2 **B.** 65.13 m^2

    C. 67.13 m^2 **D.** 68.00 m^2

Use the following information to answer the next question.

A package of three golf balls is shown.

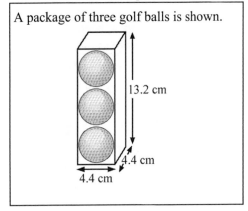

13. If the radius of each golf ball is 2.2 cm, how much extra space is there in the given package of three golf balls, rounded to the nearest tenth cubic centimetre?

    A. 121.7 cm^3 **B.** 133.8 cm^3

    C. 145.9 cm^3 **D.** 211.0 cm^3

Use the following information to answer the next question.

The front roller of a road compactor is cylindrical. It has a diameter of 1.75 m and a length of 1.5 m, and it has to compact an area of 3 300 m^2.

Numerical Response

14. The number of complete revolutions the front roller must make to compact the given area is _____.

Use the following information to answer the next question.

A tank in the shape of a right rectangular prism has a surface area of 348 yd^2. The height of the tank is 8 yd, and the width of its base is 6 yd.

Numerical Response

15. To the nearest tenth of a yard, the base of the tank has a length of _____ yd.

16. A company is designing a new game and needs to make three different solid game pieces. They want to use a cylindrical piece, a conical piece, and a spherical piece with the given dimensions. The aluminum used to make each of these game pieces costs 0.5 ¢/cm³.

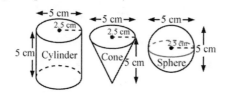

Use the following information to answer the next multipart question.

Written Response
---

a) Explain which of the given game pieces costs the most to make.

b) What is the relationship between the cost of a conical game piece and the cost of a cylindrical game piece?

10M1.4 Develop and apply the primary trigonometric ratios to solve problems that involve right triangles.

TRIGONOMETRY OF RIGHT TRIANGLES

Through investigation, you can determine the relationship between the ratios of the lengths of two sides in a right triangle relative to either **acute angle**. A **right triangle** can be labelled with respect to $\angle A$.

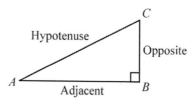

- The hypotenuse is the longest side and is always across from the 90° angle.
- The opposite side is always the side across from the given angle.
- The adjacent side is next to the given angle; it is shorter than the hypotenuse.

When you compare the lengths of the different sides of similar right triangles that hold the same acute angle, investigation will show that the ratios of the lengths of the three sides will remain the same, regardless of the right triangles that are chosen. This is summarized in the following illustration and resulting ratios.

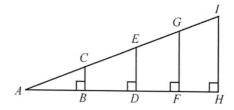

The following ratios apply to acute angle A:

- $\dfrac{BC}{AC} = \dfrac{DE}{AE} = \dfrac{FG}{AG} = \dfrac{HI}{AI}$

  $= \dfrac{\text{opposite}}{\text{hypotenuse}} = \text{sine} A = \sin A$

- $\dfrac{AB}{AC} = \dfrac{AD}{AE} = \dfrac{AF}{AG} = \dfrac{AH}{AI}$

  $= \dfrac{\text{adjacent}}{\text{hypotenuse}} = \text{cosine} A = \cos A$

- $\dfrac{BC}{AB} = \dfrac{DE}{AD} = \dfrac{FG}{AF} = \dfrac{HI}{AH}$

  $= \dfrac{\text{opposite}}{\text{adjacent}} = \text{tangent} A = \tan A$

These three ratios, the sine ratio, the cosine ratio, and the tangent ratio are known as the **primary trigonometric ratios**.

To remember these ratios, think of the mnemonic SOH CAH TOA, which stands for sine is opposite over hypotenuse, cosine is adjacent over hypotenuse, and tangent is opposite over adjacent.

Example

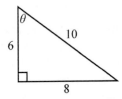

Write the three primary trigonometric ratios for angle θ.

Solution

Step 1
Label the sides of the triangle according to their positions relative to angle θ.

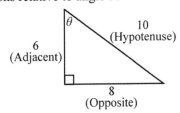

Step 2
Write the primary trigonometric ratios based on their definitions.

$\sin \theta = \dfrac{\text{opposite}}{\text{hypotenuse}} = \dfrac{8}{10} = \dfrac{4}{5}$

$\cos \theta = \dfrac{\text{adjacent}}{\text{hypotenuse}} = \dfrac{6}{10} = \dfrac{3}{5}$

$\tan \theta = \dfrac{\text{opposite}}{\text{adjacent}} = \dfrac{8}{6} = \dfrac{4}{3}$

DETERMINING THE MEASURES OF SIDES AND ANGLES IN RIGHT TRIANGLES

Depending on the given information, either the primary trigonometric ratios or the **Pythagorean theorem** are used to determine the measures of unknown sides or angles in a right triangle.

Example

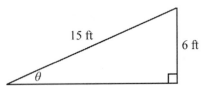

Determine the measure of angle θ to the nearest tenth of a degree.

Solution

Step 1
Label the given sides of the triangle according to their positions relative to angle θ.

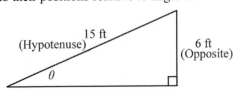

Step 2
Write the trigonometric ratio that involves the labelled sides.

$\sin \theta = \dfrac{\text{opposite}}{\text{hypotenuse}}$

$\sin \theta = \dfrac{6}{15}$

Measurement 22 Castle Rock Research

Step 3

Use the inverse trigonometric function to determine the measure of the angle.

$$\theta = \sin^{-1}\left(\frac{6}{15}\right)$$
$$\theta \approx 23.6°$$

SOLVING A TRIANGLE

Solving a triangle involves determining all the unknown sides and angles of a triangle. In order to solve a right triangle, it is common to use the Pythagorean theorem, the fact that the sum of the angles in a triangle equals 180°, and the primary trigonometric ratios.

Example

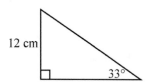

Solve the given triangle. (Round the measures of the sides to the nearest hundredth of a centimetre.)

Solution

Step 1

Use variables to label the unknown sides and angle.

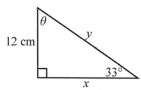

Step 2

Determine the measure of the unknown angle.
$$90° + 33° + \theta = 180°$$
$$\theta = 57°$$

Step 3

Determine the measure of one of the unknown sides by using the appropriate trigonometric ratio.

The measure of side x can be determined by using the tangent ratio of either angle.

$$\tan \theta = \frac{\text{opposite}}{\text{adjacent}}$$
$$\tan 33° = \frac{12}{x}$$
$$x\tan 33° = 12$$
$$x = \frac{12}{\tan 33°}$$
$$\approx 18.48 \text{ cm}$$

or

$$\tan 57° = \frac{x}{12}$$
$$12\tan 57° = x$$
$$x \approx 18.48 \text{ cm}$$

Step 4

Determine the measure of the other unknown side by using the Pythagorean theorem or a trigonometric ratio.

Using the Pythagorean theorem:
$$c^2 = a^2 + b^2$$
$$y^2 = 12^2 + 18.48^2$$
$$y = \sqrt{12^2 + 18.48^2}$$
$$\approx 22.03 \text{ cm}$$

Using the sine ratio:
$$\sin \theta = \frac{\text{opposite}}{\text{hypotenuse}}$$
$$\sin 33° = \frac{12}{y}$$
$$y\sin 33° = 12$$
$$y = \frac{12}{\sin 33°}$$
$$\approx 22.03 \text{ cm}$$

The lengths of the sides of the triangle are 12 cm, 18.48 cm, and 22.03 cm. The measures of the two acute angles are 33° and 57°.

SOLVING RIGHT TRIANGLE PROBLEMS

The primary trigonometric ratios and the Pythagorean theorem can be used to solve problems involving one or more right triangles in real-life applications. When solving these types of problems, recall these key definitions:

- The angle of elevation is up from the horizontal.
- The angle of depression is down from the horizontal.

Example

A cat watches a bird perched on a telephone pole. The bird is at an angle of elevation of 40° from the cat.

If the cat is 7.1 yd from the base of the pole, how high is the bird above the ground to the nearest tenth of a yard?

Solution

Step 1

Draw and label a diagram to represent the situation.

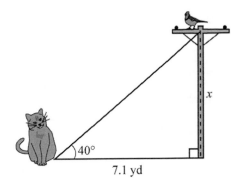

Step 2

Use the appropriate trigonometric ratio to solve for the unknown side.

$$\tan \theta = \frac{\text{opposite}}{\text{adjacent}}$$

$$\tan 40° = \frac{x}{7.1}$$

$$x = 7.1 \tan 40°$$

$$x \approx 5.9576 \text{ yd}$$

To the nearest tenth of a yard, the bird is 6.0 yd above the ground.

Sometimes, problems can be solved by making indirect or direct measurements using measuring instruments such as a clinometer, metre stick, or surveyor's transit.

Example

Lexi is standing in her yard. She sees a cat sitting directly west of her. Directly east of her is a dog. Lexi's eye level is 1.48 m high. She uses a clinometer to look directly at where the cat is sitting and measures an angle of depression of 30°. To the dog, the angle of depression is 25°.

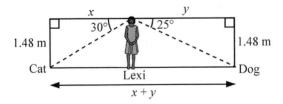

To the nearest hundredth of a metre, how far apart are the cat and dog?

Solution

Notice that $x + y$ at eye level will be the same as $x + y$ on the ground. Thus, the distance between the cat and dog is equal to $x + y$.

Step 1

Use the appropriate trigonometric ratios to solve for x and y based on the relative positions of the given angles, known sides, and unknown sides.

$$\tan \theta = \frac{\text{opposite}}{\text{adjacent}}$$

$$\tan 30° = \frac{1.48}{x}$$

$$x = \frac{1.48}{\tan 30°}$$

$$\approx 2.563\ 435 \text{ m}$$

$$\tan \theta = \frac{\text{opposite}}{\text{adjacent}}$$

$$\tan 25° = \frac{1.48}{y}$$

$$y = \frac{1.48}{\tan 25°}$$

$$\approx 3.173\ 87 \text{ m}$$

Step 2

Add the values for the variables to determine the distance between the cat and the dog, *d*.

$d = x + y$

$\approx 2.563\,435 + 3.173\,87$

$\approx 5.737\,305$ m

To the nearest hundredth of a metre, the cat and the dog are 5.74 m apart.

Use the following information to answer the next question.

Two bridges, *AB* and *CD*, are built across a pond, as shown in the given diagram.

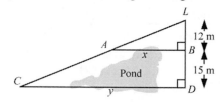

17. Which of the following statements about the relationship between sides *x* and *y* and angle *C* is **true**?

A. $\tan C = \dfrac{12}{x} = \dfrac{15}{y}$

B. $\tan C = \dfrac{12}{x} = \dfrac{27}{y}$

C. $\cos C = \dfrac{12}{x} = \dfrac{15}{y}$

D. $\cos C = \dfrac{12}{x} = \dfrac{27}{y}$

Use the following information to answer the next question.

Chico drew two right triangles and labelled them as shown.

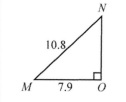

18. Which angle is the **smallest**?

A. ∠M   **B.** ∠N

C. ∠P   **D.** ∠Q

Use the following information to answer the next question.

After shoveling, Arron rests the snow shovel against the side of his shed. The shovel is 1.53 m long and the angle between the shovel and the shed is 31°.

19. To calculate how far from the base of the shed the end of the snow shovel is, Arron would use the trigonometric ratio

A. $\sin(31°) = \dfrac{1.53}{x}$

B. $\sin(31°) = \dfrac{x}{1.53}$

C. $\cos(31°) = \dfrac{1.53}{x}$

D. $\cos(31°) = \dfrac{x}{1.53}$

Use the following information to answer the next question.

A triangle with two given sides is shown.

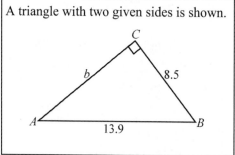

20. To the nearest tenth, what are the measures of side *b*, ∠*A*, and ∠*B*?

A. $b = 11.0$, ∠$A = 37.7°$, ∠$B = 52.3°$

B. $b = 11.0$, ∠$A = 52.3°$, ∠$B = 37.7°$

C. $b = 16.3$, ∠$A = 37.7°$, ∠$B = 52.3°$

D. $b = 11.9$, ∠$A = 31.4°$, ∠$B = 58.6°$

Use the following information to answer the next question.

A helicopter is involved in the air rescue of a person stranded in a dinghy during a fierce storm, as shown in the given illustration. The pilot determines that the angle of depression from the helicopter to the person is 15°. The helicopter is 900 ft from the person.

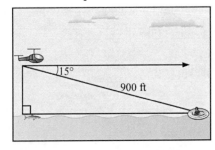

21. Rounded to the nearest foot, what is the altitude of the helicopter above the water?

   A. 233 ft   **B.** 241 ft

   C. 869 ft   **D.** 932 ft

Use the following information to answer the next question.

From a 60 m tall fire tower, a park ranger spots one fire at an angle of depression of 28° and another fire at an angle of depression of 42°.

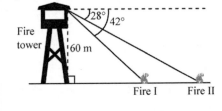

Numerical Response

22. The distance between the two fires, to the nearest tenth metre, is _____ m.

Use the following information to answer the next question.

On a sunny morning, John observes that his shadow is 0.5 m in length. At the same time, a vertical flagpole casts a shadow that has a length of 2 m.

Numerical Response

23. If John's height is 170 cm, then the height of the flagpole, to the nearest tenth of a metre, is _____ m.

Use the following information to answer the next multipart question.

24. George built a shelf that was 50 cm in length. In order to keep it secure, he built two supports, *BE* and *CD*, as shown in the given diagram.

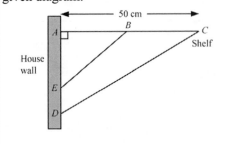

Written Response

a) If ∠*ADC* = 60°, what is the length of *CD* rounded to the nearest tenth of a centimetre?

b) If the distance between anchor points A and E is 20 cm, what is the distance between anchor points D and E, rounded to the nearest tenth of a centimetre?

Use the following information to answer the next question.

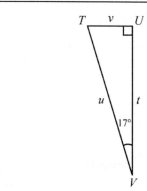

A diagram of a triangle is given.

25. Which of the following trigonometric ratios is represented by $\dfrac{t}{v}$?

A. $\sin 17°$ **B.** $\tan 17°$

C. $\sin 73°$ **D.** $\tan 73°$

ANSWERS AND SOLUTIONS
MEASUREMENT

1. D	6. D	11. A	16. WR	21. A
2. B	7. A	12. C	17. B	22. 46.2
3. B	8. B	13. A	18. D	23. 6.8
4. D	9. C	14. 401	19. B	24. WR
5. 178	10. B	15. 9.0	20. A	25. D

1. D

Millimetres are too small and metres and kilometres are too large to measure the height of the trophy. Therefore, the most appropriate unit to use is the centimetre.

2. B

Determine the perimeter, P, of the shape. This consists of three sides of a rectangle and the circumference of a semicircle. Compare it to Anjuli's estimated perimeter.

Step 1
Calculate the perimeter of the shape using the formula $C = \pi d$ for the circumference of a circle.

$$P_{shape} = P_{rectangle\ (sides)} + P_{semicircle}$$
$$= l + l + w + \frac{\pi d}{2}$$
$$= 17 + 17 + 14 + \frac{\pi(14)}{2}$$
$$= 48 + 7\pi$$
$$\approx 48 + 21.991\ 15$$
$$\approx 70.0\ yd$$

Step 2
Compare the actual perimeter to the estimated perimeter of the shape.

$$P_{difference} = P_{estimate} - P_{actual}$$
$$= 72\ yd - 70\ yd$$
$$= 2\ yd$$

Since 1yd = 1stride, the error in Anjuli's estimation is about 2 strides.

3. B

Step 1

Convert $2\frac{3}{8}$ in to cm.

There are 2.54 cm in 1 in. Set up the appropriate proportion, in which x represents the number of centimetres.

$$\frac{cm}{in} \rightarrow \frac{2.54}{1} = \frac{x}{2\frac{3}{8}}$$

Step 2
Solve for x using cross products.

$$\frac{2.54}{1} = \frac{x}{2\frac{3}{8}}$$
$$x = (2.54)\left(2\frac{3}{8}\right)$$
$$= (2.54)(2.375)$$
$$= 6.0325\ cm$$

4. D

Step 1
Convert each dimension from yards to feet by setting up and solving the appropriate proportion, where x represents the number of feet.

$$\frac{yd}{ft} \rightarrow \frac{1}{3} = \frac{40}{x}$$
$$x = 40 \times 3$$
$$x = 120\ ft$$

$$\frac{yd}{ft} \rightarrow \frac{1}{3} = \frac{15}{x}$$
$$x = 15 \times 3$$
$$x = 45\ ft$$

Step 2

Determine the number of rugs required for the hall.

Calculate the area of the hall.

$A = l \times w$
$\quad = 120 \times 45$
$\quad = 5\ 400\ \text{ft}^2$

Calculate the area of a single rug.

$A = l \times w$
$\quad = 6 \times 5$
$\quad = 30\ \text{ft}^2$

Calculate the number of rugs required.

$\dfrac{5\ 400}{30} = 180$

Step 3

Determine the cost of the rugs for the hall.

$180 \times \$35 = \$6\ 300$

It will cost $6 300 to cover the hall with rugs.

5. 178

Step 1

Convert all the units into inches.

Since 1 ft is equal to 12 in, convert 5 ft into inches by multiplying 5 by 12, then add the 10 in from the original measurement.

$5 \times 12 + 10 = 70$ in.

Step 2

Convert 70 in into centimetres by setting up the appropriate proportion, in which x represents the number of centimetres. There are 2.54 cm in 1 in.

$\dfrac{\text{inches}}{\text{cm}} \rightarrow \dfrac{1}{2.54} = \dfrac{70}{x}$

Step 3

Solve for x using cross products.

$\dfrac{1}{2.54} = \dfrac{70}{x}$
$70 \times 2.54 = 1 \times x$
$\quad\quad 177.8 = x$

When rounded to the nearest whole centimetre, 5 ft 10 in is equivalent to about 178 cm.

6. D

Calculate the surface area of one bead.

$SA_{\text{sphere}} = 4\pi r^2$
$\quad\quad\quad\ = 4\pi 0.5^2$
$\quad\quad\quad\ = 4\pi 0.25$
$\quad\quad\quad\ = 3.14\ \text{cm}^2$

There are 24 beads, so multiply the area by 24.

$3.14 \times 24 = 75.4\ \text{cm}^2$

The cost of coating is $10 per cm^2 so multiply the total area by $10 for the total cost.

$75.4 \times 10 = \$754.00$

7. A

The total surface area of a square pyramid is equal to the sum of the areas of all its surfaces. There are 4 triangular faces, each of which measures 4 ft by 2 ft. Each of these faces has an area of

$\dfrac{1}{2}(4 \times 2) = 4$ square feet.

The 4 faces have a total area of $4(4) = 16$ square feet.

The square base measures 4 ft by 4 ft. The area of the square is 4×4 or 16 square feet.

Total surface area of the square pyramid $= 16 + 16 = 32$ square feet

8. B

Step 1

Determine the radius of the cone.

The radius of the snow cone is $\dfrac{5.5}{2} = 2.75$ cm.

Step 2

Calculate the volume of the cone.

The volume of a cone is one third the volume of a cylinder with the same base and height.

$V = \dfrac{\pi r^2 h}{3}$

Use the volume formula for a cone, substitute in the values for radius and height, and evaluate.

$V = \dfrac{\pi r^2 h}{3}$
$\quad = \dfrac{\pi (2.75)^2 (13)}{3}$
$\quad \approx 102.9526\ \text{cm}^3$

The amount of ice needed to fill the snow cone to the brim, to the nearest whole cubic centimetre, is $103\ \text{cm}^3$.

9. C

Step 1

Calculate the volume of the prism-shaped water tank.

Determine the volume of the prism-shaped water tank with the dimensions $l = 60$ in, $w = 30$ in, and $h = 45$ in.

$V_{\text{prism}} = A_{\text{base}} \times h$
$\quad\quad\ = (l \times w) \times h$
$\quad\quad\ = (60 \times 30) \times 45$
$\quad\quad\ = 81\ 000\ \text{in}^3$

Step 2

Calculate the volume of the pyramid-shaped water tank.

Determine the volume of the pyramid-shaped water tank with the dimensions $l = 50$ in, $w = 30$ in, and $h = 60$ in.

$$\begin{aligned} V_{pyramid} &= \frac{(A_{base}) \times h}{3} \\ &= \frac{(l \times w) \times h}{3} \\ &= \frac{(50 \times 30) \times 60}{3} \\ &= 30\ 000\ in^3 \end{aligned}$$

Step 3

Calculate the difference between the two volumes.

The difference between these two volumes is $81\ 000\ in^3 - 30\ 000\ in^3 = 51\ 000\ in^3$.

The prism-shaped water tank can hold $51\ 000\ in^3$ more water than the pyramid-shaped water tank.

10. B

Step 1

Calculate the volume of the small box of cereal (right prism).

$$\begin{aligned} V_{small\ box} &= A_{base} \times h \\ &= (lw) \times h \\ &= (20\ cm \times 6\ cm) \times 30\ cm \\ &= 3\ 600\ cm^3 \end{aligned}$$

Step 2

Calculate the volume of the large box of cereal(right prism).

$$\begin{aligned} V_{large\ box} &= A_{base} \times h \\ &= (lw) \times h \\ &= (18\ cm \times 24\ cm) \times 40\ cm \\ &= 17\ 280\ cm^3 \end{aligned}$$

Step 3

Determine how many times greater the volume of the large box is than the volume of the small box.

$$\begin{aligned} \text{Number of times greater} &= \frac{V_{large\ box}}{V_{small\ box}} \\ &= \frac{17\ 280\ cm^3}{3\ 600\ cm^3} \\ &= 4.8 \end{aligned}$$

Step 4

Determine how much cereal the large box can hold.

Since the large cereal box is 4.8 times greater in volume than the small box, it could hold 4.8 times the amount of cereal as the small box.

$$\begin{aligned} m_{large\ box} &= m_{small\ box} \times 4.8 \\ &= 350\ g \times 4.8 \\ &= 1\ 680\ g \end{aligned}$$

The large box could hold a maximum of $1\ 680\ g$ of cereal.

11. A

Step 1

Calculate the radius of the cylinder. The cone will have the same radius.

The radius of either the given cylinder or cone is $\frac{12}{2} = 6$ cm.

Step 2

Calculate the volume of the cone.

The formula for the volume of a cylinder is $V = \pi r^2 h$.

The formula for the volume of a cone with the same base diameter and height is $V = \frac{\pi r^2 h}{3}$.

Substitute 6 for r into the formula for the volume of the cone, and simplify.

$$\begin{aligned} V_{cone} &= \frac{\pi r^2 h}{3} \\ &= \frac{\pi (6^2) h}{3} \\ &= \frac{36\pi h}{3} \\ &= 12\pi h \end{aligned}$$

The equation that can be used to determine the volume of the cone is $V_{cone} = 12\pi h$.

12. C

Step 1

Calculate the surface area of the rectangular prism.
Area of front and back rectangles (2 equal rectangles):
$$A = 2(l \times w)$$
$$= 2(3 \times 5)$$
$$= 30 \text{ m}^2$$

Area of top and bottom rectangles (2 equal rectangles):
$$A = 2(l \times w)$$
$$= 2(3 \times 2)$$
$$= 12 \text{ m}^2$$

Area of side rectangles (2 equal rectangles):
$$A = 2(l \times w)$$
$$= 2(2 \times 5)$$
$$= 20 \text{ m}^2$$

Surface area of rectangular prism
$$SA = 30 \text{ m}^2 + 12 \text{ m}^2 + 20 \text{ m}^2$$
$$= 62 \text{ m}^2$$

Step 2

Calculate the surface area of the triangular prism.
The two triangles will be subtracted from the total surface area, and the three rectangles will be added to the total surface area.
2 equal triangles:
$$A = 2\left(\frac{1}{2}b \times h\right)$$
$$= 2\left(\frac{1}{2}(1)(0.87)\right)$$
$$= 0.87 \text{ m}^2$$

3 rectangular sides:
$$A = 3(l \times w)$$
$$= 3(1 \times 2)$$
$$= 6 \text{ m}^2$$

Step 3

Calculate the total surface area.
Total surface area = rectangular prism
– two triangles + 3 rectangular sides
$$SA = 62 \text{ m}^2 - 0.87 \text{ m}^2 + 6 \text{ m}^2$$
$$= 67.13 \text{ m}^2$$

13. A

Step 1

Calculate the volume of the entire package.
The package is a right rectangular prism. Its volume can be determined using the formula
$V = A_{\text{base}} \times h$, where $A_{\text{base}} = lw$.
Substitute 4.4 cm for l, 4.4 cm for w, and 13.2 cm for h, and solve.
$$V = (lw) \times h$$
$$= (4.4 \times 4.4) \times 13.2$$
$$= 255.552 \text{ cm}^3$$

Step 2

Calculate the volume of one golf ball.
The golf balls are spherical. The volume occupied by each ball can be determined using the formula
$V_{\text{sphere}} = \dfrac{4\pi r^3}{3}$.
Substitute 2.2 cm for r.
$$V_{\text{sphere}} = \frac{4\pi r^3}{3}$$
$$= \frac{4\pi(2.2)^3}{3}$$
$$\approx 44.602\,24 \text{ cm}^3$$

The approximate volume occupied by all three balls is:
$$V_{\text{golf balls}} = 44.602\,24 \times 3$$
$$= 133.806\,72 \text{ cm}^3$$

Step 3

Determine the amount of extra space in the package.
The volume of the extra space is the difference between the volume of the package and the volume of the three golf balls.
$$V_{\text{space}} = V_{\text{prism}} - V_{\text{golf balls}}$$
$$= 255.552 \text{ cm}^3$$
$$- 133.806\,72 \text{ cm}^3$$
$$\approx 121.745 \text{ cm}^3$$

Thus, the volume of the extra space in the package, to the nearest tenth cubic centimetre, is 121.7 cm^3.

14. 401

Step 1

Determine the radius of the roller.
$$r = \frac{d}{2}$$
$$= \frac{1.75}{2}$$
$$= 0.875$$

Step 2
Determine the number of revolutions needed to cover the required area.

Total area covered = (Number of revolutions) (curved surface

$$\text{\# of revolutions} = \frac{\text{total area compacted}}{\text{curved surface area}}$$
$$= \frac{\text{total area compacted}}{2\pi r h}$$

Substitute 0.875 for r and 1.5 for h into the formula, and evaluate.

$$\text{\# of revolutions} = \frac{3\,300}{2 \times \pi \times 0.875 \times 1.5}$$
$$\approx 400.16$$

The front roller must make 401 complete revolutions to compact the given area because the entire area would not be compacted by only 400 revolutions.

15. 9.0

Step 1
Rearrange the formula for the surface area of a right rectangular prism to solve for the length. The surface area, S, of a rectangular prism is $S = 2(lw + wh + lh)$. This can be rewritten as $S = 2lw + 2wh + 2lh$.

Rearrange this formula, and solve for l.
Switch the sides of the formula around.
$2lw + 2wh + 2lh = S$
Subtract $2wh$ from both sides.
$2lw + 2lh = S - 2wh$
Factor l out of the left side of the formula.
$l(2w + 2h) = S - 2wh$
Divide both sides of the formula by $2w + 2h$.

$$\frac{l(2w + 2h)}{2w + 2h} = \frac{S - 2wh}{2w + 2h}$$
$$l = \frac{S = 2wh}{2w + 2h}$$

Step 2
Calculate the length of the tank. Substitute the given values for surface area, width, and height, and solve for the length.

$S = 348 \text{ yd}^2$, $w = 6$ yd, $h = 8$ yd

$$l = \frac{348 - 2(6)(8)}{2(6) + 2(8)}$$
$$= \frac{348 - 96}{12 + 16}$$
$$= \frac{252}{28}$$
$$= 9 \text{ yd}$$

The base of the tank has a length of 9.0 yd.

16. a) WR

Step 1
Calculate the volume of each of the pieces. For the cylinder, apply the volume formula, and substitute 2.5 cm for r and 5 cm for h.

$$V_{\text{cylinder}} = \pi r^2 h$$
$$= \pi (2.5)^2 (5)$$
$$\approx 98.175 \text{ cm}^3$$

For the cone, apply the volume formula, and substitute 2.5 cm for r and 5 cm for h.

$$V_{\text{cone}} = \frac{\pi r^2 h}{3}$$
$$= \frac{\pi (2.5)^2 (5)}{3}$$
$$\approx 32.725 \text{ cm}^3$$

For the sphere, apply the volume formula, and substitute 2.5 for r.

$$V_{\text{sphere}} = \frac{4\pi r^3}{3}$$
$$= \frac{4\pi (2.5)^3}{3}$$
$$\approx 65.54 \text{ cm}^3$$

Step 2
Calculate the cost of making the game piece with the greatest volume.

Since the game pieces are solid and the volume of the cylinder is greater than the volume of the cone or the volume of the sphere, the cylinder requires more material to construct. Because of this, it is more expensive to make.

Multiply the volume of the cylindrical piece by 0.5¢/cm³.

$$C = 98.175 \text{ cm}^3 \times 0.5\text{¢/cm}^3$$
$$= 98.175 \text{ cm}^3 \times \$0.005\text{/cm}^3$$
$$= \$0.49$$

16. b) WR

The formula for the volume of a cone $\left(V = \dfrac{\pi r^2 h}{3}\right)$ and the formula for the volume of a cylinder $\left(V = \pi r^2 h\right)$ shows that the volume of the cone is $\dfrac{1}{3}$ the volume of the cylinder.

Not for Reproduction

This can be verified using the volumes of these shapes.

$$\frac{1}{3}\left(V_{cylinder}\right) = V_{cone}$$

$$\frac{1}{3}\left(98.175 \text{ cm}^3\right) = 32.725 \text{ cm}^3$$

$$32.725 \text{ cm}^3 = 32.725 \text{ cm}^3$$

It costs $\frac{1}{3}$ the price of a cylindrical game piece to make a conical game piece, or $\frac{1}{3} \times \$0.49 = \$0.16$.

17. B

Identify the primary trigonometric ratios for angles A and C.

Since $\triangle ABL$ and $\triangle CDL$ are similar right triangles, the corresponding angles are equal, and the ratio of the lengths of the corresponding sides is constant. Based on these relationships, $\angle A = \angle C$ and the given trigonometric ratios are equivalent.

$$\sin A = \frac{12}{AL} = \sin C = \frac{27}{CL}$$

$$\cos A = \frac{x}{AL} = \cos C = \frac{y}{CL}$$

$$\tan A = \frac{12}{x} = \tan C = \frac{27}{y}$$

18. D

In $\triangle MNO$, use the cosine ratio to determine the value of $\angle M$.

$$\cos M = \frac{7.9}{10.8}$$

$$\angle M = \cos^{-1}\left(\frac{7.9}{10.8}\right)$$

$$\approx 43°$$

Since the sum of the measures of all angles in a triangle is $180°$,

$$\angle N = 180° - 90° - \angle M$$
$$= 180° - 90° - 43°$$
$$= 47°$$

In $\triangle PQR$, use the sine ratio to determine the value of $\angle P$

$$\sin P = \frac{4.9}{6.6}$$

$$\angle P = \sin^{-1}\left(\frac{4.9}{6.6}\right)$$

$$\approx 48°$$

$$\angle Q = 180° - 90° - \angle P$$
$$= 180° - 90° - 48°$$
$$= 42°$$

Therefore, $\angle Q = 42°$ is the smallest angle in the two triangles.

19. B

Begin with a sketch for clarity and label accordingly.

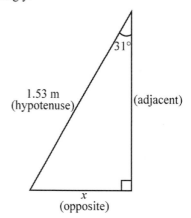

Recall,

$$\sin \theta = \frac{\text{opposite}}{\text{hypotenuse}}$$

$$\sin(31°) = \frac{x}{1.53}$$

20. A

Step 1
Determine the measure of side b using the Pythagorean theorem.

$$a^2 + b^2 = c^2$$
$$8.5^2 + b^2 = 13.9^2$$
$$b^2 = 13.9^2 - 8.5^2$$
$$b^2 = 120.96$$
$$\sqrt{b^2} = \sqrt{120.96}$$
$$b \approx 10.998$$

Rounded to the nearest tenth, the measure of side b is 11.0.

Step 2

Determine the measure of $\angle A$ using any trigonometric ratio of $\angle A$.

$\tan A = \dfrac{\text{opp}}{\text{adj}}$

$\tan A \approx \dfrac{8.5}{11.0}$

$\tan A \approx 0.7727$

$\angle A \approx \tan^{-1}(0.7727)$

$\angle A \approx 37.7°$

OR

$\sin A = \dfrac{\text{opp}}{\text{hyp}}$

$\sin A = \dfrac{8.5}{13.9}$

$\sin A = 0.6115$

$\angle A = \sin^{-1}(0.6115)$

$\angle A \approx 37.7°$

OR

$\cos A = \dfrac{\text{adj}}{\text{hyp}}$

$\cos A \approx \dfrac{11.0}{13.9}$

$\cos A \approx 0.7914$

$\angle A \approx \cos^{-1}(0.7914)$

$\angle A \approx 37.7°$

Rounded to the nearest tenth, $\angle A = 37.7°$.

Step 3

Determine the measure of $\angle B$.

The sum of the three angles in any triangle is 180°.

$\angle A + \angle B + \angle C = 180°$

$37.7° + \angle B + 90° \approx 180°$

$\angle B \approx 180°$

$\qquad\qquad -37.7° - 90°$

$\angle B \approx 52.3°$

The measures of side b, $\angle A$, and $\angle B$ are $b = 11.0$, $\angle A = 37.7°$, and $\angle B = 52.3°$.

21. **A**

Step 1

Draw a labelled diagram of the situation.

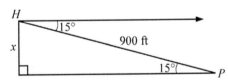

The altitude of the helicopter, H, is represented by x. Since it is equivalent to the angle of depression, the person's angle of elevation, P, to the helicopter is 15°.

Step 2

Write a trigonometric ratio involving the known side, the known angle, and the unknown side.

The ratio that includes the opposite and hypotenuse sides is the sine ratio.

$\sin 15° = \dfrac{x}{900}$

Step 3

Solve for the unknown.

Multiply both sides by 900.

$900(\sin 15°) = x$

$900(0.2588) \approx x$

$\qquad 233 \approx x$

Therefore, rounded to the nearest foot, the altitude of the helicopter above the water is 233 ft.

22. **46.2**

Step 1

Sketch and label a diagram to represent this situation. Remember that the angles of depression from the tower to the fires are equal to the angles of elevation from the fires to the tower.

Let x = horizontal distance from the tower to Fire I.
Let y = horizontal distance from the tower to Fire II.

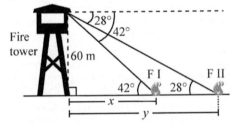

Step 2

Solve for x:

$\tan 42° = \dfrac{60}{x}$

$x(\tan 42°) = 60$

$x = \dfrac{60}{\tan 42°}$

$x = 66.636\,750\,89$

Step 3

Solve for y:

$\tan 28° = \dfrac{60}{y}$

$y(\tan 28°) = 60$

$y = \dfrac{60}{\tan 28°}$

$y = 112.843\,5879$

The distance, d, to the nearest tenth metre, between the two fires is:

$d = y - x$

$\quad = 112.843\,5879 - 66.636\,750\,89$

$\quad \approx 46.2$ m

23. 6.8

Step 1

Draw and label a diagram to represent the situation.

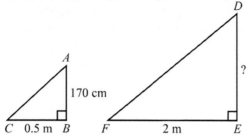

Let AB be John's height and DE be the height of the flagpole. BC and EF are the lengths of the shadows formed by John and the flag pole, respectively.

Step 2

Convert all measurements to the same units.

$$AB = 170 \text{ cm} \times \frac{1 \text{ m}}{100 \text{ cm}} = \frac{170}{100} = 1.7 \text{ m}$$

$BC = 0.5 \text{ m}$

$EF = 2 \text{ m}$

Step 3

Solve for the missing side length, DE. The measure of the angle of the sun with the ground for both shadows is the same: $\angle ACB = \angle DFE$. Therefore, $\triangle ABC$ and $\triangle DEF$ are similar triangles, since the corresponding angles are equal. In similar triangles the corresponding sides are proportional, since $\tan\angle ACB = \tan\angle DFE$.

$$\tan\angle ACB = \tan\angle DFE$$

$$\frac{AB}{CB} = \frac{DE}{FE}$$

$$\frac{1.7}{0.5} = \frac{DE}{2}$$

$$DE \times 0.5 = 2 \times 1.7$$

$$DE = \frac{3.4}{0.5}$$

$$DE = 6.8 \text{ m}$$

Therefore, the height of the flagpole, to the nearest tenth of a metre, is 6.8 m.

24. a) WR

In $\triangle ACD$, the length of CD can be determined using the trigonometric ratio for angle $\angle ACD$ that involves sides AC and CD.

This is the sine ratio.

$$\tan\angle ACB = \frac{AC}{CD}$$

$$\sin 60° = \frac{AC}{CD}$$

$$\sin 60° = \frac{50}{CD}$$

$$CD \times \sin 60° = 50$$

$$CD = \frac{50}{\sin 60°}$$

$$CD \approx 57.7 \text{ cm}$$

To the nearest tenth of a centimetre, the length of CD is 57.7 cm.

b) WR

In order to determine the distance between anchor points D and E, it is necessary to find the distance between anchor points A and D because $AD = AE + DE$. Since $AE = 20$ cm, solve for AD as follows.

Step 1

Apply the Pythagorean theorem to $\triangle ACD$. Substitute 57.74 for CD and 50 for AC.

$$(AD)^2 + (AC)^2 = (CD)^2$$

$$(AD)^2 + 50^2 = 57.74^2$$

$$(AD)^2 + 2\,500 \approx 3\,333.91$$

$$(AD)^2 \approx 833.91$$

$$(AD)^2 \approx \sqrt{833.91}$$

$$AD = 28.9$$

Step 2

Recall that $AD = AE + DE$. Substitute 20 for AE and 28.9 for AD.

$$AD = AE + DE$$

$$28.9 = 20 + DE$$

$$8.9 = DE$$

To the nearest tenth of a centimetre, the distance between anchor points D and E is 8.9 cm.

25. D

Step 1

Determine the primary trigonometric ratios for one of the acute angles.

Using 17° as the angle of reference, the sides are labelled t = adjacent, v = opposite, and u = hypotenuse.

$$\sin\theta = \frac{\text{opposite}}{\text{hypotenuse}}$$

$$\sin 17° = \frac{v}{u}$$

$$\cos\theta = \frac{\text{adjacent}}{\text{hypotenuse}}$$

$$\cos\theta = \frac{t}{u}$$

$$\tan\theta = \frac{\text{opposite}}{\text{adjacent}}$$

$$\tan 17° = \frac{v}{t}$$

Step 2

Determine the primary trigonometric ratios for the other acute triangle.

Since $180° - 90° - 17° = 73°$, the third angle in the triangle is 73°.

Using 73° as the angle of reference, the sides are labelled t = opposite, v = adjacent, and u = hypotenuse.

$$\sin\theta = \frac{\text{opposite}}{\text{hypotenuse}}$$

$$\sin 17° = \frac{t}{u}$$

$$\cos\theta = \frac{\text{adjacent}}{\text{hypotenuse}}$$

$$\cos\theta = \frac{v}{u}$$

$$\tan\theta = \frac{\text{opposite}}{\text{adjacent}}$$

$$\tan 17° = \frac{t}{v}$$

Therefore, the trigonometric ratio represented by $\frac{t}{v}$ is $\tan 73°$.

UNIT TEST — MEASUREMENT

Use the following information to answer the next question.

Roger used a pencil to trace the circular base of his water bottle. He then laid exactly four quarters in a line across the diameter of the circle. Using a ruler, he measured the diameter of each quarter, and calculated the circumference of his water bottle as 29.78 cm. The quarter could be used as a referent for one _____*i*_____, and, according to Roger's measurement, it has a diameter of _____*ii*_____ cm.

1. The given statement is completed by the information in which of the following tables?

A.

i	*ii*
centimetre	1.19

B.

i	*ii*
centimetre	2.37

C.

i	*ii*
inch	1.19

D.

i	*ii*
inch	2.37

2. Charissa ran 26 km in 3 hrs and 15 min. To the nearest hundredth metre per second, what was her average speed?

    A. 2.22 m/s   B. 2.29 m/s

    C. 3.15 m/s   D. 8.00 m/s

Use the following information to answer the next question.

A vernier calliper was used to measure the inside diameter of a pipe in centimetres. In the given diagram, the bottom scale is the sliding scale. According to the scale reading, the inside diameter of the pipe is _____*i*_____ cm and, when converted to inches, is approximately _____*ii*_____ in.

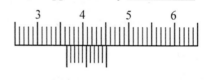

3. The given statement is completed by the information in which of the following tables?

A.

i	*ii*
3.64	$1\frac{1}{4}$

B.

i	*ii*
3.64	$1\frac{7}{16}$

C.

i	*ii*
4.04	$1\frac{3}{8}$

D.

i	*ii*
4.04	$1\frac{9}{16}$

Use the following information to answer the next question.

Mount Robson in British Columbia is 3 954 m high.

Numerical Response

4. The height of Mount Robson, to the nearest yard, is _____ yd.

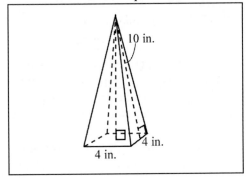

10 in.

4 in.

4 in.

5. What is the total surface area of the right square pyramid shown?

A. 68 in²   **B.** 76 in²

C. 88 in²   **D.** 96 in²

An orange with a radius of 4 cm is divided into 8 equal segments by cutting it in halves along the same axis, as shown.

6. What is the surface area of each of the 8 segments?

A. 27π cm²   **B.** 25π cm²

C. 24π cm²   **D.** 22π cm²

A circus tent is cylindrical up to a height of 3.5 yd, and conical above that.
The diameter of the base is 102 yd, and the slant height of the conical part is 55 yd.

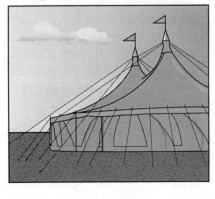

7. To the nearest hundredth square yard, the amount of canvas needed to construct the tent is

A. 9 052.23 yd²   **B.** 9 372.15 yd²

C. 9 948.25 yd²   **D.** 9 933.72 yd²

This toy has a hemispherical base and a conical top. The perpendicular height of the right cone is 14 cm, and the radius of the hemisphere is 7 cm.

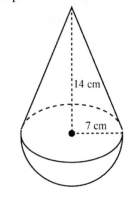

14 cm

7 cm

8. What is the approximate volume of the toy, to the nearest whole cubic centimetre?

A. 1 437 cm³   **B.** 1 337 cm³

C. 1 117 cm³   **D.** 1 028 cm³

Use the following information to answer the next question.

A right rectangular prism with the given dimensions is shown.

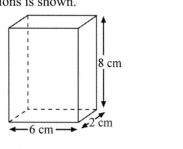

8 cm
6 cm
2 cm

Numerical Response

9. To the nearest cubic centimetre, the maximum volume of the right rectangular pyramid that would fit snugly inside the illustrated rectangular right prism is _____ cm^3.

Use the following information to answer the next question.

The Trans-Alaska Pipeline System transports oil across Alaska. One of the pipes in the system has a diameter of 1.5 m and a volume of 106 m^3.

Numerical Response

10. The length of the pipe, rounded to the nearest tenth of a metre, is _____ m.

Use the following information to answer the next question.

Jeremy makes the following measurements as a surveyor so he can determine the distance, x, between the two caves.

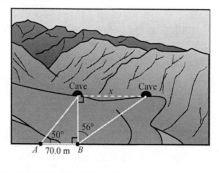

Cave x Cave
50°   56°
A 70.0 m B

11. The distance, x, to the nearest tenth metre, between the two caves is

A. 56.3 m   **B.** 69.2 m

C. 100.6 m   **D.** 123.7 m

Use the following information to answer the next question.

Michael is sitting in a movie theatre at a certain point, M, as shown in the given diagram. With a clinometer, he measures the angle of elevation to the top of the screen as 38°. With a tape measure, he measures a distance of 28 ft from his seat to the bottom of the screen.

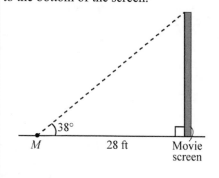

38°
M   28 ft   Movie screen

12. Rounded to the nearest foot, what is the height of the movie screen?

A. 45 ft   **B.** 35 ft

C. 22 ft   **D.** 17 ft

Use the following information to answer the next question.

A certain hiking trail has a grade of 15%. This value means that the trail climbs 15 m vertically for each 100 m of horizontal distance.

13. Rounded to the nearest tenth of a degree, what is the measure of the angle of elevation of the trail?

A. 3.8°

B. 8.5°

C. 81.5°

D. 86.2°

Use the following information to answer the next question.

A diagram of a triangle is given.

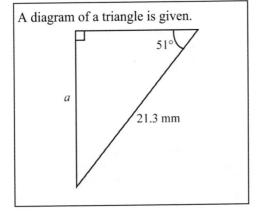

14. To the nearest tenth of a millimetre, what is the length of side *a*?

A. 13.4 mm

B. 16.6 mm

C. 26.3 mm

D. 27.4 mm

Use the following information to answer the next question.

Triangle *ABC* is given.

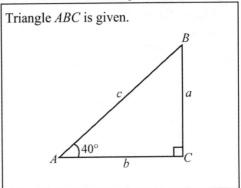

15. Which of the following equations cannot be used to solve for side *b* in the given triangle?

A. $b = c \times \cos 40°$

B. $b = c \times \sin 50°$

C. $\sin 40° = \dfrac{b}{c}$

D. $\tan 40° = \dfrac{a}{b}$

16. In which of the following triangles does $\cos \angle B = 0.8$?

A.

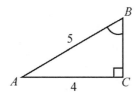

B.

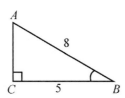

C.

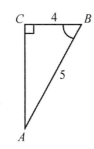

D.

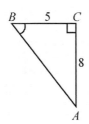

Use the following information to answer the next question.

A diagram of two right angle triangles is shown.

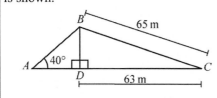

Numerical Response

17. Correct to the nearest tenth metre, the length of side *AB* is _____ m.

Use the following information to answer the next question.

A student was asked to calculate the numeric value of $x + y$.

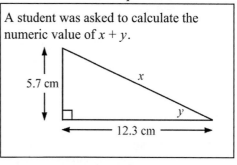

Numerical Response

18. The value, to the nearest tenth, is _____.

Use the following information to answer the next multipart question.

19. The diameter of a men's basketball is approximately 24 cm. The surface area of a volleyball is about 215 in²

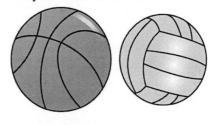

Written Response

a) Determine the volume of air needed to fill a men's basketball, rounded to the nearest cubic centimetre.

b) To the nearest cubic centimetre, what volume of air is needed to fill a volleyball?

c) In terms of volume, how many times larger is a men's basketball than a volleyball? Give the answer to the nearest tenth.

Use the following information to answer the next multipart question.

20. To estimate the amount of new water pipe required for part of a golf course, the golf course designer used the given diagram with the indicated measurements.

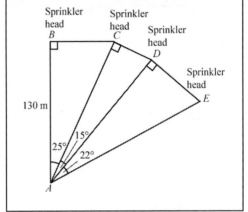

| **Written Response** |

a) What is the correct distance from the sprinkler head at point B to the sprinkler head at point C, to the nearest tenth of a metre?

b) What is the correct distance from the sprinkler head at point D to the sprinkler head at point E, to the nearest metre?

An image of a right triangular prism is given.

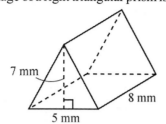

7 mm

8 mm

5 mm

21. What is the surface area of the given right triangular prism, to the nearest tenth of a square millimetre?

A. 193.9 mm^2

B. 212.6 mm^2

C. 228.9 mm^2

D. 247.6 mm^2

22. What is the volume of the given right triangular prism, rounded to the nearest whole?

A. 280 mm^3 B. 240 mm^3

C. 200 mm^3 D. 140 mm^3

The given right cylinder represents a rain barrel with an open top.

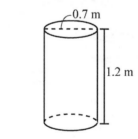

0.7 m

1.2 m

23. Rounded to the nearest hundredth of a cubic metre, how much rain water can be collected in this barrel?

A. 1.85 m^3 B. 0.82 m^3

C. 0.46 m^3 D. 0.38 m^3

24. To the nearest hundredth of a square metre, how much aluminum is required to produce this barrel?

A. 1.71 m^2 B. 3.02 m^2

C. 3.41 m^2 D. 5.24 m^2

ANSWERS AND SOLUTIONS
UNIT TEST

1. D	6. C	11. D	16. D	21. A
2. A	7. D	12. C	17. 24.9	22. D
3. B	8. A	13. B	18. 38.4	23. C
4. 4324	9. 32	14. B	19. WR	24. B
5. D	10. 60.0	15. C	20. WR	

1. D

Draw a sketch of the situation represented in the problem.

- Draw a large circle, and label it "water bottle."
- Draw four small circles side by side across the diameter of the large circle, and label them "quarters."
- Draw a dotted line across the diameter of the circle through the centres of the quarters.

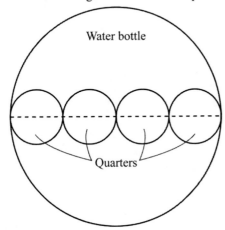

Step 2
Determine the unit of measure that the diameter of the quarter best represents.

A quarter has a diameter of approximately one inch. Therefore, it is a good referent for one inch.

Step 3
Determine the diameter, d_w, of the water bottle.

$$C_w = \pi d_w$$
$$d_w = \frac{C_w}{\pi}$$
$$= \frac{29.78}{\pi}$$
$$\approx 9.479\ 27 \text{ cm}$$

Step 4
Since there are four quarters representing the diameter, d_w, of the water bottle, the diameter of each quarter, d_q, can be determined.

$$d_w = 4 \times d_q$$
$$d_q = \frac{d_w}{4}$$
$$= \frac{9.479\ 27}{4}$$
$$\approx 2.3698 \text{ cm}$$

Therefore, each quarter has a diameter of approximately 2.37 cm.

2. A

Step 1
Convert the time into minutes.
To convert 3 hrs and 15 min into minutes, multiply 3 by 60 and add 15.
$$3 \times 60 + 15 = 195 \text{ min}$$

Step 2
Calculate Charissa's average speed.

Use unit analysis to convert $\dfrac{26 \text{ km}}{195 \text{ min}}$ into m/s.

$$\frac{26 \text{ km}}{195 \text{ min}} \times \frac{1\ 000 \text{ m}}{1 \text{ km}} \times \frac{1 \text{ min}}{60 \text{ s}} = \frac{26\ 000 \text{ m}}{11\ 700 \text{ s}}$$
$$\approx 2.22 \text{ m/s}$$

Rounded to the nearest hundredth metre per second, Charissa's average speed was 2.22 m/s.

3. B

Step 1

Determine the inside diameter of the pipe, i, as given by the scale reading.

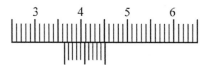

The left edge of the sliding scale shows that the reading is slightly more than 3.6. The hundredths decimal place is found by the next mark on the sliding scale that first lines up with a mark on the top scale. Counting from the left, this is at the end of the fourth space. Therefore, the reading is 3.64 cm, and the value of i is 3.64.

Step 2

Convert centimetres into inches.

There are 2.54 cm in 1 in.

Convert 3.64 cm into inches by setting up a proportion, in which x represents the measure of the unknown quantity in inches.

$$\frac{2.54 \text{ cm}}{1 \text{ in}} = \frac{3.64 \text{ in}}{x}$$
$$2.54x = 3.64 \times 1$$
$$x = \frac{3.64}{2.54}$$
$$\approx 1.433\,07 \text{ in}$$

Step 3

Convert the decimal number into a fraction.

Convert the value to the right of the decimal, 0.433 07, into a fraction with a denominator of 16.

$$\frac{0.433\,07}{1} \times \frac{16}{16} = \frac{6.929\,12}{16} \approx \frac{7}{16}$$

When 3.64 cm is converted to inches, it is approximately $1\frac{7}{16}$ in.

Therefore, ii $= 1\frac{7}{16}$.

4. 4324

There is 0.9144 m in 1 yd.
Convert 3 954 m into yards. Set up the appropriate proportion, where x represents the number of yards.

$$\frac{\text{m}}{\text{yd}} \rightarrow \frac{0.9144}{1} = \frac{3\,954}{x}$$
$$(0.9144)(x) = (1)(3\,954)$$
$$0.9144x = 3\,954$$
$$x = \frac{3\,954}{0.9144}$$
$$\approx 4\,324.147 \text{ yd}$$

Rounded to the nearest yard, the height of Mount Robson is 4 324 yd.

5. D

Step 1

Determine the formula for the total surface area of the pyramid.

$$SA_{\text{pyramid}} = SA_{\text{base}} + SA_{\text{triangular faces}}$$
$$= (l \times w) + 4\left(\frac{l \times h}{2}\right)$$

Step 2

Substitute the known values into the formula.

$$(l \times w) + 4\left(\frac{l \times h}{2}\right)$$
$$= (4 \times 4) + 4\left(\frac{4 \times 10}{2}\right)$$

Step 3

Evaluate following the order of operations.

$$(4 \times 4) + 4\left(\frac{4 \times 10}{2}\right)$$
$$= 16 + 4\left(\frac{40}{2}\right)$$
$$= 16 + 4(20)$$
$$= 16 + 80$$
$$= 96 \text{ in}^2$$

6. C

After being cut, the orange will have 8 segments, each with the same volume and surface area.

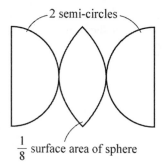

$\frac{1}{8}$ surface area of sphere

A net diagram can be drawn as follows:

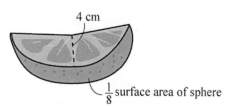

2 semi-circles

$\frac{1}{8}$ surface area of sphere

The surface area of each piece:
piece = area outside peel +2 (area of the semicircles).

The surface area of the outside peel will be an eighth of the total surface area of a sphere

$$\text{area} = \frac{1}{8} \times 4\pi r^2$$
$$= \frac{1}{2}\pi r^2$$

Each semicircle has a radius of 4 cm. Therefore,
$\therefore$ 2(area of semicircle)

$$= 2\left[\frac{1}{2}\right]\pi r^2$$
$$= \pi r^2$$

The surface area of each piece

$$= \left(\frac{1}{2}\right)\pi r^2 + \pi r^2$$
$$= \left(\frac{1}{2}\right)\pi(4)^2 + \pi(4)^2$$
$$= 8\pi + 16\pi$$
$$= 24\pi \text{ cm}^2$$

7. D

Step 1
Create a formula to determine the surface area of the tent.
Total surface area =
curved surface area of cylinder
+curved surface area of cone
$$SA_{\text{total}} = A_{\text{cylinder's lateral face}} + A_{\text{cone's lateral face}}$$
$$SA_{\text{total}} = 2\pi rh + \pi rs$$

Step 2
Calculate the amount of canvas used to make the tent. Since the diameter is 102 yd, the radius is 51 yd. Substitute the height of the cylinder is 3.5 yd for h, the radius of both the cylinder and the cone is 102 yd for r, and the slant height of the cone 55 yd for s.
$$SA_{\text{total}} = 2\pi rh + \pi rs$$
$$= 2\pi \times 51 \times 3.5 + \pi \times 51 \times 55$$
$$\approx 1\ 121.548\ 58 + 8\ 812.1674$$
$$\approx 9\ 933.72 \text{ yd}^2$$
The amount of canvas needed to construct the tent, to the nearest hundredth square yard, is
9 933.72 yd^2.

8. A
Determine the volume of the toy.

Using the appropriate volume formulas, add the volume of the right cone to the volume of the hemisphere.
$$V_{\text{toy}} = V_{\text{cone}} + V_{\text{hemisphere}}$$
$$V_{\text{toy}} = \frac{\pi r^2 h}{3} + \frac{2\pi r^3}{3}$$

Notice that in the formula for a hemisphere, $\frac{2}{3}$ is used rather than $\frac{4}{3}$ because you are only calculating half of a sphere.

Substitute the given values into the formulas and solve.
$$V_{\text{toy}} = \frac{\pi \times (7)^2 \times (14)}{3} + \frac{2 \times \pi \times (7)^3}{3}$$
$$= \frac{\pi \times 49 \times 14}{3} + \frac{2 \times \pi \times 343}{3}$$
$$= 718.38 + 718.38$$
$$\approx 1436.76 \text{ cm}^3$$

Therefore, the approximate volume of the toy, to the nearest whole cubic centimetre, is 1 437 cm^3.

9. 32

The volume of a right pyramid is $\frac{1}{3}$ the volume of a right prism with the same length, width, and height. Determine the maximum volume of the pyramid.
$$V_{\text{pyramid}} = \frac{1}{3}V_{\text{prism}}$$
$$= \frac{1}{3}\left(A_{\text{base}} \times h\right)$$
$$= \frac{1}{3}(lw) \times h$$

Substitute 6 for l, 2 for w, and 8 for h.
$$V_{\text{pyramid}} = \frac{1}{3}(6 \times 2 \times 8)$$
$$= \frac{1}{3}(96)$$
$$= 32 \text{ cm}^3$$

The maximum volume of the pyramid that would fit snugly inside the prism is 32 cm^3.

10. 60.0

Step 1

Determine the radius of the pipe.

$$r = \frac{d}{2}$$
$$= \frac{1.5}{2}$$
$$= 0.75 \text{ m}$$

Step 2

Calculate the length of the pipe, h, by applying the formula for the volume of a cylinder, $V = \pi r^2 h$. Substitute the known values into the formula, and solve.

$$V = \pi r^2 h$$
$$106 = \pi (0.75)^2 h$$
$$106 = \pi \times 0.5625 \times h$$

Divide both sides by ($\pi \times 0.5625$).

$$\frac{106}{\pi \times 0.5625} = h$$
$$59.98 \approx h$$

Rounded to the nearest tenth of a metre, the length of the pipe is 60.0 m.

11. D

Draw and label a diagram that represents this situation. Let C_1 and C_2 be the points that represent the cave.

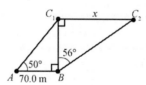

First, find the distance of BC_1.

$$\tan 50° = \frac{BC_1}{70.0}$$
$$70.0(\tan 50°) = BC_1$$
$$BC_1 = 83.422\ 751\ 48$$

Next, find the distance between the caves, x.

$$\tan 56° = \frac{x}{83.422\ 751\ 48}$$
$$83.422\ 751\ 48(\tan 56°) = x$$
$$x \approx 123.7$$

The distance between the caves, to the nearest tenth metre, is 123.7 m.

12. C

Step 1

Draw a diagram representing the situation. Label the triangle with a variable for the unknown measurement.

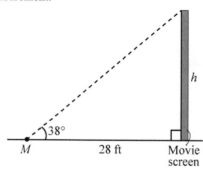

Step 2

Apply the appropriate trigonometric ratio to solve for the unknown height.

$$\tan \theta = \frac{\text{opposite}}{\text{hypotenuse}}$$
$$\tan 38° = \frac{h}{28}$$
$$28 \times \tan 38° = h$$
$$21.88 \text{ ft} \approx h$$

Therefore, the height of the movie screen is approximately 22 ft.

13. B

Step 1

Draw and label a diagram to represent the situation.

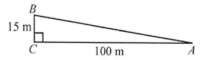

Step 2

Determine and apply the appropriate trigonometric ratio to find the measure of the angle of elevation. Since the angle of elevation is the angle formed by the horizontal and side AB, the angle of elevation is angle A. The measures of the opposite and adjacent sides are known, so use the tangent ratio to find the measure of angle A.

$$\tan A = \frac{\text{opposite}}{\text{adjacent}}$$
$$= \frac{15}{100}$$
$$= 0.15$$

Step 3

Use the inverse tangent function to determine the measure of angle A. The inverse tangent function is accessed with the keys [inv] [tan] or the key $\left[\tan^{-1}\right]$ on a calculator.

$A = \tan^{-1}(0.15)$
$ \approx 8.531°$

Rounded to the nearest tenth, the measure of the angle of elevation is 8.5°.

14. B

Use the sine ratio to determine the length of side a.

$\sin \theta = \dfrac{\text{opposite}}{\text{hypotenuse}}$

$\sin 51° = \dfrac{a}{21.3}$

$\ a = (21.3)(\sin 51°)$

$\ a \approx 16.6 \text{ mm}$

To the nearest tenth of a millimetre, the length of side a is 16.6 mm.

15. C

Step 1

Determine if the equation $b = c \times \cos 40°$ is correct. The cosine ratio is used to solve for b.

$\cos A = \dfrac{\text{adjacent}}{\text{hypotenuse}}$

$\cos 40° = \dfrac{b}{c}$

$\cos 40° \times c = b$

Hence, this equation can be used to solve for b.

Step 2

Determine if the equation $b = c \times \sin 50°$ is correct. The sine ratio is used to solve for b.

Given that there is a right angle triangle and that the sum of all angles within a triangle equals 180°, angle B must equal $180° - 90° - 40° = 50°$.

$\sin B = \dfrac{\text{opposite}}{\text{hypotenuse}}$

$\sin 50° = \dfrac{b}{c}$

$\sin 50° \times c = b$

Therefore, this equation can be used to solve for b.

Step 3

Determine if the equation $\sin 40° = \dfrac{b}{c}$ is correct.

The value of $\sin 40°$ is given as $\dfrac{b}{c}$.

However, from the diagram, $\sin 40° = \dfrac{a}{c}$ because $\sin \theta = \dfrac{\text{opposite}}{\text{hypotenuse}}$.

Therefore, this equation cannot be used to derive a value for side b.

Step 4

Determine if the equation $\tan 40° = \dfrac{a}{b}$ is correct.

The tangent ratio is used to solve for b.

$\tan A = \dfrac{\text{opposite}}{\text{adjacent}}$

$\tan 40° = \dfrac{a}{b}$

Therefore, this equation can be used to solve for side b.

The only equation that is incorrect and cannot be used is $\sin 40° = \dfrac{b}{c}$.

16. D

Since $\cos \angle B = 0.8$, this value represents the ratio of the adjacent side to the hypotenuse. Identify the triangle in which this ratio is equal to 0.8.

Step 1

Determine if triangle A is correct.

Determine the length of the adjacent side using the Pythagorean theorem.

$(BC)^2 = (AB)^2 - (AC)^2$
$BC^2 = 5^2 - 4^2$
$BC^2 = 25 - 16$
$BC^2 = 9$
$\sqrt{BC^2} = \sqrt{9}$
$BC = 3$
$\cos \angle B = \dfrac{BC}{AB} = \dfrac{3}{5} = 0.6$

This ratio is not correct.

Step 2

Determine if triangle B is correct.

$\cos \angle B = \dfrac{BC}{AB} = \dfrac{5}{8} = 0.625$

This ratio is not correct.

Step 3

Determine if triangle C is correct.

Determine the length of the hypotenuse, AB.

$$AB^2 = BC^2 + AC^2$$
$$AB^2 = 4^2 + 5^2$$
$$AB^2 = 16 + 25$$
$$AB^2 = 41$$
$$\sqrt{AB^2} = \sqrt{41}$$
$$AB = \sqrt{41}$$
$$\cos \angle B = \frac{BC}{AB} = \frac{4}{\sqrt{41}} \approx 0.62$$

This ratio is not correct.

Step 4

Determine if triangle D is correct.

$$\cos \angle B = \frac{BC}{AB} = \frac{4}{5} = 0.8$$

This ratio is correct.

17. **24.9**

Step 1

Apply the Pythagorean theorem in $\triangle BDC$ in order to determine by length of side BD.

$$(BD)^2 + (CD)^2 = (BC)^2$$

Substitute 63 for CD and 65 for BC

$$(BD)^2 + (63)^2 = (65)^2$$
$$(BD)^2 + 3\ 969 = 4\ 225$$
$$(BD)^2 = 256$$
$$BD = \sqrt{256}$$
$$BD = 16 \text{ m}$$

Step 2

Apply the sine ratio in $\triangle ADB$ in order to determine the length of side AB.

$$\sin 40° = \frac{BD}{AB}$$

Substitute 16 for BD.

$$\sin 40° = \frac{16}{AB}$$
$$AB \sin 40° = 16$$
$$AB = \frac{16}{\sin 40°}$$
$$AB \approx 24.89 \text{ m}$$

Correct to the nearest tenth of a metre, the length of side AB is 24.9 m.

18. **38.4**

Step 1

Use the Pythagorean theorem to determine the value of x.

$$a^2 + b^2 = c^2$$
$$(5.7)^2 + (12.3)^2 = x^2$$
$$32.49 + 151.29 = x^2$$
$$183.78 = x^2$$
$$13.56 \text{ cm} \approx x$$

Step 2

Use the tangent ratio to determine the value of y.

$$\tan \theta = \frac{\text{opposite}}{\text{adjacent}}$$
$$\tan y = \frac{5.7}{12.3}$$
$$y = \tan^{-1}\left(\frac{5.7}{12.3}\right)$$
$$y \approx 24.86°$$

Rounded to the nearest tenth, the numeric value of $x + y = 13.56 + 24.86 = 38.4$.

19. **a) WR**

Step 1

Calculate the radius, r, of the basketball.

$$r = \frac{d}{2}$$
$$= \frac{24}{2}$$
$$= 12 \text{ cm}$$

Step 2

Using the formula for the volume of a sphere, determine the volume of air needed.

$$V_{\text{sphere}} = \frac{4\pi r^3}{3}$$
$$= \frac{4\pi(12)^3}{3}$$
$$= \frac{4\pi(1\ 728)}{3}$$
$$\approx 7\ 238.229\ 474 \text{ cm}^3$$

Rounded to the nearest cubic centimetre, the volume of air needed to fill a men's basketball is 7 238 cm^3.

b) WR

Use the formula for the surface area of a sphere to determine the radius, r, of the volleyball.

$$SA_{sphere} = 4\pi r^2$$
$$215 = 4\pi r^2$$
$$\frac{215}{4\pi} = r^2$$
$$r = \sqrt{\frac{215}{4\pi}}$$
$$r \approx 4.136\ 3216\ \text{in}$$

The radius of the volleyball is approximately 4.136 3216 in.

Step 2

Convert 4.136 3216 in into centimetres by setting up the appropriate proportion, in which x represents the number of centimetres.

$$\frac{\text{in}}{\text{cm}} = \frac{1}{1.54} = \frac{4.136\ 3216}{x}$$
$$x = (4.136\ 3216)(1.54)$$
$$x \approx 10.506\ 256\ 87\ \text{cm}$$

The radius of the volleyball is approximately 10.506 256 87 cm.

Step 3

Determine the volume of the volleyball using the formula for the volume of a sphere.

$$V_{sphere} = \frac{4\pi r^3}{3}$$
$$= \frac{4\pi (10.506\ 256\ 87)^3}{3}$$
$$\approx 4\ 857.7\ \text{cm}^3$$

To the nearest cubic centimetre, 4 858 cm³ of air is needed to fill a volleyball.

c) WR

Compare the volumes of the basketball and the volleyball.

$$\frac{V_{basketball}}{V_{volleyball}} = \frac{7\ 238\ \text{cm}^3}{4\ 858\ \text{cm}^3} \approx 1.49$$

The volume of a men's basketball is about 1.5 times the volume of a volleyball.

20. a) WR

In $\triangle ABC$, the distance BC can be determined as follows:

$$\tan 25° = \frac{BC}{AB}$$

Substitute 130 for AB.

$$\tan 25° = \frac{BC}{130}$$
$$BC = 130 \times \tan 25°$$
$$BC \approx 60.62$$

The distance from the sprinkler head at point B to the sprinkler head at point C, to the nearest tenth of a metre, is 60.6 m.

b) WR

In order to determine the distance from the sprinkler head at point D to the sprinkler head at point E, first find the length of AD. This can be done as follows:

In $\triangle ABC$, $\cos 25° = \frac{AB}{AC}$.

Substitute 130 for AC.

$$\cos 25° = \frac{130}{AC}$$
$$AC \times \cos 25° = 130$$
$$AC \approx 143.44$$

In $\triangle ACD$, $\cos 15° = \frac{AC}{AD}$.

Substitute 143.44 for AB.

$$\cos 15° = \frac{143.44}{AD}$$
$$AD \times \cos 15° = 146.44$$
$$AD \approx 148.50$$

Now use the tangent ratio.

$$\tan(A) = \frac{DE}{AD}$$
$$\tan(22°) = \frac{DE}{148.50}$$
$$DE = 60$$

The distance from the sprinkler head at point D to the sprinkler head at point E, to the nearest metre, is 60 m.

21. A

Calculate the widths of the two rectangles located along the sides of the triangular prism. Use the Pythagorean theorem to calculate the width of each of the two rectangles.

$$a^2 + b^2 = c^2$$
$$(7)^2 + (2.5)^2 = c^2$$
$$49 + 6.25 = c^2$$
$$55.25 = c^2$$
$$7.43 \text{ mm} = c^2$$

The width of each of the rectangles located along the sides of the triangular prism is 7.43 mm.

Step 2

Calculate the surface area of the triangular prism. Use the value for the widths of the rectangles, along with the other given values, to determine the sum of the surface areas of the five faces of the triangular prism.

$$SA = 2\left(\frac{bh}{2}\right)_{\text{faces}} + 2(lw)_{\text{sides}} + (lw)_{\text{bottom}}$$
$$\approx 2\left(\frac{7 \times 5}{2}\right) + 2(8 \times 7.43) + (8 \times 5)$$
$$\approx 35 + 118.88 + 40$$
$$= 193.88 \text{ mm}^2$$

Rounded to the nearest tenth of a square millimetre, the surface area of the triangular prism is 193.9 mm².

22. D

Step 1

Construct a formula to calculate the volume of a right triangular prism.

The volume of a right triangular prism is equal to the area of the triangular base multiplied by the height of the prism.

$$V = A_{\text{base}} \times h$$
$$= \left(\frac{b \times h_{\text{t}}}{2}\right) \times h$$

Step 2

Substitute the given values into the formula, and evaluate.

$$V = \left(\frac{b \times h_{\text{t}}}{2}\right) \times h$$
$$V = \frac{5 \times 7}{2} \times 8$$
$$V = 140 \text{ mm}^3$$

Rounded to the nearest whole, the volume of the given right triangular prism is 140 mm³.

23. C.

First, find the radius of the base.

$$r = \frac{d}{2}$$
$$= \frac{0.7}{2}$$
$$= 0.35 \text{ m}$$

Now, determine how much water the rain barrel can hold, by calculating the volume of the right cylinder, using the volume formula.

$$V_{\text{cylinder}} = (\text{area of base})(\text{height})$$
$$= (\pi r^2)(h)$$
$$= \pi \times (0.35)^2 \times (1.2)$$
$$\approx 0.46 \text{ m}^3$$

24. B

Step 1

Construct a formula for the total surface area. Only the base is included in the surface area since there is no cover on the barrel. The total surface consists of a circle (the bottom) and a rectangle (the lateral side of the cylinder).

$$SA = \pi r2 + 2\pi rh$$

Step2

Substitute the given dimensions into the formula, and evaluate.

The radius of the cylinder is $\frac{0.7}{2} = 0.35$ m.

$$SA = \pi r^2 + 2\pi rh$$
$$SA = \pi (0.35)^2 + 2\pi (0.35)(1.2)$$
$$SA \approx 3.02 \text{ m}^2$$

NOTES

$$c^2 - a^2 = b^2$$

$$5^2 - 3^2 = b^2$$

$$25 - 9 = b^2$$

$$16 = b^2$$

$$\sqrt{16} = \sqrt{b^2}$$

$$4 = b$$

ALGEBRA AND NUMBER

	Table of Correlations				
	Outcome	**Practice Questions**	**Unit Test Questions**	**Practice Test 1**	**Practice Test 2**
10AN1	Develop algebraic reasoning and number sense.				
10AN1.1	Demonstrate an understanding of factors of whole numbers.	1, 2, 3, 4	1, 2, 3, 4	1	1
10AN1.2	Demonstrate an understanding of irrational numbers.	5, 6, 7, 8, 9	5, 6, 7, 8, 9	2, 3	2, 3
10AN1.3	Demonstrate an understanding of powers with integral and rational exponents.	10, 11, 12, 13, 14, 15, 16	10, 11, 12, 13, 14, 15, 16	4, 5, 6, 7	4, 5, 6
10AN1.4	Demonstrate an understanding of the multiplication of polynomial expressions, concretely, pictorially and symbolically.	17, 18, 19, 20, 21, 22	17, 18, 19, 20, 21, 22, 23	8, 9	7, 8, 9
10AN1.5	Demonstrate an understanding of common factors and trinomial factoring, concretely, pictorially and symbolically.	23, 24, 25, 26, 27, 28, 29, 30	24, 25, 26, 27, 28, 29, 30	10, 11, 12	10, 11, 12

10AN1.1 Demonstrate an understanding of factors of whole numbers.

WORKING WITH WHOLE NUMBERS

Whole numbers can be grouped into specific sets as a result of their common factors and multiples.

PRIME FACTORIZATION OF A WHOLE NUMBER

The process of writing a whole number (other than 0 and 1) as the product of its prime factors is called **prime factorization**. Recall some of the terminology related to the process of factoring:

- A **factor** is a number that divides evenly into another number, and a **prime factor** is a factor that is also a prime number.
- A **prime number** is any whole number that has only two factors, the number 1 and itself. The first eight prime numbers are: 2, 3, 5, 7, 11, 13, 17, and 19.
- A **composite number** is any whole number that has more than two factors. For example, the number 16 is a composite number with the five factors of 1, 2, 4, 8, and 16.

Every composite number can be written as a product of its prime factors. A **factor tree** is a useful diagram to show the process of prime factorization. The tree can appear in different forms depending on the initial two factors found.

Example

Determine the prime factorization of 24 using a factor tree.

Solution

Write 24 as a product of two factors.
Then, continue to factor the resulting values until prime factors appear at the bottom of the factor tree.

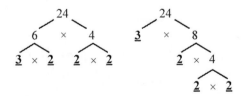

According to the factor trees, the prime factorization of 24 is as follows:
$3 \times 2 \times 2 \times 2$.

DETERMINING THE GREATEST COMMON FACTOR (GCF) OF WHOLE NUMBERS

The **greatest common factor (GCF)** of two or more whole numbers is the largest factor shared by these numbers. There are several methods for finding the GCF of a set of numbers and solve related problems.

Example

Determine the greatest common factor of 126 and 98.

Solution

Method 1—List Factors
1. List the factors of each number.
   126 = 1, 2, 3, 6, 7, 9, **14**, 18, 21, 42, 63, 126
   98 = 1, 2, 7, **14**, 49, 98
2. Select the greatest factor common to both 126 and 98. The greatest common factor is 14.

Method 2—Prime Factorization
1. Determine the prime factors of each number.
   $126 = 2 \times 7 \times 3 \times 3$
   $98 = 2 \times 7 \times 7$
2. Determine the greatest common factor.
   - The product of the shared prime factors is the greatest common factor.
   - The shared prime factors are 2×7, so the greatest common factor of 126 and 98 is 14.

Example

Cliff has 252 blue marbles, 270 red marbles, and 324 green marbles. He wants to distribute them among the greatest number of bags possible so that each bag contains the same number of each colour of marble.

How many bags will Cliff need to separate the marbles evenly?

Solution

Determine the maximum number of groupings with the same number of each type of marble by identifying the GCF of 252, 270, and 324.

The prime factorizations of the three numbers are as follows:
$252 = \mathbf{2} \times 2 \times \mathbf{3} \times \mathbf{3} \times 7$
$270 = \mathbf{2} \times \mathbf{3} \times \mathbf{3} \times 3 \times 5$
$324 = \mathbf{2} \times 2 \times \mathbf{3} \times \mathbf{3} \times 3 \times 3$

The GCF is $2 \times 3 \times 3 = 18$.
Therefore, Cliff will need 18 bags.

Each bag will contain $\dfrac{252}{18} = 14$ blue marbles,

$\dfrac{270}{18} = 15$ red marbles, and $\dfrac{324}{18} = 18$ green marbles.

DETERMINING THE LEAST COMMON MULTIPLE (LCM) OF WHOLE NUMBERS

A **multiple** is a number that is the product of a natural number and another natural number.
For example, the first three multiples of 17 are as follows:
$17 \times 1 = 17$
$17 \times 2 = 34$
$17 \times 3 = 51$

A common multiple is a number that is a multiple of two or more numbers.
The **least common multiple**(LCM) of two or more numbers is the lowest multiple common to all the numbers. There are several methods for finding the LCM of a set of numbers and solve related problems.

Example

A particular factory has three signals. A bell rings every 8 hours, a whistle blows every 9 hours, and a light flashes every 12 hours.

If the power to the bell, whistle, and light are all turned on at the same time, how often will the three signals happen at the same time?

Solution

Determine the least common multiple of 8, 9, and 12.

Method 1
Make a list of the multiples of each number.

- Multiples of 8: 8, 16, 24, 32, 40, 48, 56, 64, **72**…
- Multiples of 9: 9, 18, 27, 36, 45, 54, 63, **72**, 81…
- Multiples of 12: 12, 24, 36, 48, 60, **72**, 84, 96…

Identify the lowest multiple shared by all three numbers.
The LCM is 72.

Method 2
Write the prime factorization of each number, and select the combination of the largest set of each prime factor in the factorizations.

$8 = \mathbf{2 \times 2 \times 2} \qquad 9 = \mathbf{3 \times 3} \qquad 12 = 2 \times 2 \times 3$

Largest set of 2   Largest set of 3

The LCM is the product of these factors.
$2 \times 2 \times 2 \times 3 \times 3 = 72$

Since the LCM is $2 \times 2 \times 2 \times 3 \times 3 = 72$, the bell, whistle, and light signal will happen at the same time every 72 hours.

PERFECT SQUARES, SQUARE ROOTS, PERFECT CUBES, AND CUBE ROOTS

A **perfect square** is a whole number that can be expressed as the product of two identical numbers. A positive **square root** is a natural number that, when multiplied by itself, produces a perfect square.

For example, $3 \times 3 = 9$, so 9 is a perfect square and 3 is the positive square root of 9. This square root can be expressed as $\sqrt{9} = 3$.

A perfect square can be represented by drawing a square, where the area is the perfect square and the length of each side is the square root.

Example

Use a diagram to show that 25 is a perfect square with a square root of 5.

Solution

Draw a square with an area of 25 square units. Each side of the square has a length of 5 units.

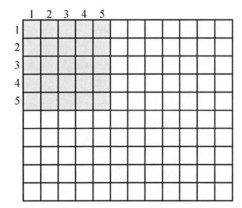

$$A = s \times s \qquad s = \sqrt{A}$$
$$= 5 \times 5 \text{ and } = \sqrt{25}$$
$$= 25 \qquad = 5$$

A **perfect cube** is a number that can be expressed as the product of three identical numbers.
A **cube root** is a number that, when multiplied by itself three times, produces a perfect cube.
For example, $6 \times 6 \times 6 = 216$, so 216 is a perfect cube and 6 is the cube root of 216. This cube root can also be expressed as $\sqrt[3]{216} = 6$.

A perfect cube can be represented by drawing a cube, where the volume is the perfect cube and the length of each side is the cube root.

Example

Represent the perfect cube 1 728 and its corresponding cube root of 12.

Solution

Draw a cube that represents the volume of 1 728 cubic units. Each side of the cube has a length of 12 units.

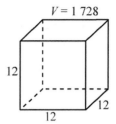

$$V = s \times s \times s$$
$$= 12 \times 12 \times 12$$
$$= 1\ 728$$
and
$$s = \sqrt[3]{V}$$
$$= \sqrt[3]{1\ 728}$$
$$= 12$$

Problems involving square roots and cube roots can be solved using prime factorization, a graphing calculator, or other strategies.

Example

Determine the cube root of 3 375.

Solution

Step 1

Write 3 375 as a product of its prime factors.
$$3\ 375 = 3 \times 3 \times 3 \times 5 \times 5 \times 5$$

Step 2

Group the factors into three matching sets.
$$3\ 375 = (3 \times 5) \times (3 \times 5) \times (3 \times 5)$$

Step 3

Simplify each set of factors.

3 375 = 15 × 15 × 15

Thus, the cube root of 3 375 is 15.

Using a graphing calculator like the TI–83+, the cube root of 3 375 ($\sqrt[3]{3\ 375}$) can be evaluated using the $\sqrt[3]{}$ feature and the following keystrokes:

| MATH | 4 | 3 | 3 | 7 | 5 |) | ENTER |

The calculator screen shows the resulting value of 15.

Example

Nine square floor mats in a gymnasium are connected together to form a large square area of 11 664 in².

What is the length of the side of each square floor mat?

Solution

Step 1

Determine the area, A, of each square mat.

$A = 11\ 664 \div 9$

$\quad = 1\ 296\ \text{in}^2$

Step 2

Calculate the length of the side, s, of each mat using the square root feature ($\sqrt{\ }$) on the graphing calculator.

$s \times s = A$

$\quad s^2 = 1\ 296$

$\quad\quad s = \sqrt{1\ 296}$

$\quad\quad\ = 36$

The length of the side of each square floor mat is 36 in.

Use the following information to answer the next question.

When Yannick went to the grocery store for hotdogs and buns for a family picnic, he discovered that the hotdogs were sold in packages of 12 and that the buns were sold in packages of 8.

1. The **least** number of packages of hotdogs and buns that Yannick must buy in order to have the same number of hotdogs and buns is

   A. 2 packages of hotdogs and 3 packages of buns

   B. 3 packages of hotdogs and 2 packages of buns

   C. 4 packages of hotdogs and 6 packages of buns

   D. 6 packages of hotdogs and 4 packages of buns

2. Which one of the following diagrams of square tiles can be used to find the square root of 64?

   A.

   B.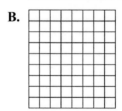

   C.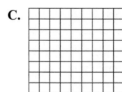

   D.

3. Which of the following statements is **true**?

   A. The number 1 has prime factors.

   B. The whole number 144 has 16 factors.

   C. A composite number has only two factors.

   D. The greatest common factor of 420 and 504 is 84.

Written Response
---

4. Identify a whole number that is both a perfect square and perfect cube found between 2 000 and 10 000.

10AN1.2 Demonstrate an understanding of irrational numbers.

UNDERSTANDING IRRATIONAL NUMBERS

Irrational numbers are a special subset of real numbers. Most irrational numbers are written as radicals. To understand the values of irrational numbers, it is important to know how to estimate, simplify, and evaluate them.

THE REAL NUMBER SYSTEM

Within the real number system, there are several subsets:

- Natural numbers (N)—the set of counting numbers $\{1, 2, 3, 4, \ldots\}$.
- Whole numbers (W)—the set of counting numbers and zero $\{0, 1, 2, 3, 4, \ldots\}$.
- Integers (I)—the set of natural numbers, their additive inverses, and zero $\{\ldots -3, -2, -1, 0, 1, 2, 3, \ldots\}$.
- Rational numbers (Q)—all numbers that can be written in the form of $\frac{a}{b}$, in which a and b are integers and $b \neq 0$.
- Irrational numbers ($\overline{Q}$)—all numbers that cannot be written in the form of $\frac{a}{b}$, in which a and b are integers and $b \neq 0$.

The set of rational numbers includes all integers (e.g., $-\frac{3}{1}$, 5, $\frac{110}{5}$, $\sqrt{16}$, $\sqrt[3]{-8}$) and all terminating and repeating decimals (e.g., $\frac{3}{4} = 0.75$, $-\frac{5}{3} = -1.\bar{6}$, $3\frac{3}{7} = 3.485\ 714\ 2857\ (1)\ldots$, $-\frac{11}{16} = -0.6875, \ldots$).

The set of irrational numbers include all non-terminating and non-repeating decimals (e.g., $0.252\ 252\ 225\ldots$, $\sqrt{2} = 1.414\ 213\ 56\ldots$, $\pi = 3.141\ 592\ 65\ldots$, $e = 2.718\ 281\ 82\ldots$, $\sqrt[3]{-120} = -4.932\ 4241\ldots$).

Together, the rational and irrational numbers make up the set of real numbers ($\mathbb{R}$). The relationships between the various number sets within the real number system are shown in this diagram.

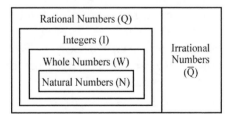

Understanding Radicals and Irrational Numbers

Irrational and rational numbers can be expressed as radicals. A **radical** is an expression consisting of the radical sign ($\sqrt{}$), a quantity under the sign called the **radicand**, and an **index** that indicates which root the radicand needs to be taken to.

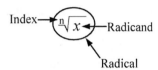

For example, the radical $\sqrt[4]{-81}$ reads "fourth root of negative 81." The index 4 means to find a root that will result in the radicand value of -81 when multiplied by itself four times.

Since $-81 = (-3) \times (-3) \times (-3) \times (-3)$, or $(-3)^4$, $\sqrt[4]{-81} = -3$.

By convention, square roots of radicands are written without their index of 2. ($\sqrt{8}$ means $\sqrt[2]{8}$)

Radicals with indexes greater than 3, such as $\sqrt[5]{2.4}$, can be converted to decimal approximations using the $\sqrt[x]{}$ feature on a graphing calculator like the TI-83+. Use the following key strokes:

$\boxed{5}$ $\boxed{\text{MATH}}$ $\boxed{5}$ $\boxed{\text{ENTER}}$ $\boxed{2}$ $\boxed{.}$ $\boxed{4}$ $\boxed{\text{ENTER}}$

The calculator screen shows the resulting evaluation.

```
5×√2.4
        1.191357898
```

Radicals that are square roots of perfect squares, cube roots of perfect cubes, and so on are rational numbers. Radicals that are not square roots of perfect squares, cube roots of perfect cubes, and so on are irrational numbers.

Example

$$\left\{ \sqrt[3]{-27},\ \sqrt{\frac{40}{3}},\ \sqrt[4]{2.4},\ \sqrt{\frac{25}{64}} \right\}$$

A set of numbers is given.

Identify the rational and irrational numbers in the given set of numbers.

Solution

The following numbers from the set are rational numbers:

- $\sqrt[3]{-27}$ is rational since -27 is a perfect cube: $-3 \times -3 \times -3 = -27$. The resulting value of -3 is an integer.

- $\sqrt{\dfrac{25}{64}}$ is rational since $\dfrac{25}{64}$ is a perfect square: $\dfrac{5}{8} \times \dfrac{5}{8} = \dfrac{25}{64}$. The resulting value of $\dfrac{5}{8} = 1.6$ is a terminating decimal.

The following numbers from the set are irrational numbers:

- $\sqrt{\dfrac{40}{3}}$ is irrational since $\dfrac{40}{3}$ is not a perfect square. The resulting value of $\sqrt{\dfrac{40}{3}} = 3.651\ 483\ 71\ldots$ is a non-terminating, non-repeating decimal number.

- $\sqrt[4]{2.4}$ is irrational since 2.4 is not a perfect fourth power. The resulting value of $\sqrt[4]{2.4} = 1.244\ 665\ 95\ldots$ is a non-terminating, non-repeating decimal number.

Radicals can be written in two forms:

- **Entire radicals** are radicals of the form $\sqrt[n]{x}$, such as $\sqrt{1.69}$, $\sqrt[3]{142}$, and $\sqrt[5]{-6}$.

- **Mixed radicals** are radicals of the form $a\sqrt[n]{x}$, where a is any rational number (except 0), such as $\sqrt[5]{2}$, $\dfrac{2}{3}\sqrt[3]{6}$, and $-1.2\sqrt[4]{32}$.

CONVERTING RADICAL FORMS

When converting radicals, it is important to remember the multiplication property of radicals: $\sqrt[n]{xy} = \sqrt[n]{x} \times \sqrt[n]{y}$. Any mixed radical, $a\sqrt[n]{x}$, can be converted to an entire radical by rewriting a as $\sqrt[n]{a^n}$ and then multiplying the simplified result with $\sqrt[n]{x}$.

Example

Convert $5\sqrt[3]{4}$ into an entire radical.

Solution

Step 1
Raise the coefficient value of 5 to an exponent of 3, and multiply it to the existing value underneath the radical sign.
$$5\sqrt[3]{4} = \sqrt[3]{4 \times 5^3}$$

Step 2
Multiply the two values underneath the radical sign together.
$$5\sqrt[3]{4} = \sqrt[3]{4 \times 125}$$
$$= \sqrt[3]{500}$$

Many radicals that are written as entire radicals, $\sqrt[n]{x}$, can be converted to mixed radicals (or simplified) if the radicand, x, can be written as the product of two factors, in which one of the factors is a perfect nth power. When simplifying entire radicals, choose the greatest perfect nth power. Several methods can be used to determine the greatest nth power.

Example

Write the radical $\sqrt[3]{320}$ in simplest mixed radical form.

Solution

Step 1
Determine two numbers that have a product equal to the value of the radicand, one of which must be a perfect cube.
These numbers are 64 and 5.

Step 2
Express the radicand as a product of these two numbers.
$$\sqrt[3]{320} = \sqrt[3]{64 \times 5}$$

Step 3
Separate the expression to isolate the perfect cube.
$$\sqrt[3]{320} = \sqrt[3]{64} \times \sqrt[3]{5}$$

Step 4
Take the cube root of the perfect cube, and place this value in front of the remaining radical.
$$\sqrt[3]{64} \times \sqrt[3]{5} = 4 \times \sqrt[3]{5}$$
$$= 4\sqrt[3]{5}$$

LOCATING IRRATIONAL NUMBERS ON A NUMBER LINE

The approximate location of an irrational number on a real number line can be determined.

Example

$$\{\sqrt[3]{-43}, \sqrt{10}, 2\sqrt{3}, -2\sqrt[4]{13}\}$$
A set of irrational numbers is given.

Use a number line to order the given set of irrational numbers.

Solution

Step 1
Convert all the irrational numbers into the same format.
Convert mixed radicals into entire form.
$$2\sqrt{3} = \sqrt{2^2 \times 3}$$
$$= \sqrt{4 \times 3}$$
$$= \sqrt{12}$$
$$-2\sqrt[4]{13} = -\sqrt[4]{2^4 \times 13}$$
$$= -\sqrt[4]{16 \times 13}$$
$$= -\sqrt[4]{208}$$

61

Step 2

Calculate their estimated position between roots of neighbouring perfect powers.

- The irrational number $\sqrt[3]{-43}$ lies about halfway between the perfect cubes -27 and -64. Since $\sqrt[3]{-27} = -3$ and $\sqrt[3]{-64} = -4$, its estimated value is -3.5.

- The irrational number $\sqrt{10}$ is slightly more than $\sqrt{9}$, and $\sqrt{9} = 3$, so its estimated value is 3.1.

- The irrational number $\sqrt{12}$ lies about halfway between the perfect squares 9 and 16. Since $\sqrt{9} = 3$ and $\sqrt{16} = 4$, its estimated value is 3.5.

- The irrational number $-\sqrt[4]{208}$ lies between the perfect powers of 256 and 81. Since $-\sqrt[4]{256} = -4$ and $-\sqrt[4]{81} = -3$, and $-\sqrt[4]{208}$ is closer to $-\sqrt[4]{256}$ than it is to $-\sqrt[4]{81}$, its estimated value is -3.8.

Step 3

Place each irrational number in ascending order on a number line.

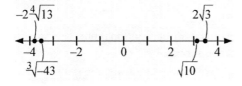

Use the following information to answer the next question.

Four statements about numbers are given.

I. The set of rational numbers is a subset of the set of real numbers.
II. The set of real numbers contains the set of irrational numbers.
III. The set of integers contains the set of whole numbers.
IV. The set of whole numbers is a subset of the set of natural numbers.

5. Which of the given statements are **true**?
   A. II, III, and IV
   B. I, III, and IV
   C. I, II, and IV
   D. I, II, and III

Use the following information to answer the next question.

A set of numbers is given.
$$\sqrt{0.64}, \sqrt{3}, \sqrt{6.4}, \sqrt{\frac{9}{16}}$$

6. Which of the given numbers are irrational?
   A. $\sqrt{0.64}, \sqrt{3}, \sqrt{6.4}, \sqrt{\frac{9}{16}}$
   B. $\sqrt{0.64}, \sqrt{3}, \sqrt{6.4}$
   C. $\sqrt{0.64}, \sqrt{\frac{9}{16}}$
   D. $\sqrt{3}, \sqrt{6.4}$

Use the following information to answer the next question.

> The approximate speed of a car prior to a collision can be determined using the formula $s = \sqrt{169d}$, in which d is the length of the skid marks, in metres, after the brakes were applied, and s is the speed of the car, in kilometres per hour, prior to the brakes being applied.

7. If the skid marks were 8 m long, what is the speed of the car, s, in simplest radical form?

   A. $13\sqrt{2}$ km/h

   B. $25\sqrt{5}$ km/h

   C. $26\sqrt{2}$ km/h

   D. $52\sqrt{2}$ km/h

8. What is the order of the irrational numbers $2\sqrt[4]{5}$, $3\sqrt[3]{4}$, $\sqrt[3]{69}$, and $\sqrt[4]{231}$ when ordered from least to greatest?

   A. $2\sqrt[4]{5}$, $3\sqrt[3]{4}$, $\sqrt[3]{69}$, $\sqrt[4]{231}$

   B. $2\sqrt[4]{5}$, $\sqrt[4]{231}$, $\sqrt[3]{69}$, $3\sqrt[3]{4}$

   C. $3\sqrt[3]{4}$, $\sqrt[3]{69}$, $2\sqrt[4]{5}$, $\sqrt[4]{231}$

   D. $3\sqrt[3]{4}$, $\sqrt[4]{231}$, $\sqrt[3]{69}$, $2\sqrt[4]{5}$

Numerical Response

9. When $3.5\sqrt[4]{32}$ is converted into the entire radical $\sqrt[4]{x}$, the value of x is _____.

10AN1.3 Demonstrate an understanding of powers with integral and rational exponents.

POWERS AND EXPONENT LAWS

Powers are expressions with exponents that can be simplified or converted using the exponent laws.

UNDERSTANDING POWERS

A **power** consists of a base and an exponent.

Power $\{2^3$

To evaluate a power with a positive integral exponent, factor the base the number of times the exponent indicates, and then perform the necessary multiplication.

$$2^3 = (2)(2)(2)$$
$$= 8$$

EXPONENT LAWS

The exponent rules or laws explain how to evaluate and simplify expressions containing powers. Here, the laws are applied to expressions with rational and variable bases and integral and rational exponents.

- Product of powers law: when multiplying powers that have the same base, add the exponents.
$$x^m \times x^n = x^{m+n}$$

- Quotient of powers law: when dividing powers that have the same base, subtract the exponents.
$$x^m \div x^n = x^{m-n}, \; x \neq 0$$

- Power of a power law: when a base is raised to multiple exponents, keep the base the same and multiply the exponents.
$$\left(x^m\right)^n = x^{mn}$$

- Power of a product law: when different multiplied bases are raised to an exponent, distribute the exponent to each base.
$$(xy)^m = x^m y^m$$

- Power of a quotient law: when different divided bases are raised to an exponent, distribute the exponent to each base.
$$\left(\frac{x}{y}\right)^m = \frac{x^m}{y^m}, \; y \neq 0$$

In addition to the five laws, the following two agreements are applications of the given laws:

A power with an exponent of zero has a value of 1 ($x^0 = 1$, $x \neq 0$). This agreement is an application of the quotient of powers law, $x^m \div x^n = x^{m-n}$, in which $m = n$. For example, since $2^3 \div 2^3 = 2^{3-3} = 2^0$ and $2^3 \div 2^3 = 8 \div 8 = 1$, then $2^0 = 1$.

The powers with negative exponents agreement $\left(x^{-n} = \dfrac{1}{x^n}, \ x \neq 0\right)$ is an application of the quotient of powers law $(x^m \div x^n = x^{m-n}$, in which $m = 0)$ and the previous agreement $\left(x^0 = 1, \ x \neq 0\right)$. For example, since $2^0 \div 2^3 = 2^{0-3} = 2^{-3}$ and $2^0 \div 2^3 = \dfrac{1}{2^3}$, then $2^{-3} = \dfrac{1}{2^3}$.

A result of this agreement is that a power with a base raised to a negative exponent can be rewritten as (or is equivalent to) a power with the **reciprocal** of the base raised to a positive exponent. For example, $\left(\dfrac{3}{5}\right)^{-2} = \left(\dfrac{5}{3}\right)^{2}$ and $(-1.2)^{-3} = \left(-\dfrac{1}{1.2}\right)^{3}$.

Example

Use patterning to show that $\left(\dfrac{1}{2}\right)^{-3} = 2^3$ and $2^{-2} = \left(\dfrac{1}{2}\right)^{2}$.

Solution

Write the patterns of 2^3 to 2^{-2} and $\left(\dfrac{1}{2}\right)^{2}$ to $\left(\dfrac{1}{2}\right)^{-3}$ with their corresponding simplified values.

$$2^3 = 8$$
$$2^2 = 4$$
$$2^1 = 2$$
$$2^0 = 1$$
$$2^{-1} = \dfrac{1}{2}$$
$$2^{-2} = \dfrac{1}{4}$$
$$\left(\dfrac{1}{2}\right)^{2} = \dfrac{1}{4}$$
$$\left(\dfrac{1}{2}\right)^{1} = \dfrac{1}{2}$$
$$\left(\dfrac{1}{2}\right)^{0} = 1$$
$$\left(\dfrac{1}{2}\right)^{-1} = 2$$
$$\left(\dfrac{1}{2}\right)^{-2} = 4$$
$$\left(\dfrac{1}{2}\right)^{-3} = 8$$

It is evident from the patterns that $\left(\dfrac{1}{2}\right)^{-3} = 2^3$ and $2^{-2} = \left(\dfrac{1}{2}\right)^{2}$.

POWERS WITH RATIONAL EXPONENTS

Powers with rational exponents can be expressed as radicals, and vice versa. One such relationship, namely $x^{\frac{1}{n}} = \sqrt[n]{x}$, can be verified using various strategies.

Example

Show that $8^{\frac{1}{3}}$ is equivalent to $\sqrt[3]{8}$.

Solution

Based upon the product of powers law $\left(x^m \times x^n = x^{m+n}\right)$, the following mathematical statement can be written:

$$8^{\frac{1}{3}} \times 8^{\frac{1}{3}} \times 8^{\frac{1}{3}} = 8^{\frac{1}{3}+\frac{1}{3}+\frac{1}{3}}$$
$$= 8^{\frac{3}{3}}$$
$$= 8^1$$
$$= 8$$

Similarly, since 8 is a perfect cube and $\sqrt[3]{8} = 2$, a second mathematical statement can be written:

$$\sqrt[3]{8} \times \sqrt[3]{8} \times \sqrt[3]{8} = 2 \times 2 \times 2$$
$$= 8$$

Upon analysis of both statements, it can be seen that $8^{\frac{1}{3}}$ is equivalent to $\sqrt[3]{8}$.

Furthermore, a power in the form of $x^{\frac{m}{n}}$, in which m and n are natural numbers and $\frac{m}{n}$ is in simplest (reduced) form, can be expressed in radical form as follows:

$$x^{\frac{m}{n}} = \sqrt[n]{x^m} \text{ or } x^{\frac{m}{n}} = \left(\sqrt[n]{x}\right)^m$$

Example

Convert $\left(\frac{8}{27}\right)^{-\frac{2}{3}}$ to radical form, and evaluate.

Solution

Step 1

Use the negative exponent principle to convert the power into a power with a positive exponent.

$$\left(\frac{8}{27}\right)^{-\frac{2}{3}} = \left(\frac{27}{8}\right)^{\frac{2}{3}}$$

Step 2

Convert the power into radical form.

$$\left(\frac{27}{8}\right)^{\frac{2}{3}} = \left(\sqrt[3]{\frac{27}{8}}\right)^2$$

Step 3

Evaluate the expression.

$$\left(\sqrt[3]{\frac{27}{8}}\right)^2 = \left(\frac{3}{2}\right)^2$$
$$= \frac{3^2}{2^2}$$
$$= \frac{9}{4}$$

APPLYING THE LAW OF EXPONENTS

The exponent laws can be used to simplify powers and solve problems.

Example

Use the laws of exponents to simplify the expression $\left(\frac{\sqrt{25a^3b^{-3}}}{0.2a^{\frac{3}{2}}b^{-\frac{1}{2}}}\right)^{-\frac{1}{2}}$, in which $a, b > 0$.

Solution

Step 1

Evaluate the numerical part of the radical, and convert the variable parts to powers with rational exponents.

$$\left(\frac{\sqrt{25a^3b^{-3}}}{0.2a^{\frac{3}{2}}b^{-\frac{1}{2}}}\right)^{-\frac{1}{2}} = \left(\frac{5a^{\frac{3}{2}}b^{-\frac{3}{2}}}{0.2a^{\frac{3}{2}}b^{-\frac{1}{2}}}\right)^{-\frac{1}{2}}$$

Step 2

Use the quotient of powers law to simplify the expressions in the brackets.

$$\left(\frac{5a^{\frac{3}{2}}b^{-\frac{3}{2}}}{0.2a^{\frac{3}{2}}b^{-\frac{1}{2}}}\right)^{-\frac{1}{2}} = \left[\frac{5}{0.2}a^{\frac{3}{2}-\frac{3}{2}}b^{-\frac{3}{2}-\left(-\frac{1}{2}\right)}\right]^{-\frac{1}{2}}$$

$$= \left(25a^0b^{-1}\right)^{-\frac{1}{2}}$$

Step 3

Use the power of a product law and zero exponent and negative exponent principles to simplify the expression further.

$$\left(25a^0b^{-1}\right)^{-\frac{1}{2}} = \left(25^{-\frac{1}{2}}\right)(1)\left(b^{-1\times-\frac{1}{2}}\right)$$

$$= \left(\frac{1}{25^{\frac{1}{2}}}\right)b^{\frac{1}{2}}$$

Step 4

Evaluate the numerical part of the expression.

$$\left(\frac{1}{25^{\frac{1}{2}}}\right)b^{\frac{1}{2}} = \left(\frac{1}{\sqrt{25}}\right)b^{\frac{1}{2}}$$

$$= \frac{b^{\frac{1}{2}}}{5}$$

$$= \frac{\sqrt{b}}{5}$$

Example

The growth of a colony of 800 bacteria can be modelled by the equation $N = 800(2)^{\frac{t}{3}}$, in which N is the number of bacteria after t hours.

How many bacteria are present after 12.7 hours?

Solution

Substitute the value 12.7 for t in the equation $N = 800(2)^{\frac{t}{3}}$, and solve for N.

$$N = 800(2)^{\frac{t}{3}}$$
$$= 800(2)^{\frac{12.7}{3}}$$
$$\approx 800(18.808\ 7665)$$
$$\approx 15\ 047.0132$$

There are 15 047 bacteria present after 12.7 hours.

Use the following information to answer the next question.

To evaluate $(0.04)^{-\frac{3}{2}}$, Anjuli went through the following steps using paper and pencil:

$$(0.04)^{-\frac{3}{2}} = (k)^{\frac{3}{2}} = l$$

10. Her respective values of k and l are

    A. 0.04, 125   **B.** 0.04, 0.032

    C. 25, 125   **D.** 25, 7.8125

Use the following information to answer the next question.

Mark simplified the expression

$$\frac{\sqrt[3]{8a^2b^{-2}}}{(2a^{-2}b)^{-1}}$$ using the given steps.

I. $\dfrac{\left(8a^2b^{-2}\right)^{\frac{1}{3}}}{2^{-1}a^2b^{-1}}$

II. $\dfrac{2a^{\frac{2}{3}}b^{-\frac{2}{3}}}{2^{-1}a^2b^{-1}}$

III. $\dfrac{2}{-2}a^{\frac{2}{3}-2}b^{-\frac{2}{3}+1}$

IV. $-a^{-\frac{4}{3}}b^{\frac{1}{3}}$

11. In which step did Mark make his first error?

A. I   **B.** II

C. III   **D.** IV

12. If the exponential expression $\left(\dfrac{1}{4}\right)^k$ is equivalent to $(2)(2)(2)$, then the value of k is

A. $\dfrac{3}{2}$ **B.** $\dfrac{2}{3}$

C. $-\dfrac{1}{2}$ **D.** $-\dfrac{3}{2}$

13. For $\left(\dfrac{5}{9}\right)^{\frac{2}{3}} = \sqrt[n]{\left(\dfrac{9}{5}\right)^m}$, the values of m and n are

A. $m = 2, n = 3$

B. $m = 3, n = 2$

C. $m = -2, n = 3$

D. $m = -3, n = 2$

Use the following information to answer the next question.

The measure of the acidity in any aqueous solution is called its pH, and is related exponentially to the concentration of hydrogen ions, H^+, in moles per litre, by the function: $H^+ = 10^{-pH}$.

A student used this function to determine the hydrogen ion concentration of three types of water solution.

- Rain water: pH = 5.6
- Distilled water: pH = 6.9
- Acid rain: pH = 4.0

14. Which of the following statements about these calculated hydrogen ion concentrations is **incorrect**?

A. The concentration of H^+ in acid rain is the highest.

B. The concentration of H^+ in rain water is greater than 10^{-7} mol/L.

C. The difference in the H^+ concentration between acid rain and rain water is 9.75×10^{-5} mol/L

D. The difference in the H^+ concentration between acid rain and rain water is less than the difference in the H^+ concentration between rain water and distilled water.

Numerical Response

15. When the expression $\dfrac{\left(0.8^3\right)^{-2}}{(0.8)^{-3}(0.8)^{-2}}$ is evaluated to the nearest hundredth, the resulting value is _____.

Use the following information to answer the next question.

Raoul wanted to understand the exponential expression $8^{\frac{m}{3}}$. He used the following patterning method:

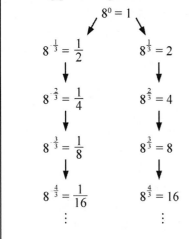

$$8^0 = 1$$

$$8^{-\frac{1}{3}} = \frac{1}{2} \qquad 8^{\frac{1}{3}} = 2$$

$$8^{-\frac{2}{3}} = \frac{1}{4} \qquad 8^{\frac{2}{3}} = 4$$

$$8^{-\frac{3}{3}} = \frac{1}{8} \qquad 8^{\frac{3}{3}} = 8$$

$$8^{-\frac{4}{3}} = \frac{1}{16} \qquad 8^{\frac{4}{3}} = 16$$

$$\vdots \qquad \qquad \vdots$$

Written Response

16. Continue this pattern to discover the values of $8^{\frac{m}{3}}$ when $m = -5$ and $m = 7$. Show your work.

10AN1.4 Demonstrate an understanding of the multiplication of polynomial expressions, concretely, pictorially and symbolically.

MULTIPLYING POLYNOMIALS

A **polynomial** is an algebraic expression that is a monomial or the sum or difference of two or more monomials. A **monomial** is a term consisting of a number, a variable, or a product of numbers and variables (e.g., 5, $-2x$, $2m^2n$); a **binomial** is a polynomial with two terms (e.g., $2x + 9$, $3x - 7y$); and a **trinomial** is a polynomial with three terms (e.g., $5x^2 - 5x + 1$, $-2x + 3y - xy$). A variety of strategies can be used to multiply and simplify polynomial expressions.

MULTIPLYING POLYNOMIALS BY MONOMIALS

When determining the product of a monomial and a polynomial that is in brackets, the monomial must be multiplied by each term of the polynomial in the brackets. This process is an application of the **distributive property**. When the multiplication is complete, the like terms are collected and often written in descending order of degree.

Example

Simplify the polynomial expression $3x(4x - 1) + 2x(2x + 6)$.

Solution

Multiply each term located on the outside of the brackets by each term located on the inside of the brackets. Then, gather the like terms and simplify.

$$(3x)(4x - 1) + (2x)(2x + 6)$$
$$3x(4x) + 3x(-1) + 2x(2x) + 2x(6)$$
$$12x^2 - 3x + 4x^2 + 12x$$
$$16x^2 + 9x$$

MULTIPLYING TWO BINOMIALS

When two binomials are multiplied, such as $(2x + 3)(3x - 2)$ or $(3x + 2y)^2$, several unique approaches and models can be used.

METHOD 1—ALGEBRA TILES

Algebra tiles can be used to represent the product of two binomials. Representations of positive values are shaded, and representations of negative values are unshaded.

To represent the product of $(2x + 3)(x + 2)$, make a rectangle that is two x-tiles and three unit tiles wide, and one x-tile and two unit tiles long.

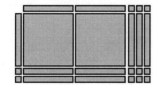

Using x^2-tiles, x-tiles, and unit tiles, fill in the rectangle. The rectangle formed consists of two x^2-tiles, seven x-tiles, and six unit tiles.

Therefore, $(2x + 3)(x + 2) = 2x^2 + 7x + 6$.

METHOD 2—FOIL

FOIL is a mnemonic device used to help remember how to multiply two binomials.

- **F**: Multiply the **first** term in each binomial together.
- **O**: Multiply the two **outside** terms together.
- **I**: Multiply the two **inside** terms together.
- **L**: Multiply the **last** two terms together.

After multiplying the terms together, gather like terms.

Example

Simplify the polynomial expression $(2x + 1)(x - 3)$.

Solution

Use the FOIL method, by multiplying each term in the first binomial by each term in the second binomial.

$= 2x(x) + 2x(-3) + 1(x) + 1(-3)$

$\boxed{F} \quad \boxed{O} \quad \boxed{I} \quad \boxed{L}$

$= 2x^2 - 6x + x - 3$

Now, collect like terms.

$2x^2 - 6x + x - 3$
$= 2x^2 - 5x - 3$

METHOD 3—VERTICAL MULTIPLICATION

The product of two binomials can be determined using a procedure similar to the multiplication of two-digit numbers. The terms in the bottom row are each multiplied by the terms in the top row, and then like terms are added.

$$\begin{array}{r} 34 \\ \times\ 25 \\ \hline 170 \\ 68 \\ \hline 850 \end{array}$$

$$\begin{array}{r} x + 1 \\ \times\ x + 2 \\ \hline 2x + 2 \\ x^2 + x \\ \hline x^2 + 3x + 2 \end{array}$$

MULTIPLYING TWO POLYNOMIALS

The distributive property can be used to multiply and simplify multiple-termed polynomials. Multiply each term in the first polynomial by each term in the second polynomial. After multiplying, simplify by gathering the like terms.

Example

Simplify the polynomial expression $(3x + 4)(2xy - 5y + 1)$.

Solution

Step 1

Simplify the polynomial expression.

Multiply each term in the binomial by each of the terms in the trinomial.

$= \begin{pmatrix} 3x(2xy) + 3x(-5y) + 3x(1) \\ +4(2xy) + 4(-5y) + 4(1) \end{pmatrix}$

$= 6x^2y - 15xy + 3x + 8xy - 20y + 4$

$= 6x^2y - 7xy + 3x - 20y + 4$

$(3x + 4)(2xy - 5y + 1)$

Step 2

Verify the solution.

The simplified expression can be verified by substituting numbers for the variables in both the original product and its simplified form. For example, substitute $x = -2$ and $y = 1$.

Left side

$(3x, +4)(2xy - 5y + 1)$
$= [3(-2) + 4][2(-2)(1) - 5(1) + 1]$
$= (-6 + 4)(-4 - 5 + 1)$
$= (-2)(-8)$
$= 16$

Right side

$6x^2y - 7xy + 3x - 20y + 4$
$= \begin{pmatrix} 6(-2)^2(1) - 7(-2) \\ \times (1) + 3(-2) - 20(1) + 4 \end{pmatrix}$
$= 24 + 14 - 6 - 20 + 4$
$= 16$

Since the left-side value is equal to the right-side value, the product has been correctly expanded and simplified.

Use the following information to answer the next question.

The design of the side view of a specialized cement staircase is shown, with expressions for all side lengths.

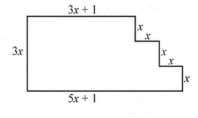

17. Which of the following simplified expressions describes the area of the side view of the staircase?

A. $6x^2$ **B.** $15x^2$

C. $12x^2 + 3x$ **D.** $13x^2 + 3x$

18. When $(2x + 3)(x^2 + 4x - 7)$ is expanded and simplified, the coefficient of the x^2-term is

A. -2 **B.** 2

C. 8 **D.** 11

19. When the algebraic expression $5x(2 - x) - (x + 3)^2$ is expanded and simplified, the resulting expression is

A. $-6x^2 + 16x + 9$

B. $-6x^2 + 10x - 9$

C. $-6x^2 - 4x + 9$

D. $-6x^2 + 4x - 9$

Use the following information to answer the next question.

Josh wanted to expand and simplify the quadratic expression $(-2x + 3)(3x - 4)$. To find all terms in the multiplication process he used a rectangular grid as shown.

	$-2x$	3
$3x$	$-6x^2$	A
-4	B	-12

20. When the terms represented by A and B are combined, the resulting term is

A. x **B.** $-x$

C. $12x$ **D.** $17x$

Use the following information to answer the next question.

Kara attempted to simplify the expression $4x(-x^2 + 2x - 3)$ using the following four steps:

1. $(4x)(-x^2) + (4x)(2x) + (4x)(-3)$
2. $(4)(-1)(x)(x^2)$
   $+(4)(2)(x)(x) + (4)(-3)(x)$
3. $-4x^2 + 8x^2 - 12x$
4. $4x^2 - 12x$

21. In which step did Kara's first error in multiplication occur?

A. Step 1   **B.** Step 2

C. Step 3   **D.** Step 4

Numerical Response

22. If $2x + 3$ is multiplied by $3x + 4$, what is the minimum number of algebra tiles required to display the product?_____

10AN1.5 Demonstrate an understanding of common factors and trinomial factoring, concretely, pictorially and symbolically.

FACTORING POLYNOMIALS

Factoring is the process of expressing a polynomial as a product of polynomials of a lesser degree. Factoring is the inverse process of multiplying or expanding a polynomial.

FACTORING OUT THE GREATEST COMMON FACTOR

When factoring out the greatest common factor or GCF (the largest factor common to two or more terms), look at what is common in each term of the polynomial expression. Once the greatest common factor has been identified, divide it out of each term in the polynomial.

Example

Factor $30x^2y^3 - 12xy^2 + 24x^2y$.

Solution

First, find the GCF of the three terms of the polynomial expression.

Method 1: Division List
Determine the factors of each term, and then find the GCF.
$30x^2y^3 \rightarrow$
1, 2, 3, 5, **6**, 10, 15, 30, $\boldsymbol{x}$, x^2, $\boldsymbol{y}$, y^2, y^3
$12xy^2 \rightarrow$
1, 2, 3, 4, **6**, 12, $\boldsymbol{x}$, $\boldsymbol{y}$, y^2
$24x^2y \rightarrow$
1, 2, 3, 4, **6**, 8, 12, 24, $\boldsymbol{x}$, x^2, $\boldsymbol{y}$
The greatest common factor is $6xy$.

Method 2: Prime Factorization
Determine the prime factors of each term, and then select the maximum shared prime factors.
$30x^2y^3 = \boldsymbol{2} \times \boldsymbol{3} \times 5 \times \boldsymbol{x} \times x \times \boldsymbol{y} \times y \times y$
$12xy^2 = 2 \times \boldsymbol{2} \times \boldsymbol{3} \times \boldsymbol{x} \times \boldsymbol{y} \times y$
$24x^2y = 2 \times 2 \times \boldsymbol{2} \times \boldsymbol{3} \times \boldsymbol{x} \times x \times \boldsymbol{y}$

The greatest common factor is
$2 \times 3 \times x \times y = 6xy$.

Now, divide each term by the GCF.
$30x^2y^3 - 12xy^2 + 24x^2y$
$= 6xy(5xy^2 - 2y + 4x)$

The factored expression can be verified by multiplying the factors and then comparing the result to the original polynomial.
$6xy(5xy^2 - 2y + 4x)$
$= 6xy(5xy^2) + 6xy(-2y) + 6xy(4x)$
$= 30x^2y^3 - 12xy^2 + 24x^2y$

FACTORING BY GROUPING

Factoring by grouping involves rewriting a polynomial that has an even number of terms into smaller groups that contain a common factor.
To use this method, remove the greatest common factor (GCF) from each group, and then factor out the common binomial.

Example

Factor the expression $x^2 + 2x + x + 2$.

Solution

Step 1
Group the terms.
$x^2 + 2x + x + 2$
$= (x^2 + 2x) + (x + 2)$

Step 2
Remove the GCF from each group.
$(x^2 + 2x) + (x + 2)$
$= x(x + 2) + 1(x + 2)$

Step 3
Factor out the common binomial.
$x(x + 2) + 1(x + 2)$
$= (x + 2)(x + 1)$

FACTORING TRINOMIALS USING ALGEBRA TILES

To factor a trinomial using algebra tiles, begin by arranging the algebra tiles into a rectangle and then add algebra tiles to the outside of the rectangle.

The tiles representing $x^2 + 5x + 6$ can be arranged into the following rectangle:

Now, add algebra tiles to the left and upper sides of the rectangle to form the two factors.

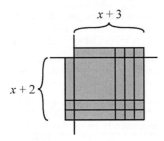

Therefore, the factors are $(x + 2)(x + 3)$.

FACTORING TRINOMIALS IN THE FORM OF $x^2 + bx + c$ USING ALGEBRA

To factor a quadratic trinomial in the form of $x^2 + bx + c$, you need to find two integers, d and e, that have a **product** of $d \times e = c$ and a **sum** of $d + e = b$. To help determine the two integers with a sum of b and a product of c, it is often useful to list all the factors of c. Then, the trinomial will factor as follows: $x^2 + bx + c = (x + d)(x + e)$

Example

Factor the expression $x^2 - 7x + 12$.

Solution

In the expression $x^2 - 7x + 12$, note that c is 12.

List the factors of 12.
1×12
2×6
3×4
and
-1×-12
-2×-6
-3×-4

Only one of these combinations will result in a sum of $b = -7$, namely -3 and -4.

Therefore, $x^2 - 7x + 12 = (x - 4)(x - 3)$.

FACTORING TRINOMIALS OF THE FORM $ax^2 + bx + c$ USING ALGEBRA

One commonly used procedure for factoring trinomials of the form $ax^2 + bx + c$ is called decomposition. **Decomposition** splits the term bx into two separate terms and then factors the four terms by grouping.

Example

Factor $2x^2 - 5x - 3$.

Solution

Step 1
Find two numbers that have a product equal to $a \times c$ and a sum of b.

These two numbers are -6 and 1, since the product $(-6) \times (1)$ is equal to $a \times c = -6$ and the sum $(-6) + (1)$ is equal to $b = -5$.

Step 2
Split the middle term bx into two terms of x that contain the two numbers found in step 1.

Step 3

Group the four terms, and factor out the greatest common factor from each pair of two terms.

$$(2x^2 - 6x) + (1x - 3)$$
$$2x(x - 3) + 1(x - 3)$$

Step 4

Factor out the common binomial.

$$2x(x - 3) + 1(x - 3)$$
$$(2x + 1)(x - 3)$$

Therefore, $2x^2 - 5x - 3$ factors to $(2x + 1)(x - 3)$.

Factoring Trinomials with Perfect Squares Using Algebra

A perfect square is a whole number that can be expressed as the product of two identical numbers; for example, 9, 25, or 144. Perfect squares can also be algebraic expressions that are the product of two identical terms; for example, $4x^2$, $36y^4$, or x^2y^2. Some special trinomials have perfect squares as first and last terms. If the first term, a^2, is a perfect square and the last term, b^2, is a perfect square, such that the middle term is $2ab$ or $-2ab$, then the trinomial is called a **perfect square trinomial**, and it is factored as follows:

$$a^2 + 2ab + b^2$$
$$= (a + b)(a + b) \text{ or } (a + b)^2$$
$$a^2 - 2ab + b^2$$
$$= (a - b)(a - b) \text{ or } (a - b)^2$$

Example

Factor $8x^2 - 40x + 50$.

Solution

First, divide out the greatest common factor from each term of the trinomial. The greatest common factor of $8x^2$, $-40x$, and 50 is 2.

$$8x^2 - 40x + 50$$
$$= 2(4x^2 - 20x + 25)$$

Notice that the trinomial in the brackets is a perfect square trinomial in the form of $a^2 - 2ab + b^2$.

$$a^2 = 4x^2$$
$$\sqrt{a^2} = \sqrt{4x^2}$$
$$a = 2x$$
$$b^2 = 25$$
$$\sqrt{b^2} = \sqrt{25}$$
$$b = 5$$
$$-2ab = -2(2x)(5)$$
$$= -20x$$

Since $a^2 - 2ab + b^2 = (a - b)(a - b)$,

$$2(4x^2 - 20x + 25)$$
$$= 2(2x - 5)(2x - 5) \text{ or } 2(2x - 5)^2$$

If the first term, a^2, is a perfect square and the last term, b^2, is a **subtracted** perfect square, such that the middle term is missing (or equal to zero), then this special trinomial (which technically has become a binomial), is referred to as a **difference of squares**, and it is factored as follows:

$$a^2 - b^2 = (a + b)(a - b)$$

Example

Factor $x^2 - 9$.

Solution

This is a difference of squares in the form of $a^2 - b^2$.

$$a^2 = x^2 \qquad b^2 = 9$$
$$\sqrt{a^2} = \sqrt{x^2} \quad \sqrt{b^2} = \sqrt{9}$$
$$a = x \qquad b = 3$$

Since $a^2 - b^2 = (a + b)(a - b)$, it follows that $x^2 - 9 = (x + 3)(x - 3)$.

Note: If the binomial $x^2 - 9$ is rewritten as a trinomial, $x^2 + 0x - 9$, it can be factored using the strategy for trinomials in the form of $x^2 + bx + c$. Find two numbers with a sum of $b = 0$ and a product of $c = -9$. The values are 3 and −3, since $3 - 3 = 0$ and $(3)(-3) = -9$.

Therefore,
$$x^2 - 9 = x^2 + 0x - 9$$
$$= (x + 3)(x - 3)$$

---

23. What is the greatest common factor of $3m^2np^3$, $15m^3n^3p^4$, and $36m^2n^2p^3$?

   A. m^2np^3 **B.** $m^2n^2p^2$

   C. $3m^2np^3$ **D.** $3m^3n^3p^4$

24. Which of the following algebra tile arrangements represents the factorization of $x^2 - 2x - 24$?

   A.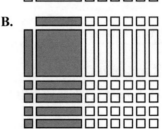

   B.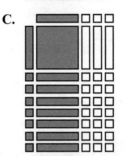

   C.

   D.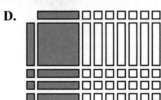

25. What is one of the factors of the binomial $16a^2b^2 - 9c^2$?

   A. $8ab - 3c$ **B.** $8ab - 9c$

   C. $4ab + 3c$ **D.** $4ab - 9c$

26. Which of the following binomials is a factor of both $x^2 - 15x - 34$ and $x^2 + 5x + 6$?

   A. $x - 17$ **B.** $x - 16$

   C. $x + 2$ **D.** $x + 3$

Use the following information to answer the next question.

A student factored four quadratic expressions as shown.

I. $x^2 - 19x + 60 = (x - 15)(x - 4)$

II. $3x^3 - 75x = 3x(x - 5)(x + 5)$

III. $-9x^2 + 12x - 4 = (3x + 2)(3x + 2)$

IV. $4x^2 + 6x + 2 = 2(x + 1)(2x + 1)$

27. The quadratic expression that the student factored **incorrectly** is

　　A. quadratic I　　**B.** quadratic II

　　C. quadratic III　　**D.** quadratic IV

Numerical Response

28. The factored form of the polynomial $x^2 - 2x - 15$ can be written as $(x - m)(x + n)$. The value of $m + n$ is

　　_____.

Use the following information to answer the next question.

The factored form of the perfect square trinomial $4x^2 + Bx + 25$ can be written as $(Ax + C)^2$.

Numerical Response

29. Written in order from left to right, the value of *ABC* is _____.

Use the following information to answer the next question.

A student was asked to factor a quadratic expression in the form $ax^2 + bx + c$ by means of decomposition. Part of this process is shown.

Step 1 → $6x^2 - 3x + 4x - \square$

Step 2 → $3x(\underline{\quad\quad}) + \square(\underline{\quad\quad})$

Step 3 → $(\underline{\quad\quad\quad})(\underline{\quad\quad\quad})$

Written Response

30. Complete the decomposition by filling in the missing terms.

ANSWERS AND SOLUTIONS
ALGEBRA AND NUMBER

1. A	7. C	13. C	19. D	25. C
2. D	8. B	14. D	20. D	26. C
3. D	9. 4802	15. 1.25	21. C	27. C
4. WR	10. C	16. WR	22. 35	28. 8
5. D	11. C	17. C	23. C	29. 2205
6. D	12. D	18. D	24. B	30. WR

1. A

To find the least number of packages of hotdogs and buns that Yannick must buy to get the same number of each. Find the least common multiple of the number of buns in a package (8) and the number of hotdogs in a package (12).

- The multiples of 8 are 8, 16, 24, 32, 40, 48, 56...
- The multiples of 12 are 12, 24, 36, 48, 60, 72, 84...

The least common multiple of 8 and 12 is 24. However, keep in mind that the question asks for the number of packages not the number of buns or the number of hotdogs. To get 24;hotdogs, you need 2 packages; to get 24 buns, you need 3 packages.

2. D

To find the square root of 64, a square with an area of 64 square units is required. The length of each side of the square will be the number's square root.

In alternative D, the square has an area of 64 units and the length of each side is 8 units.

3. D

A prime factor is a factor that is a prime number. The number 1 is not a prime number, and does not have prime number factors.

The factors of 144 are 1, 2, 3, 4, 6, 8, 9, 12, 16, 18, 24, 36, 48, 72, and 144. The total number of factors 144 has is 15.

A composite number is a whole number that has more than two factors.

To determine the greatest common factor (GCF) of 420 and 504, write the prime factorization of each number, and then select the shared factors.
$420 = 2 \times 2 \times 3 \times 5 \times 7$
$504 = 2 \times 2 \times 2 \times 3 \times 3 \times 7$

Therefore, the GCF of 420 and 504 is
$2 \times 2 \times 3 \times 7 = 84$.

4. WR

Step 1
Determine the smallest and largest possible numbers.
A perfect cube is a whole number that can be expressed as the product of three identical natural numbers. Between 2 000 and 10 000, the smallest perfect cube is $13^3 = 2\ 197$ and the largest perfect cube is $21^3 = 9\ 261$.

Step 2
Determine perfect cubes that are also perfect squares.
For a number to also be a perfect square, the cube root of the number must be a perfect square.
The only number in the list of cube roots (13, 14... 20, 21) that is a perfect square is 16.
Therefore, $16^3 = 4\ 096$ is also a perfect square, since $\sqrt{4\ 096} = 64$ or $64^2 = 4\ 096$.
The answer can also be supported by analyzing the prime factorization of 4 096.
$$4\ 096 = \left(\begin{array}{c} 2 \times 2 \times 2 \times 2 \times 2 \times 2 \\ \times 2 \times 2 \times 2 \times 2 \times 2 \times 2 \end{array}\right)$$
The prime factors can be grouped into three and two matching sets.
$$4\ 096 = \left(2^6\right) \times \left(2^6\right)$$
$$= 64 \times 64$$
$$4\ 096 = \left(2^4\right) \times \left(2^4\right) \times \left(2^4\right)$$
$$= 16 \times 16 \times 16$$
Therefore, 4 096 is a whole number that is both a perfect square and a perfect cube located between 2 000 and 10 000.

5. D

Analyze each definition to determine which is correct.

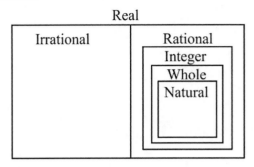

Real

Irrational	Rational
	Integer
	Whole
	Natural

Rational numbers are real numbers that can be written in the form $\frac{m}{n}$, where $n \neq 0$ and m and n are integers. These numbers are also real numbers, so statement I is true.

Irrational numbers are real numbers that cannot be written in the form $\frac{m}{n}$, where m and n are integers. Irrational numbers belong to the set of real numbers, so statement II is true.

Integers are the set of natural numbers, their negative values, and the number 0. Whole numbers are all positive natural numbers and 0. Since whole numbers are a subset of integers, statement III is true.

Whole numbers are the set of natural numbers and 0, so statement IV is false.

Statements I, II, and III are true.

6. D

An irrational number is a real number that cannot be written in the form $\frac{m}{n}$, where m and n are integers and $n \neq 0$. Irrational numbers have a decimal representation that does not repeat or terminate.

- Since 0.64 is a perfect square, $\sqrt{0.64} = 0.8$, it is a rational number.
- Since 3 is not a perfect square, $\sqrt{3} = 1.732\ 0508\ldots$, it is an irrational number.
- Since 6.4 is not a perfect square, $\sqrt{6.4} = 2.529\ 822\ 12\ldots$, it is an irrational number.
- Since $\frac{9}{16}$ is a perfect square, $\sqrt{\frac{9}{16}} = \frac{3}{4}$, it is a rational number.

Therefore, $\sqrt{3}$ and $\sqrt{6.4}$ are irrational.

7. C

Determine the speed of the car, s, in simplified radical form.

Step 1
Substitute 8 for d in the formula $s = \sqrt{169d}$.
$s = \sqrt{169d}$
$ = \sqrt{169 \times 8}$

Step 2
Factor 8 into two factors, in which one factor is the greatest perfect square.
Since the factors of 8 are 1, 2, 4, and 8, in which 4 is the largest perfect square, the expression can be simplified as follows:
$s = \sqrt{169 \times 8}$
$ = \sqrt{169 \times 4 \times 2}$

Step 3
Use the multiplication property of radicals, $\sqrt[n]{xy} = \sqrt[n]{x} \times \sqrt[n]{y}$, to rewrite the radical.
$s = \sqrt{169 \times 4 \times 2}$
$ = \sqrt{169} \times \sqrt{4} \times \sqrt{2}$

Step 4
Evaluate the radicals that are square roots of perfect squares, and simplify.
$s = \sqrt{169} \times \sqrt{4} \times \sqrt{2}$
$ = 13 \times 2 \times \sqrt{2}$
$ = 26\sqrt{2}$

In simplest radical form, the speed of the car, s, is $26\sqrt{2}$ km/h.

8. B

Step 1
Convert the mixed radicals into entire form.
$2\sqrt[4]{5} = \sqrt[4]{2^4} \times \sqrt[4]{5}$
$\phantom{2\sqrt[4]{5}} = \sqrt[4]{16} \times \sqrt[4]{5}$
$\phantom{2\sqrt[4]{5}} = \sqrt[4]{80}$
$3\sqrt[3]{4} = \sqrt[3]{3^3} \times \sqrt[3]{4}$
$\phantom{3\sqrt[3]{4}} = \sqrt[3]{27} \times \sqrt[3]{4}$
$\phantom{3\sqrt[3]{4}} = \sqrt[3]{108}$

Step 2

Find the approximate values of the radicals by estimating their positions between the roots of neighbouring perfect powers.

- Since $\sqrt[3]{69}$ is slightly more than $\sqrt[3]{64} = 4$, its estimated value is 4.1.
- Since $\sqrt[3]{108}$ is closer to $\sqrt[3]{125} = 5$ than $\sqrt[3]{81} = 4$, its estimated value is 4.8.
- Since $\sqrt[4]{80}$ is almost equal to $\sqrt[4]{81} = 3$, its estimated value is 3.0.
- Since $\sqrt[4]{231}$ is closer to $\sqrt[4]{256} = 4$ than $\sqrt[4]{81} = 3$, its estimated value is 3.9.

Based on the estimated values, the order of the numbers from least to greatest is $2\sqrt[4]{5}, \sqrt[4]{231}, \sqrt[3]{69}$, and $3\sqrt[3]{4}$.

Note: These radicals can also be approximated using the $\sqrt[3]{}$ and $\sqrt[x]{}$ features of a graphing calculator.

9. 4802

Step 1

Since the index is 4, rewrite 3.5 as the fourth root of 3.5 raised to the fourth power.

$$3.5 = \sqrt[4]{3.5^4}$$
$$= \sqrt[4]{150.0625}$$

Step 2

Substitute $\sqrt[4]{150.0625}$ for 3.5 in the expression $3.5\sqrt[4]{32}$, and then multiply the radicands.

$$3.5\sqrt[4]{32} = \sqrt[4]{150.0625} \times \sqrt[4]{32}$$
$$= \sqrt[4]{150.0625 \times 32}$$
$$= \sqrt[4]{4\ 802}$$

Therefore, when $3.5\sqrt[4]{32}$ is converted into entire radical form, $\sqrt[4]{x}$, the value of x is $4\ 802$.

10. C

Before evaluating k in the expression $(k)^{\frac{3}{2}}$, convert 0.04 to a fraction.

$$0.04 = \frac{4}{100}$$
$$= \frac{4 \div 4}{100 \div 4}$$
$$= \frac{1}{25}$$

Thus, $(0.04)^{-\frac{3}{2}}$ is equivalent to $\left(\frac{1}{25}\right)^{-\frac{3}{2}}$.

Since $\left(\frac{1}{x}\right)^{-n} = x^n$, you can convert this expression from $\left(\frac{1}{25}\right)^{-\frac{3}{2}}$ to $(25)^{\frac{3}{2}}$.

Therefore, in $(k)^{\frac{3}{2}}$, the value of k must be 25.

You know that $x^{\frac{m}{n}} = \sqrt[n]{x^m}$, so you can convert the expression of $(25)^{\frac{3}{2}}$ to the radical form of $\sqrt{25^3}$ or $(\sqrt{25})^3$.

Since $\sqrt{25} = 5$ ($5 \times 5 = 25$),

$$(\sqrt{25})^3 = 5^3$$
$$= 5 \times 5 \times 5$$
$$= 125$$

The value of l is 125.

11. C

The correct steps for the simplification of the expression $\dfrac{\sqrt[3]{8a^2b^{-2}}}{(2a^{-2}b)^{-1}}$ are given.

Step 1

Convert the radical expression in the numerator into a power with a rational exponent, and apply the power of product law to the expression in the denominator.

$$\frac{\sqrt[3]{8a^2b^{-2}}}{(2a^{-2}b)^{-1}} = \frac{(8a^2b^{-2})^{\frac{1}{3}}}{2^{-1}a^2b^{-1}}$$

Step 2

Apply the power of a product law to the expression in the numerator.

$$\frac{\left(8a^2b^{-2}\right)^{\frac{1}{3}}}{2^{-1}a^2b^{-1}} = \frac{8^{\frac{1}{3}}a^{\frac{2}{3}}b^{-\frac{2}{3}}}{2^{-1}a^2b^{-1}}$$

$$= \frac{2a^{\frac{2}{3}}b^{-\frac{2}{3}}}{2^{-1}a^2b^{-1}}$$

Step 3

Apply the quotient of powers law to the powers.

$$\frac{2a^{\frac{2}{3}}b^{-\frac{2}{3}}}{2^{-1}a^2b^{-1}} = \frac{2}{2^{-1}}a^{\frac{2}{3}-2}b^{-\frac{2}{3}-(-1)}$$

$$= \frac{2}{\frac{1}{2}}a^{\frac{2}{3}-2}b^{-\frac{2}{3}+1}$$

Step 4

Simplify the expression.

$$\frac{2}{\frac{1}{2}}a^{\frac{2}{3}-2}b^{-\frac{2}{3}+1} = 4a^{\frac{2}{3}-\frac{6}{3}}b^{-\frac{2}{3}+\frac{3}{3}}$$

$$= 4a^{-\frac{4}{3}}b^{\frac{1}{3}}$$

By comparing Mark's process with the correct solution, it can be seen that Mark's first error was made in step III.

12. D

According to the product rule $(x^m)(x^n) = x^{m+n}$,

$(2)(2)(2) = (2^1)(2^1)(2^1)$

$\quad = 2^{1+1+1}$

$\quad = 2^3$

Since $\sqrt{4} = 2$ because $2 \times 2 = 4$, rewrite this expression as follows:

$(2)^3 = (\sqrt{4})^3 = (4)^{\frac{3}{2}}$, since $\left(\sqrt[n]{x}\right)^m = x^{\frac{m}{n}}$.

You also know that $x^n = \left(\frac{1}{x}\right)^{-n}$, so

$(4)^{\frac{3}{2}} = \left(\frac{1}{4}\right)^{-\frac{3}{2}}$. Therefore, for $\left(\frac{1}{4}\right)^k$ to be equivalent

to $(2)(2)(2)$, the value of k is $-\frac{3}{2}$.

13. C

The expression $\left(\frac{5}{9}\right)^{\frac{2}{3}}$ can be written in the form

$\left(\frac{1}{\frac{5}{9}}\right)^{-\frac{2}{3}}$, since $x^n = \left(\frac{1}{x}\right)^{-n}$.

Since dividing a fraction by a second fraction is the same as multiplying by the reciprocal of the second fraction, the result is

$$\left(\frac{1}{\frac{5}{9}}\right)^{-\frac{2}{3}} = \left(\frac{1}{1} \times \frac{9}{5}\right)^{-\frac{2}{3}}$$

$$= \left(\frac{9}{5}\right)^{-\frac{2}{3}}$$

A power with a rational exponent can be rewritten as a radical expression.

$$x^{\frac{m}{n}} = \sqrt[n]{x^m}$$

Therefore, $\left(\frac{9}{5}\right)^{-\frac{2}{3}} = \sqrt[3]{\left(\frac{9}{5}\right)^{-2}}$

The values of $m = -2$ and $n = 3$ for $\sqrt[n]{\left(\frac{9}{5}\right)^m}$ to be

equivalent to $\left(\frac{5}{9}\right)^{\frac{2}{3}}$.

14. D

Substitute each pH value into the function to solve for the H^+ concentration in each type of water:

- Rain water:
$H^+ = 10^{-pH}$
$\quad = 10^{-5.6} = 2.51E - 6$
$\quad = 2.51 \times 10^{-6}$ mol/L
Distilled water:
$H^+ = 10^{-pH}$
$\quad = 10^{-6.9} = 1.26E - 7$
$\quad = 1.26 \times 10^{-7}$ mol/L
Acid rain:
$H^+ = 10^{-pH}$
$\quad = 10^{-4.0} = 1E - 4$
$\quad = 1 \times 10^{-4}$ mol/L

Based on these results, you can see which choice is incorrect.

The concentration of H^+ in acid rain is 1×10^{-4} mol/L, which is higher than the concentration of H^+ in the other two solutions.

The concentration of H^+ in rain water, namely 2.51×10^{-6} mol/L, is greater than 10^{-7} mol/L.

The difference between the H^+ concentrations of acid rain and rain water is
$$(1 \times 10^{-4}) - (2.51 \times 10^{-6}) = 9.75 \times 10^{-5} \text{ mol/L}$$

The difference between the H^+ concentrations of rain water and distilled water is
$$(2.51 \times 10^{-6}) - (1.26 \times 10^{-7}) = 2.384 \times 10^{-6} \text{ mol/L}$$

The difference between the H^+ concentrations of acid rain and rain water is **greater** than the difference between the H^+ concentrations of rain and water and distilled water. Therefore, choice D is incorrect.

15. **1.25**

Step 1
Use the power of a power and product of powers laws to simplify the numerator and denominator of the expression.
$$\frac{(0.8^3)^{-2}}{(0.8)^{-3}(0.8)^{-2}} = \frac{0.8^{3 \times -2}}{0.8^{-3 + (-2)}}$$
$$= \frac{0.8^{-6}}{0.8^{-5}}$$

Step 2
Use the quotient of powers law to simplify the expression.
$$\left(\frac{0.8^{-6}}{0.8^{-5}}\right) = 0.8^{-6 - (-5)}$$
$$= 0.8^{-1}$$

Step 3
Use the negative exponent principle to convert the power into a power with a positive exponent, and evaluate.
$$0.8^{-1} = \frac{1}{0.8^1}$$
$$= 1.25$$

16. **WR**

The pattern shows that as $\frac{1}{3}$ is added to the exponent of 8, the corresponding resulting values increase by a ratio of 2($\times$ 2).

Therefore, you can find the value for $m = 7$ by the right side of the pattern as follows:
$$8^{\frac{4}{3}} = 16$$
$$\rightarrow 8^{\frac{5}{3}} = 16 \times 2 = 32$$
$$\rightarrow 8^{\frac{6}{3}} = 32 \times 2 = 64$$
$$\rightarrow 8^{\frac{7}{3}} = 64 \times 2 = 128$$

Similarly, the pattern shows that as $\frac{1}{3}$ is subtracted from the exponent, the resulting values decrease by a ratio of 2($\div$ 2).

Therefore, you can find the value for $m = -5$ by following the left side of the pattern as follows:
$$8^{-\frac{4}{3}} = \frac{1}{16}$$
$$\rightarrow 8^{-\frac{5}{3}} = \frac{1}{16} \div 2$$
$$= \frac{1}{16} \times \frac{1}{2}$$
$$= \frac{1}{32}$$

According to the pattern of $8^{\frac{m}{3}}$, the values for $m = 7$ is 128 and for $m = -5$ is $\frac{1}{32}$.

17. **C**

Method 1
Multiply $3x(5x + 1)$ to find the total rectangular area and then subtract three squares represented by $(x)(x)$.

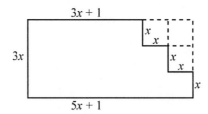

$$A_{\text{rectangle}} = 3x(5x + 1)$$
$$= 15x^2 + 3x$$
$$A_{\text{square}} = (x)(x) = x^2$$
$$A_{3 \text{ squares}} = 3(x^2) = 3x^2$$
$$A_{\text{staircase}} = A_{\text{rectangle}} - A_{3 \text{ squares}}$$
$$= 15x^2 + 3x - 3x^2$$
$$= 12x^2 + 3x$$

Method 2

Multiply three horizontal strips (A, B, and C), making up the stair as shown below.

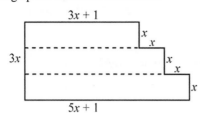

$\text{Area}_A = (x)(3x + 1)$

$\text{Area}_B = (x)(3x + 1 + x)$

$\text{Area}_C = (x)(5x + 1)$

$\text{Area}_{\text{staircase}} = \text{Area}_A + \text{Area}_B + \text{Area}_C$

$= (x)(3x + 1) + (x)(4x + 1) + (x)(5x + 1)$

$= 3x^2 + x + 4x^2 + x + 5x^2 + x$

$= 12x^2 + 3x$

The simplified expression describing the area of the staircase is $12x^2 + 3x$.

18. D

In order to determine the coefficient of the x^2-term, expand and simplify the expression.

Step 1

Use the distributive property.

Multiply each term of the first binomial by each term of the second trinomial and simplify each term.

$(2x + 3)(x^2 + 4x - 7)$

$= \begin{pmatrix} 2x(x^2) + 2x(4x) + 2x(-7) \\ +3(x^2) + 3(4x) + 3(-7) \end{pmatrix}$

$= 2x^3 + 8x^2 - 14x + 3x^2 + 12x - 21$

Step 2

Collect like terms.

$2x^3 + 8x^2 - 14x + 3x^2 + 12x - 21$

$= 2x^3 + 11x^2 - 2x - 21$

The coefficient of the x^2-term is 11.

19. D

To expand and simplify the algebraic expression $5x(2 - x) - (x + 3)^2$, use the distributive property and FOIL method, as shown below.

$5x(2 - x) - (x + 3)^2$

$= 5x(2 - x) - (x + 3)(x + 3)$

$= (5x)(2) + (5x)(-x) - $
$[(x)(x) + (3)(x) + 3(x) + (3)(3)]$

$= 10x - 5x^2 - (x^2 + 3x + 3x + 9)$

$= 10x - 5x^2 - x^2 - 3x - 3x - 9$

Collect like terms.

$= (-5x^2 - x^2) + (10x - 3x - 3x) - 9$

$= -6x^2 + 4x - 9$

20. D

To find the term represented by A, you need to multiply $(3)(3x) = 9x$. Similarly, to find the term represented by B, you need to multiply $(-4)(-2x) = 8x$. When the two terms are combined or added, the result is $17x$.

21. C

The correct steps for the simplification of the expression $4x(-x^2 + 2x - 3)$ are as follows:

Step 1

Multiply each term of the trinomial by the monomial.

$4x(-x^2 + 2x - 3)$

$= (4x)(-x^2) + (4x)(2x) + (4x)(-3)$

Step 2

Factor each term into its individual components.

$(4x)(-x^2) + (4x)(2x) + (4x)(-3)$

$= \begin{pmatrix} (4)(-1)(x)(x^2) + (4)(2)(x)(x) \\ +(4)(-3)(x) \end{pmatrix}$

Step 3

In each term, multiply all the components together.

$(4)(-1)(x)(x^2) + (4)(2)(x)(x) + (4)(-3)(x)$

$= -4x^{2+1} + 8x^{1+1} - 12x$

$= -4x^3 + 8x^2 - 12x$

Kara's first error occurred in step 3 when she incorrectly simplified $-4x^{2+1}$ to $-4x^2$ rather than $-4x^3$.

22. 35

When these two binomials are multiplied,

$(2x + 3)(3x + 4) = 6x^2 + 17x + 12$

Therefore, the algebra tiles needed are

$6\ x^2$ tiles $+ 17\ x$ tiles $+ 12$ unit tiles $= 35$ tiles

23. C

A common factor of all three numerical coefficients of the terms is 3, and m^2, n, and p^3 are all common variable factors of the three terms. Thus, the greatest common factor for these three terms is $3m^2np^3$.

To verify, divide each term by $3m^2np^3$.

$$\frac{3m^2np^3}{3m^2np^3} = 1$$

$$\frac{15m^3n^3p^4}{3m^2np^3} = 5mn^2p$$

$$\frac{36m^2n^2p^3}{3m^2np^3} = 12n$$

24. B

The correct arrangement of algebra tiles has a total of 35 tiles.

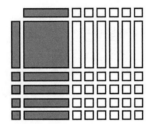

There is 1 shaded "x^2" tile.

There are 4 shaded "x" tiles and 6 white "x" tiles which cancel out to 2 white tiles.

There are 24 white "one" tiles.

25. C

Step 1
Since this expression is a differences of squares, set up a product of two binomials, one with an addition operation and one with a subtraction operation. The order of the binomials does not matter.
$(+)(-)$

Step 2
Determine the square root of the first term in the difference-of-squares expression, and use the root as the first term in each of the bracketed binomials.
$16a^2b^2 = \sqrt{16a^2b^2}$
$\qquad = 4ab$
Therefore, $(4ab +)(4ab -)$.

Step 3
Calculate the square root of the second term in the difference-of-squares expression, and use the root as the second term in each of the bracketed binomials.
$9c^2 = \sqrt{9c^2}$
$\qquad = 3c$
Therefore, $(4ab + 3c)(4ab - 3c)$.
One factor is $4ab + 3c$.

26. C

The first expression is $x^2 - 15x - 34$.

Find two numbers such that their product is -34 and their sum is -15. The number -34 can be factored as -17×2. The sum of these factors is -15 $(-17 + 2)$.

Thus, the expression $x^2 - 15x - 34$ can be factored as

$x^2 - 15x - 34 = (x - 17)(x + 2)$

The second expression is $x^2 + 5x + 6$.

Find two numbers such that their product is 6 and their sum is 5. The number 6 can be factored as 2×3. The sum of these factors is $5 (5 = 2 + 3)$.

Thus, the expression $x^2 + 5x + 6$ can be factored as:
$x^2 + 5x + 6 = (x + 3)(x + 2)$

- The factors of $x^2 - 15x - 34$ are $(x - 17)$ and $(x + 2)$.

- The factors of $x^2 + 5x + 6$ are $(x + 3)$ and $(x + 2)$.

The binomial $(x + 2)$ is a factor of both expressions.

27. C

Quadratic I: trinomial, where $a = 1$, $x^2 - 19x + 60$

Find two integers whose product is 60 and whose sum is -19. The two numbers are -15 and -4. Then, split the trinomial into two binomial factors, one with -15 and the other with -4.
$x^2 - 19x + 60 = (x - 15)(x - 4)$
This expression is factored correctly.

Quadratic II: binomial, with differences of squares:
$3x^3 - 75x$

Factor out the GCF of $3x$.
$3x^3 - 75x = 3x(1x^2 - 25)$
Since 1 and 25 are perfect squares, the expression factors to $3x(\sqrt{1}x - \sqrt{25})(\sqrt{1}x + \sqrt{25})$
$\qquad = 3x(x - 5)(x + 5)$
This expression is also factored correctly

Quadratic III: trinomial, where
$a \neq 1$, $-9x^2 + 12x - 4$

Find two numbers that multiply to give
$(-9)(-4) = 36$ and that have a sum of 12. The two
numbers are 6 and 6. Split the middle term.

$-9x^2 + 12x - 4$

$-9x^2 + 6x + 6x - 4$

Group the four terms, factor out the GCF of each
pair, and then factor out the common binomial.
$(-9x^2 + 6x) + (6x - 4)$
$-3x(3x - 2) + 2(3x - 2)$
$(-3x + 2)(3x - 2)$
This expression is factored incorrectly.

Quadratic IV: trinomial, where $a \neq 1$,
$4x^2 + 6x + 2$

First, factor out the GCF of 2.
$2(2x^2 + 3x + 1)$
Find two numbers that multiply to give $(2)(1) = 2$
and have a sum of 3. The two numbers are 2 and 1.
Split the middle term.

$2(2x^2 + 3x + 1)$

$2(2x^2 + 2x + 1x + 1)$

Group the four terms, factor out the GCF of each
pair, and then factor out the common binomial.
$2[(2x^2 + 2x) + (1x + 1)]$
$2[2x(x + 1) + 1(x + 1)]$
$2(x + 1)(2x + 1)$
This expression is factored correctly.

Therefore, quadratic III is factored incorrectly.

28. 8

In order to factor $x^2 - 2x - 15$, find two numbers
that have a product of -15 (c-value) and a sum of
-2 (b-value). In this case the two numbers are -5
and 3.

Thus, the factored form of $x^2 - 2x - 15$ is
$(x - 5)(x + 3)$.

Since $m = 5$ and $n = 3$, the value of
$m + n = 5 + 3 = 8$.

29. 2205

A perfect square trinomial in the form of
$a^2 + 2ab + b^2$ factors to $(a + b)(a + b)$ or $(a + b)^2$.
For the perfect square trinomial $4x^2 + Bx + 25$,
$4x^2$ represents a^2 and 25 represents b^2.

Step 1
Determine the values of a and b.
$a^2 = 4x^2$
$\sqrt{a^2} = \sqrt{4x^2}$
$a = 2$
$b^2 = 25$
$\sqrt{b^2} = \sqrt{25}$
$b = 5$

Step 2
For the perfect square trinomial $4x^2 + Bx + 25$, the
middle term Bx represents $2ab$. Determine the value
of B.
Substitute $2x$ for a and 5 for c in the equation
$Bx = 2ab$, and then solve for B.
$Bx = 2ab$
$\quad = 2(2x)(5)$
$\quad = 20x$
$\dfrac{Bx}{x} = \dfrac{20x}{x}$
$B = 20$

Step 3
When the perfect square trinomial is written in the
factored form of $(Ax + C)^2$, Ax represents a, and C
represents b. Determine the values of A and C.

- Since $a = 2x$ and $a = Ax$, then $A = 2$.
- Since $b = 5$ and $b = C$, then $C = 5$.

Step 4
Write the value of ABC in order from left to right.
Since $A = 2$, $B = 20$, and $C = 5$, the values of ABC
are 2, 20, and 5, or **2 205**.

30. WR

Step 1
The student shows the splitting of the middle
term bx into two terms.
$bx = -3x + 4x$
$\quad = 1x$
Therefore, $b = 1$ in the original expression.
The two numbers -3 and 4 also need to multiply to
produce the product of $(a)(c)$ in the original
expression $ax^2 + bx + c$, that is $(a)(c) = (-3)(4)$.
$ac = -12$, and since $a = 6$
$6c = -12$
$\quad c = -2$ or $-(2)$
The completed first step
should be $6x^2 - 3x + 4x - \boxed{2}$

Step 2
The four terms are grouped, and the GCF is factored out of each binomial.

$\left(6x^2 - 3x\right) + (4x - 2)$
$3x(2x - 1) + 2(2x - 1)$

The completed second step

should be $3x(\underline{2x - 1}) + \boxed{2}(2x - 1)$

Step 3
Factor out the common binomial.
The completed third step should be
$(\underline{3x + 2})(\underline{2x - 1})$ or $(\underline{2x - 1})(\underline{3x + 2})$.

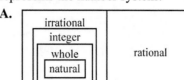

UNIT TEST — ALGEBRA AND NUMBER

1. Which of the following numbers has the **fewest** prime factors?

　A. 13 552　　**B.** 23 598

　C. 32 032　　**D.** 47 250

Use the following information to answer the next question.

> Derek owns a rectangular plot of land measuring 792 ft by 840 ft. He wants to split this plot into square sections, where each section has the maximum possible area.

2. How many square sections can be formed?

　A. 576　　　**B.** 1 155

　C. 4 620　　**D.** 10 395

3. The expression $\sqrt[3]{\sqrt{100-36}}$ is equivalent to

　A. $\sqrt[3]{4}$　　**B.** $\sqrt[3]{2}$

　C. 4　　　　**D.** 2

Use the following information to answer the next question.

> Brittany multiplies three whole numbers to form the smallest possible perfect square.

Numerical Response

4. If the first two numbers are 8 and 105, then the third number is _____.

5. Which of the following diagrams represents the number system?

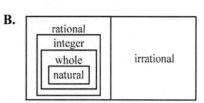

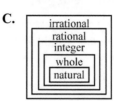

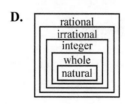

Use the following information to answer the next question.

> On the given number line, the letters represent real numbers.

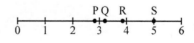

6. Which letter represents the approximate value of $\sqrt{10}$?

　A. P　　　**B.** Q

　C. R　　　**D.** S

7. When the numbers $3\sqrt[3]{-10}$, $-4\sqrt[3]{5}$, $2\sqrt[3]{-36}$, and $-5\sqrt[3]{3}$ are ordered from least to greatest, what is the order?

 A. $3\sqrt[3]{-10}$, $2\sqrt[3]{-36}$, $-4\sqrt[3]{5}$, $-5\sqrt[3]{3}$

 B. $3\sqrt[3]{-10}$, $-4\sqrt[3]{5}$, $-5\sqrt[3]{3}$, $2\sqrt[3]{-36}$

 C. $-5\sqrt[3]{3}$, $2\sqrt[3]{-36}$, $-4\sqrt[3]{5}$, $3\sqrt[3]{-10}$

 D. $-5\sqrt[3]{3}$, $-4\sqrt[3]{5}$, $2\sqrt[3]{-36}$, $3\sqrt[3]{-10}$

Use the following information to answer the next question.

> Lisa examined the following list of numbers:
>
> $\sqrt{\dfrac{23}{92}}$, $-\dfrac{1}{9}$, $2.636\,363...$, $\sqrt[3]{28}$, $2\sqrt[4]{625}$, $\dfrac{\pi}{3}$

8. How many rational numbers did Lisa find in the list?

 A. 2   B. 3

 C. 4   D. 5

Numerical Response

9. When $\sqrt{432}$ is converted to the simplified mixed radical form $a\sqrt{b}$, the sum of a and b is _____.

10. Which of the following exponential expressions is equivalent to $\left(\left(\dfrac{1}{2}\right)^3\right)^{-1}$?

 A. $\left(\dfrac{1}{2}\right)^3 \times \left(\dfrac{1}{2}\right)^{-1}$

 B. $\left(\dfrac{1}{2}\right)^3 \div \left(\dfrac{1}{2}\right)^{-1}$

 C. $\dfrac{1}{2} \times \dfrac{1}{2} \times \dfrac{1}{2}$

 D. $2 \times 2 \times 2$

11. For $8^r \times 8^r \times 8^r = \dfrac{1}{64}$, the value of r must be

 A. $\dfrac{3}{2}$ B. $\dfrac{2}{3}$

 C. $-\dfrac{2}{3}$ D. $-\dfrac{3}{2}$

12. The **most** simplified form of the expression $\left(\dfrac{4x^3y^8}{2x^5y^6}\right)^3$ is

 A. $\dfrac{8y^6}{x^6}$ B. $\dfrac{16x^9}{y^9}$

 C. $\dfrac{8x^9}{y^9}$ D. $8x^6y^6$

Use the following information to answer the next question.

> The half-life of iodine-131 is every 8.04 days; that is, after 8.04 days, half of the iodine-131 decays. The amount, N_t, of iodine-131, in kilograms, with an initial mass of 12 600 kg, remaining after t days is given by the formula:
>
> $$N_t = 12\,600\left(\dfrac{1}{2}\right)^{\frac{t}{8.04}}$$

13. The approximate mass of iodine-131 remaining after 30 days, to the nearest whole kilogram, is

 A. 131 kg   B. 475 kg

 C. 949 kg   D. 3 378 kg

Use the following information to answer the next question.

> A possible way to estimate the value of a car can be calculated using the formula $V_t = V_0(1 - r)^t$, where V_t is the value after t years, V_0 is the original value, and r is the depreciation rate expressed as a decimal. In 1996, a particular car was valued at $27 500. Its value decreased exponentially each year afterward. For the first 7 years, the value of the car decreased by 24% of the previous year's value.

14. What will be the value of the car after 7 years?

 A. $942.85   B. $3 060.75

 C. $4 027.43   D. $5 299.25

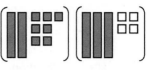

Numerical Response

15. When the expression $\dfrac{\left(\frac{1}{7}\right)^{-\frac{2}{3}}\left(49^{\frac{1}{2}}\right)^{3}}{(7^{2})}$ is
evaluated, the resulting value is
_____. (Record your answer to the
nearest tenth.)

Numerical Response

16. When the expression $\left(\sqrt[5]{\left(\frac{1}{5}\right)^{-3}}\right)^{\frac{7}{2}}$ is
converted to a simplified power of the
form 5^{n}, the value of n is _____.
(Record your answer to the nearest tenth.)

17. The expression $(3x - 2)(x + 5)$ is
represented by which of the following
algebra tile grids?

A.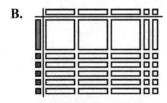

B.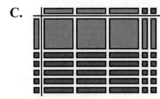

C.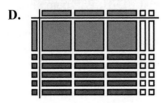

D.

*Use the following information to
answer the next question.*

The algebra tiles represent an algebraic
expression.

18. When the algebraic representations of the
algebra tiles are multiplied and simplified,
the result is

   A. $6x^{2} + 13x - 28$

   B. $6x^{2} + 21x + 3$

   C. $5x^{2} + 13x + 3$

   D. $5x^{2} + 7x - 4$

19. In order for the polynomial expression
$(3x + 2)(2x - 3) - 2(x - 2)^{2}$
$+ Ax^{2} + Bx + C$ to equal 0, the values
of A, B, and C are

   A. $A = 4$, $B = 3$, $C = 14$

   B. $A = -4$, $B = -3$, $C = 14$

   C. $A = 4$, $B = -3$, $C = 2$

   D. $A = -4$, $B = 3$, $C = 2$

20. When expanded, the expression
$(2x - 5)(3x + 4)^{2}$ equals

   A. $5x^{3} - 80$

   B. $18x^{3} + 3x^{2} - 88x - 80$

   C. $18x^{3} - 45x^{2} + 32x - 80$

   D. $18x^{3} + 93x^{2} - 88x - 80$

Use the following information to answer the next question.

Jennifer expanded and simplified the given expression as shown.

$-2(2x + 5y)^2 = -8x^2 - 20xy - 25y^2$

To verify her work, she substituted the values $x = 1$ and $y = -2$ into both the left and right sides of the equation. According to the verification, Jennifer's final expression is _____*i*_____, because the left side is equal to _____*ii*_____ and the right side is equal to _____*iii*_____.

21. The given statement is completed by the information in which of the following tables?

A.

i	*ii*	*iii*
correct	-128	-128

B.

i	*ii*	*iii*
correct	128	128

C.

i	*ii*	*iii*
incorrect	-128	-68

D.

i	*ii*	*iii*
incorrect	128	68

Numerical Response

22. If $(3x + 2)(2x + 3) = 6x^2 + bx + c$, where b and c are real numbers, then the value of $b + c$ is _____.

Written Response

23. Find the product of $(2x - 3)(x - 4)$ using the vertical multiplication strategy.

24. One factor of the expression $k^2 + 6k - 2k - 12$ is
- **A.** $k - 6$
- **B.** $k + 6$
- **C.** $k + 2$
- **D.** $-k - 2$

25. The expression $x + 3$ is **not** a factor of
- **A.** $x^2 - 2x - 15$
- **B.** $-2x^2 + 18$
- **C.** $-3x^2 - 9x$
- **D.** $x^2 + 7x + 15$

26. Which of the following expressions is **not** a factor of $9mn^2 - 12mn - 12m$?
- **A.** $3n + 2$
- **B.** $n - 4$
- **C.** $n - 2$
- **D.** $3m$

Use the following information to answer the next question.

Rachel is asked to factor four different polynomials. The given table shows the four polynomials and the student's solutions.

	Polynomial	Student's Solution
I	$8x^3 + 4x^2$	$4x^2(2x + 1)$
II	$25a^2 - 4b^2c^2$	$(5a + 2bc)(5a - 2bc)$
III	$2x^2 - 18y^2$	$2(x + 3y)(x - 3y)$
IV	$4a^3 - a$	$a(2a - 1)^2$

27. Which polynomial did Rachel factor **incorrectly**?
- **A.** Polynomial I
- **B.** Polynomial II
- **C.** Polynomial III
- **D.** Polynomial IV

28. Which of the following forms is the completely factored form of the expression $x^4 - 81$?

   A. $(x^2 + 9)(x + 3)(x - 3)$

   B. $(x^2 + 9)(x^2 - 9)$

   C. $(x^2 - 9)^2$

   D. $(x^2 + 9)^2$

Use the following information to answer the next question.

The polynomial expression $x^2 - 3x - 4$ is factored as $(x - m)(x + n)$.

Numerical Response

29. The value of $m + n$ is _____.

Written Response

30. When the two polynomial expressions given by, $18x^2 - 8$ and $6x^2 - 11x - 10$ are factored, what common factor do they share?

Copyright Protected

ANSWERS AND SOLUTIONS — UNIT TEST

1. B	7. D	13. C	19. B	25. D
2. B	8. C	14. C	20. B	26. B
3. D	9. 15	15. 25.6	21. C	27. D
4. 210	10. D	16. 2.1	22. 19	28. A
5. B	11. C	17. D	23. WR	29. 5
6. B	12. A	18. A	24. B	30. WR

1. B

Step 1

Determine the prime factorization of each number. Factor trees can be used to determine prime factorization.

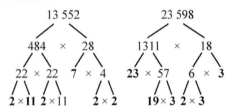

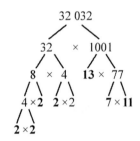

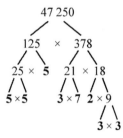

Step 2

Determine the number that has the fewest prime factors.

According to the factor trees, 13 552 has 7 prime factors, 23 598 has 6 prime factors, 32 032 has 8 prime factors, and 47 250 has 8 prime factors. Therefore, 23 598 has the fewest prime factors.

2. B

The side length of the square section with the maximum possible area will be the greatest common factor (GCF) of each dimension of the rectangular plot.

Step 1

Determine the GCF of 792 and 840 using one of the two methods.

Method 1—Use a division list.

Use a calculator to determine all the factors of each number, and pick the GCF.

Factors of 792	
1 × 792	9 × 88
2 × 396	11 × 72
3 × 264	12 × 66
4 × 198	18 × 44
6 × 132	22 × 36
8 × 99	24 × 33

Factors of 840	
1 × 840	10 × 84
2 × 420	12 × 70
3 × 280	14 × 60
4 × 210	15 × 56
5 × 168	20 × 42
6 × 140	21 × 40
7 × 120	24 × 35
8 × 105	28 × 30

The GCF is 24.

Method 2— Prime factorization

Determine the prime factors of each number, and select the maximum shared prime factors.

$792 = 2 \times 2 \times 2 \times 3 \times 3 \times 11$
$840 = 2 \times 2 \times 2 \times 3 \times 5 \times 7$

The GCF is $2 \times 2 \times 2 \times 3 = 24$.

Therefore, the side length of the square section with the maximum possible area is 24 ft.

Step 2

Determine the total number of square sections, n, that can be formed by dividing the total area, A, of the plot by the area, A_s, of each square section.

$$n = \frac{A}{A_s}$$
$$= \frac{l \times w}{s \times s}$$
$$= \frac{840 \times 792}{24 \times 24}$$
$$= \frac{665\ 280}{576}$$
$$= 1\ 155$$

Therefore, the number of square sections that could be formed in the rectangular plot of land is 1 155.

3. D

Step 1

Determine the difference between 100 and 36.
$100 - 36 = 64$

Step 1

Evaluate $\sqrt{64}$.

A possible set of key strokes are $\boxed{\text{2nd}} \rightarrow \boxed{x^2}$
$\rightarrow \boxed{64} \rightarrow \boxed{)} \rightarrow \boxed{\text{ENTER}}$.
$\sqrt{64} = 8$

Step 2

Evaluate $\sqrt[3]{8}$.

A possible set of key strokes are $\boxed{\text{MATH}} \rightarrow \boxed{4}$
$\rightarrow \boxed{8} \rightarrow \boxed{)} \rightarrow \boxed{\text{ENTER}}$.
$\sqrt[3]{8} = 2$

Note that the approximate value of $\sqrt[3]{\sqrt{100 - 36}}$ can be determined in one step using the following sequence of key strokes on a graphing calculator:

$\boxed{\text{MATH}} \rightarrow \boxed{4} \rightarrow \boxed{\text{2nd}} \rightarrow \boxed{x^2} \rightarrow \boxed{100} \rightarrow \boxed{-}$
$\rightarrow \boxed{36} \rightarrow \boxed{)} \rightarrow \boxed{)} \rightarrow \boxed{\text{ENTER}}$

4. 210

The smallest perfect square of the three multiplied numbers consists of the minimum groups of paired prime factors.

Step 1

Determine the prime factors of 8×105.
$8 \times 105 = 2 \times 2 \times 2 \times 3 \times 5 \times 7$

Step 2

Determine the third number, x, that has the necessary prime factors to create the minimum sets of paired factors for 8×105.

Since a perfect square is required, multiply the left side of the equation by x and square each **unpaired** prime factor on the right side of the equation.

$8 \times 105 = 2 \times 2 \times 2 \times 3 \times 5 \times 7$
$840(x) = 2 \times 2 \times (2^2)(3^2)(5^2)(7^2)$
$840x = (4)(4)(9)(25)(49)$
$840x = 176\ 400$
$x = \frac{176\ 400}{840}$
$x = 210$

Therefore, the third number is 210. When 210 is multiplied by 105 and 8, the product is the smallest perfect square of 176 400 (or 420^2).

5. B

The set of rational numbers and the set of irrational numbers are distinct, meaning they do not contain any common values. The set of rational numbers includes integers, whole numbers, and natural numbers. Therefore, the diagram of a number system looks like this..

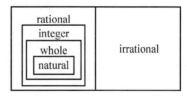

6. B

Step 1

Determine the two perfect squares that 10 is between.

The two perfect squares that 10 is between are 9 and 16.

Step 2

Determine the square roots of these perfect squares.
$\sqrt{9} = 3$
$\sqrt{16} = 4$

Therefore, the square root of 10 is between the whole numbers 3 and 4.

Step 3

Determine the letter that represents the approximate square root of 10.

The square root of 10 is either Q or R.

Since 10 is closer to 9 than 16, $\sqrt{10}$ is closer to 3 than 4.

The letter Q is the best approximation.

7. D

One of the best ways to compare radicals is to convert them from mixed radicals into entire radicals.

Step 1

Since the index is 3, rewrite each coefficient value as the cube root of its value cubed, and multiply it to the radicand.

$$3\sqrt[3]{-10} = \sqrt[3]{3^3} \times \sqrt[3]{-10}$$
$$= \sqrt[3]{27} \times \sqrt[3]{-10}$$
$$= \sqrt[3]{-270}$$

$$-4\sqrt[3]{5} = \sqrt[3]{(-4)^3} \times \sqrt[3]{5}$$
$$= \sqrt[3]{-64} \times \sqrt[3]{5}$$
$$= \sqrt[3]{-320}$$

$$2\sqrt[3]{-36} = \sqrt[3]{(2)^3} \times \sqrt[3]{-36}$$
$$= \sqrt[3]{8} \times \sqrt[3]{-36}$$
$$= \sqrt[3]{-288}$$

$$-5\sqrt[3]{3} = \sqrt[3]{(-5)^3} \times \sqrt[3]{3}$$
$$= \sqrt[3]{-125} \times \sqrt[3]{3}$$
$$= \sqrt[3]{-375}$$

Step 2

Determine the order of the radicals from least to greatest.

$$\sqrt[3]{-375} < \sqrt[3]{-320} < \sqrt[3]{-288} < \sqrt[3]{-270}$$

Therefore, the order from least to greatest is $-5\sqrt[3]{3}$, $-4\sqrt[3]{5}$, $2\sqrt[3]{-36}$, and $3\sqrt[3]{-10}$.

8. C

A rational number is a real number that can be written in the form $\frac{a}{b}$, where a and b are integers and $b \neq 0$. This includes all integers and all terminating and repeating decimals.

- The number $\sqrt{\frac{23}{92}} = \sqrt{\frac{1}{4}} = \frac{1}{2}$. Since $\frac{1}{4}$ is a perfect square, $\sqrt{\frac{23}{92}}$ is a rational number.

- The number $-\frac{1}{9}$ is a rational number in the form $\frac{a}{b}$.

- The number $2.636\,363\ldots$ is a repeating decimal, so it is a rational number.

- The number $\sqrt[3]{28} = 3.036\,588\,97\ldots$ is not a rational number because 28 is not a perfect cube and the resulting decimal is non-repeating and non-terminating.

- The number $2\sqrt[4]{625} = 2 \times 5 = 10$. Since 625 is a perfect fourth power, $2\sqrt[4]{625}$ is a rational number.

- The number $\frac{\pi}{3} = 1.047\,197\,55\ldots$, is a non-repeating, non-terminating decimal. It is not a rational number.

There are four rational numbers in the list.

9. 15

Step 1

Determine the greatest perfect square of all the factors of 432.
The factors of 432 are 1, 2, 3, 4, 6, 8, 9, 12, 16, 18, 24, 27, 36, 48, 54, 72, 108, 144, 216, and 432.
The greatest perfect square is 144.

Step 2

Simplify the entire radical using the factors 144 and 3.

$$\sqrt{432} = \sqrt{144 \times 3}$$
$$= \sqrt{144} \times \sqrt{3}$$
$$= 12 \times \sqrt{3}$$
$$= 12\sqrt{3}$$

Step 3

Determine the value of $a + b$.
When $\sqrt{432}$ is written as $a\sqrt{b} = 12\sqrt{3}$, the sum of a and b is $12 + 3 = 15$.

10. D

The original expression $\left(\left(\frac{1}{2}\right)^3\right)^{-1}$ can be simplified according to the power rule $\left(x^m\right)^n = x^{mn}$ as follows:

$$\left(\left(\frac{1}{2}\right)^3\right)^{-1} = \left(\frac{1}{2}\right)^{3\times -1} = \left(\frac{1}{2}\right)^{-3}$$

Since $\left(\frac{1}{x}\right)^{-n} = x^n$, the expression $\left(\frac{1}{2}\right)^{-3}$ can also be written as 2^3.

The expression $\left(\frac{1}{2}\right)^3 \times \left(\frac{1}{2}\right)^{-1}$ can be simplified using the product rule $x^m \times x^n = x^{m+n}$ as follows:

$$\left(\frac{1}{2}\right)^3 \times \left(\frac{1}{2}\right)^{-1} = \left(\frac{1}{2}\right)^{3+-1}$$
$$= \left(\frac{1}{2}\right)^2$$

This expression is not equivalent to either form of the simplified original expression $\left(\frac{1}{2}\right)^{-3}$ or 2^3.

The expression $\left(\frac{1}{2}\right)^3 \div \left(\frac{1}{2}\right)^{-1}$ can be simplified using quotient rule $x^m \div x^n = x^{m-n}$ as follows:

$$\left(\frac{1}{2}\right)^3 \div \left(\frac{1}{2}\right)^{-1} = \left(\frac{1}{2}\right)^{3--1}$$
$$= \left(\frac{1}{2}\right)^4$$

This expression is not equivalent to either form of the simplified original expression $\left(\frac{1}{2}\right)^{-3}$ or 2^3.

The expression $\frac{1}{2} \times \frac{1}{2} \times \frac{1}{2}$ can also be simplified using the product rule.

$$\frac{1}{2} \times \frac{1}{2} \times \frac{1}{2} = \left(\frac{1}{2}\right)^1 \times \left(\frac{1}{2}\right)^1 \times \left(\frac{1}{2}\right)^1$$
$$= \left(\frac{1}{2}\right)^{1+1+1}$$
$$= \left(\frac{1}{2}\right)^3$$

This expression is not equivalent to either form of the simplified original expression $\left(\frac{1}{2}\right)^{-3}$ or 2^3.

The expression $2 \times 2 \times 2$ can also be simplified using the product rule.

$$2 \times 2 \times 2 = 2^1 \times 2^1 \times 2^1$$
$$= 2^{1+1+1}$$
$$= 2^3$$

This expression is equivalent to the second form of the simplified original expression 2^3.

11. C

The value $\frac{1}{64}$ written as an expression with a base of 8 is $\frac{1}{8^2}$, since $64 = 8 \times 8 = 8^1 \times 8^1 = 8^{1+1} = 8^2$.

The expression $\frac{1}{8^2}$ can also be written in the form 8^{-2} since $\frac{1}{x^n} = x^{-n}$.

Therefore, $8^r \times 8^r \times 8^r = 8^{-2}$.

According to the product rule $\left(x^m\right) \times (x)^n = x^{m+n}$, the expression on the left side of the equal sign can be simplified as follows:

$$\left(8^r\right)\left(8^r\right)\left(8^r\right) = 8^{r+r+r} = 8^{3r}$$

In the simplified expression $8^{3r} = 8^{-2}$, the exponents must be equal since the bases are equal.
$$3r = -2$$
$$r = -\frac{2}{3}$$

The correct value of r is $-\frac{2}{3}$.

12. A

Step 1

Use the quotient of powers law to simplify the expression in the brackets.

$$\left(\frac{4x^3y^8}{2x^5y^6}\right)^3 = \left(\frac{4}{2}x^{3-5}y^{8-6}\right)^3$$
$$= \left(2x^{-2}y^2\right)^3$$

Step 2

Use the power of a product law to simplify the expression further.

$$\left(2x^{-2}y^2\right)^3 = 2^3x^{-2\times 3}y^{2\times 3}$$
$$= 8x^{-6}y^6$$

Step 3

Rewrite the expression in terms of positive exponents applying the negative exponent principle.

$$8x^{-6}y^6 = \frac{8y^6}{x^6}$$

13. C

The formula for the decay of iodine-131 is given as:

$$N_t = 12\ 600\left(\frac{1}{2}\right)^{\frac{t}{8.04}}$$

where t is the time in days and N_t is the amount of iodine remaining after t days.

To find the amount of iodine remaining after 30 days, substitute $t = 30$ in the formula, and then evaluate.

$$N_{30} = 12\ 600\left(\frac{1}{2}\right)^{\frac{30}{8.04}}$$

$$\approx 12\ 600(0.075\ 292\ 8519)$$

$$\approx 948.689\ 9342\ \text{kg}$$

Therefore, the approximate mass remaining after 30 days, to the nearest whole kilogram, is 949 kg.

14. **C**

Substitute 27 500 into the equation for V_0, 0.24 for r, and 7 for t, and then evaluate.

$$V_t = V_0(1 - r)^t$$

$$= 27\ 500(1 - 0.24)^7$$

$$= 27\ 500(0.76)^7$$

$$\approx 27\ 500(0.146\ 451\ 9457)$$

$$\approx 4\ 027.4285$$

Therefore, the value of the car after 7 years is $4 027.43, to the nearest cent.

15. **25.6**

Step 1

Using the negative exponent principle, rewrite the power with the negative exponent as a power with a positive exponent.

$$\frac{\left(\frac{1}{7}\right)^{-\frac{2}{3}}\left(49^{\frac{1}{2}}\right)^3}{(7^2)} = \frac{\left(49^{\frac{1}{2}}\right)^3}{\left(\frac{1}{7}\right)^{\frac{2}{3}}(7^2)}$$

$$= \frac{(7)^{\frac{2}{3}}\left(49^{\frac{1}{2}}\right)^3}{(7^2)}$$

Step 2

Rewrite $49^{\frac{1}{2}}$ as a radical, and evaluate.

$$\frac{(7)^{\frac{2}{3}}\left(49^{\frac{1}{2}}\right)^3}{(7^2)} = \frac{(7)^{\frac{2}{3}}(\sqrt{49})^3}{(7^2)}$$

$$= \frac{(7)^{\frac{2}{3}}(7)^3}{(7^2)}$$

Step 3

Use the product and quotient of powers laws to simplify the expression, and evaluate it using a calculator.

$$\frac{(7)^{\frac{2}{3}}(7)^3}{(7^2)} = 7^{\frac{2}{3}+3-2}$$

$$= 7^{\frac{2}{3}+\frac{9}{3}-\frac{6}{3}}$$

$$= 7^{\frac{5}{3}}$$

$$\approx 25.615\ 139\ 97$$

Therefore, to the nearest tenth, the resulting value is 25.6.

16. **2.1**

Step 1

Convert the expression in the brackets to a power with a rational exponent.

$$\left(\sqrt[5]{\left(\frac{1}{5}\right)^{-3}}\right)^{\frac{7}{2}} = \left(\left(\frac{1}{5}\right)^{-\frac{3}{5}}\right)^{\frac{7}{2}}$$

Step 2

Rewrite the power in the brackets to a power with a positive exponent, using the negative exponent principle.

$$\left(\left(\frac{1}{5}\right)^{-\frac{3}{5}}\right)^{\frac{7}{2}} = \left(5^{\frac{3}{5}}\right)^{\frac{7}{2}}$$

Step 3

Apply the power of a power law.

$$\left(5^{\frac{3}{5}}\right)^{\frac{7}{2}} = 5^{\frac{3}{5}\times\frac{7}{2}}$$

$$= 5^{\frac{21}{10}}$$

$$= 5^{2.1}$$

When the expression is simplified to the form 5^n, the value of n is 2.1, to the nearest tenth.

17. **D**

Step 1

Use the FOIL strategy to expand the polynomial.

$$(3x - 2)(x + 5)$$

$$= 3x^2 + 15x - 2x - 10$$

$$= 3x^2 + 13x - 10$$

Step 2

Eliminate the algebra tiles that do not include a mix of positive and negative tiles.

Positive tiles are shaded and negative tiles are white.

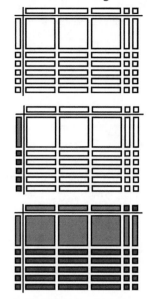

are not correct because they do not include a mix of positive and negative tiles.

Step 3

The correct grid will represent $3x$ as three shaded rectangles and -2 as two white squares.

18. A

Step 1

Determine the algebraic representation of the algebra tiles.

The shaded tiles are positive $1x$ and positive 1 unit tiles, and the unshaded tiles are $-1x$ and -1 unit tiles. The algebraic representation of the algebra tiles is $(2x + 7)(3x - 4)$.

Step 2

Determine the product of $(2x + 7)(3x - 4)$ using the FOIL method, and simplify.

$(2x + 7)(3x - 4)$

$= \begin{pmatrix} (2x)(3x) + (2x)(-4) \\ +7(3x) + 7(-4) \end{pmatrix}$

$= 6x^2 - 8x + 21x - 28$

$= 6x^2 + 13x - 28$

When the algebraic representations of the algebra tiles are multiplied and simplified, the result is $6x^2 + 13x - 28$.

19. B

Use the FOIL method and the distributive property to simplify the expressions given below.

$(3x + 2)(2x - 3) - 2(x - 2)^2$

$= (3x + 2)(2x-3) - 2(x - 2)(x - 2)$

$= (3x)(2x) + (-3)(3x) + 2(2x) + (2)(-3) - 2$
$[(x)(x) + (-2)(x) + (-2)(x) + (-2)(-2)]$

$= 6x^2 - 9x + 4x - 6 - 2(x^2 - 2x - 2x + 4)$

$= \begin{pmatrix} 6x^2 - 9x + 4x - 6 \\ -2x^2 + 4x + 4x - 8 \end{pmatrix}$

$= \begin{pmatrix} (6x^2 - 2x^2) \\ +(-9x + 4x + 4x + 4x) \\ +(-6 - 8) \end{pmatrix}$

$= 4x^2 + 3x - 14$

Now, for $Ax^2 + Bx + C + (4x^2 + 3x - 14)$ to equal 0, $Ax^2 + Bx + C$ must be the additive inverse of $4x^2 + 3x - 14$. This means that $Ax^2 = -4x^2$, $Bx = -3x$, and $C = -(-14)$.

Therefore, $A = -4$, $B = -3$, and $C = 14$.

20. B

To expand the expression $(2x - 5)(3x + 4)^2$, multiply the three terms.

Step 1

Multiply and simplify $(3x + 4)^2$.

$(3x + 4)^2 = (3x + 4)(3x + 4)$

$= \begin{pmatrix} 3x(3x) + 3x(4) \\ +4(3x) + 4(4) \end{pmatrix}$

$= 9x^2 + 12x + 12x + 16$

$= 9x^2 + 24x + 16$

Step 2

Multiply the expression $9x^2 + 24x + 16$ by the first term, $(2x - 5)$, and simplify.

$(2x - 5)(9x^2 + 24x + 16)$

$= \begin{pmatrix} 2x(9x^2) + 2x(24x) + 2x(16) \\ +(-5)(9x^2) + (-5)(24x) + (-5)(16) \end{pmatrix}$

$= \begin{pmatrix} 18x^3 + 48x^2 + 32x \\ -45x^2 - 120x - 80 \end{pmatrix}$

$= 18x^3 + 3x^2 - 88x - 80$

21. C

Step 1

Substitute the values $x = 1$ and $y = -2$ into both expressions in the equation, and evaluate each side. Determine the value of the left side of the equation.

$-2(2x + 5y)^2$

$= -2(2(1) + 5(-2))^2$

$= -2(-8)^2$

$= -2(64)$

$= -128$

Determine the value of the right side of the equation.

$-8x^2 - 20xy - 25y^2$

$= -8(1)^2 - 20(1)(-2) - 25(-2)^2$

$= -8 + 40 - 25(4)$

$= -8 + 40 - 100$

$= -68$

Step 2

Determine if the simplification is correct.

Since the left-side value of -128 does not equal the right-side value of -68, Jennifer's expanded and simplified expression is incorrect. The correct expansion and simplification is given as follows:

$-2(2x + 5y)^2$

$= -2(2x + 5y)(2x + 5y)$

$= (-4x - 10y)(2x + 5y)$

$= \begin{pmatrix} -4x(2x) - 4x(5y) \\ -10y(2x) - 10y(5y) \end{pmatrix}$

$= -8x^2 - 20xy - 20xy - 50y^2$

$= -8x^2 - 40xy - 50y^2$

22. 19

Step 1

For the left side of the given equation, use the distributive property of multiplication (FOIL) to multiply each term within the first set of brackets by each term within the second set of brackets.

$(3x + 2)(2x + 3)$

$= 3x(2x) + 3x(3) + 2(2x) + 2(3)$

$= 6x^2 + 9x + 4x + 6$

Step 2

Collect like terms.

$6x^2 + 9x + 4x + 6 = 6x^2 + 13x + 6$

Step 3

Compare the expression $6x^2 + 13x + 6$ to the expression $6x^2 + bx + c$.

$6x^2 + 13x + 6 = 6x^2 + bx + c$

In order for the expressions to be equal, $b = 13$ and $c = 6$.

The value of $b + c = 13 + 6 = 19$.

23. WR

Step 1

Write the two binomials, one on top of the other.

$$\begin{array}{r} 2x - 3 \\ \times \quad x - 4 \\ \hline \end{array}$$

Step 2

Multiply the first term from the bottom row by each term in the top row.

$$\begin{array}{r} 2x - 3 \\ \times \quad x - 4 \\ \hline -8x + 12 \end{array}$$

Step 3

Multiply the second term from the bottom row by each term in the top row. Write like terms one on top of the other to make adding easier in the next step.

$$\begin{array}{r} 2x - 3 \\ \times \quad x - 4 \\ \hline -8x + 12 \\ 2x^2 - 3x \end{array}$$

Step 4

Add like terms together.

$$\begin{array}{r} 2x - 3 \\ \times \quad x - 4 \\ \hline -8x + 12 \\ +2x^2 - 3x \\ \hline 2x^2 - 11x + 12 \end{array}$$

24. B

Step 1

Factor the expression by grouping.

Group the terms, and remove the greatest common factor from each group.

$k^2 + 6k - 2k - 12$

$= (k^2 + 6k) + (-2k - 12)$

$= k(k + 6) - 2(k + 6)$

Step 2

Factor out the common binomial from each group.

$k(k + 6) - 2(k + 6)$

$= (k - 2)(k + 6)$

Therefore, one factor of the expression $k^2 + 6k - 2k - 12$ is $k + 6$.

25. **D**

To determine the expression that does not have $x + 3$ as a factor, you need to factor each given choice.

Alternative A: Trinomial, where $a = 1$, $(x^2 - 2x - 15)$.

Find two numbers that have a product of -15 and a sum of -2. These numbers are -5 and 3. Factor the trinomial to two binomials containing -5 and 3.

$x^2 - 2x - 15 = (x - 5)(x + 3)$. This trinomial does have a factor of $x + 3$.

Alternative B: Binomial, with a difference of squares $(-2x^2 + 18)$.

Factor out the GCF of -2.

$-2x^2 + 18 = -2(x^2 - 9)$

Since 1 and 9 are perfect squares, the expression factors to

$-2(\sqrt{x^2} - \sqrt{9})(\sqrt{x^2} + \sqrt{9}) = -2(x - 3)(x + 3)$

This binomial also has a factor of $x + 3$.

Alternative C: Binomial, with a common GCF $(-3x^2 - 9x)$C.

Factor out the common GCF.

$-3x^2 - 9x = -3x(x + 3)$

This alternative also has a factor of $x + 3$.

Alternative D: Trinomial, where $a = 1$, $(x^2 + 7x + 15)$.

Find two numbers that have a product of 15 and a sum of 7. There are no two numbers that produce this result. This expression cannot be factored, therefore, $x + 3$ is not one of its factors.

26. **B**

Step 1

To factor $9mn^2 - 12mn - 12m$, begin by factoring out the greatest common factor (GCF) of $3m$ from each term of the expression.

$9mn^2 - 12mn - 12m = 3m(3n^2 - 4n - 4)$

Step 2

Factor the trinomial in the expression $3m(3n^2 - 4n - 4)$.

To factor $(3n^2 - 4n - 4)$, find two numbers that have a product of -12 (from $a \times c$) and a sum of -4 (the b-value). In this case, the numbers are 2 and -6.

Rewrite the expression by replacing the term $-4n$ with $2n$ and $-6n$.

$= 3m[3n^2 - 4n - 4]$
$= 3m[3n^2 + 2n - 6n - 4]$

Group the terms inside the brackets.

$= 3m[3n^2 + 2n - 6n - 4]$
$= 3m[(3n^2 + 2n) + (-6n - 4)]$

Step 3

Remove the GCF from each group.

$= 3m[(3n^2 + 2n) + (-6n - 4)]$
$= 3m[n(3n + 2) - 2(3n + 2)]$

Factor out the common binomial.

$= 3m[n(3n + 2) - 2(3n + 2)]$
$= 3m(n - 2)(3n + 2)$

The expression that is not a factor of $9mn^2 - 12mn - 12m$ is $n - 4$.

27. **D**

Step 1

Factor polynomial I by removing the greatest common factor of $4x^2$ from each term.

$8x^3 + 4x^2 = 4x^2(2x + 1)$

Polynomial I was factored correctly by Rachel.

Step 2

Factor polynomial II as a difference of squares:

$a^2 - b^2 = (a + b)(a - b)$.

$25a^2 - 4b^2c^2$
$= \begin{pmatrix} (\sqrt{25a^2}) + (\sqrt{4b^2c^2}) \\ \times \ (\sqrt{25a^2}) - (\sqrt{4b^2c^2}) \end{pmatrix}$
$= (5a + 2bc)(5a - 2bc)$

Polynomial II was factored correctly by Rachel.

Step 3

Factor polynomial III by removing the greatest common factor of 2 from each term and factoring the result as a difference of squares.

$2x^2 - 18y^2$
$= 2(x^2 - 9y^2)$
$= 2(\sqrt{x^2} + \sqrt{9y^2}) \times (\sqrt{x^2} - \sqrt{9y^2})$
$= 2(x + 3y)(x - 3y)$

Polynomial III was factored correctly by Rachel.

Step 4

Factor polynomial IV by removing the greatest common factor of a and factoring the result as a difference of squares.

$4a^3 - a$
$= a(4a^2 - 1)$
$= a(\sqrt{4a^2} + \sqrt{1}) \times (\sqrt{4a^2} - \sqrt{1})$
$= a(2a + 1)(2a - 1)$

Polynomial IV was not factored correctly by Rachel.

28. A

Step 1

Factor $x^4 - 81$ into a difference of squares.

$x^4 - 81 = (\sqrt{x^4} - \sqrt{81})(\sqrt{x^4} + \sqrt{81})$
$\qquad\quad = (x^2 - 9)(x^2 + 9)$

The factor $(x^2 + 9)$ cannot be factored further, but $(x^2 - 9)$ can be since it is also a difference of squares.

Step 2

Factor $(x^2 - 9)$.

$(x^2 - 9) = (\sqrt{x^2} - \sqrt{9})(\sqrt{x^2} + \sqrt{9})$
$\qquad\quad = (x - 3)(x + 3)$

Therefore, the fully factored form of the expression is $(x^2 + 9)(x + 3)(x - 3)$.

29. 5

Step 1

Factor $x^2 - 3x - 4$.

In order to factor $x^2 - 3x - 4$, find two numbers that have a product of -4 (c-value) and a sum of -3 (b-value). In this case, the two numbers are -4 and 1.

The factored form of $x^2 - 3x - 4$ is $(x - 4)(x + 1)$.

Step 2

Determine the value of $m + n$.

$m = 4$ and $n = 1$
$m + n = 4 + 1$
$\qquad\quad = 5$

30. WR

Step 1

Factor the first expression as a binomial with differences of squares.

Factor out the GCF of 2 out of each term.

$18x^2 - 8 = 2(9x^2 - 4)$

Since 9 and 4 are perfect squares the expression factors to

$2(\sqrt{9}x - \sqrt{4})(\sqrt{9}x + \sqrt{4})$
$= 2(3x - 2)(3x + 2)$

Step 2

Factor the second expression as a trinomial using decomposition.

Find two numbers that multiply to give $(6)(-10) = -60$, and that have a sum of -11. The two numbers are -15 and 4. Split the middle term.

$\qquad = 6x^2 - 11x - 10$

$\qquad = 6x^2 + 4x - 15x - 10$

Group the four terms and factor the GCF of each pair.

$(6x^2 + 4x) + (-15x - 10)$
$= 2x(3x + 2) - 5(3x + 2)$

Factor out the common binomial.

$2x(3x + 2) - 5(3x + 2)$
$= (2x - 5)(3x + 2)$

Step 3

Identify the common factor.

The common factor is $(3x + 2)$.

RELATIONS AND FUNCTIONS

Table of Correlations				
Outcome	**Practice Questions**	**Unit Test Questions**	**Practice Test 1**	**Practice Test 2**
10RF1 Develop algebraic and graphical reasoning through the study of relations.				
10RF1.1 Interpret and explain the relationships among data, graphs and situations.	1, 2, 3, 4, 5, 6	1, 2, 3, 4, 5, 6	22, 23	23, 24
10RF1.2 Demonstrate an understanding of relations and functions.	7	7	24	
10RF1.3 Demonstrate an understanding of slope.	8, 9, 10, 11, 12, 13, 14, 15, 16	8, 9, 10, 11, 12, 13, 14, 15, 16	25, 26, 27, 28	25, 26, 27
10RF1.4 Describe and represent linear relations.	17, 18, 19, 20, 21, 22	17, 18, 19, 20, 51a, 51b	29, 30	28, 29
10RF1.5 Determine the characteristics of the graphs of linear relations.	23, 24, 25, 26a, 26b	21, 22, 23, 50a, 50b	31, 32	30, 31
10RF1.6 Relate linear relations to their graphs.	27, 28, 29, 30, 31	24, 25, 26, 27, 28	33	32
10RF1.7 Determine the equation of a linear relation to solve problems.	32, 33, 34, 35, 36, 37, 38a, 38b	29, 30, 31, 32, 33, 34, 35	34, 35, 41a, 41b, 41c	33, 34, 35
10RF1.8 Represent a linear function, using function notation.	39, 40, 41	36, 37, 38	36, 37	36, 37
10RF1.9 Solve problems that involve systems of linear equations in two variables, graphically and algebraically.	42, 43, 44, 45, 46, 47, 48, 49, 50, 51, 52	39, 40, 41, 42, 43, 44, 45, 46, 47, 48, 49	38, 39, 40a, 40b	38, 39, 40, 41, 42a, 42b

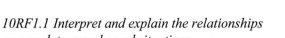

10RF1.1 Interpret and explain the relationships among data, graphs and situations.

RELATIONS

In order to understand relations, it is important to understand domain and range, how to graph relations, and how to interpret graphs.

UNDERSTANDING RELATIONS

Data is collected from real-life situations for the purpose of understanding the relationship between two variables. A **relation** is a set of ordered pairs (x, y) that indicates the association between the input elements of one variable, x, with the corresponding output elements of another variable, y.

Relations can be represented in many ways, such as ordered pairs, tables of values, mapping diagrams, equations, and graphs.

DOMAIN AND RANGE

The **domain** of a relation is the set of all input elements, x, and the **range** is the set of all output elements, y, for which a particular relation is defined. The domain and range of a relation can be expressed in a variety of ways, such as words, lists, and inequalities (set notation).

Example

Consider the following relation comparing the height and mass of four boys.

Height in cm (x)	Mass in kg (y)
180	75
188	90
190	88
194	95

State the domain and range of the given relation.

Solution

The domain and range for the relation can be expressed as a list.

The domain is 180, 188, 190, 194, or {180, 188, 190, 194}.

The range is 75, 90, 88, 95, or {75, 90, 88, 95}.

Example

Consider the given relation comparing the number of cars in a parking lot at different times of the day:

Time (x)	Number of Cars (y)
08:00	52
10:30	46
12:00	28
14:30	39
16:00	12
18:00	4

State the domain and range of the relation.

Solution

The domain and range for the given relation can be expressed as a list.

The domain is the times of day: 08:00, 10:30, 12:00, 14:30, 16:00, 18:00.

The range is the number of corresponding cars in the parking lot: 52, 46, 28, 39, 12, 4.

Example

Consider the relation shown in the graph of $y = -x^2 + 4x + 2$.

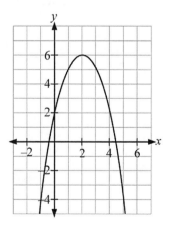

State the domain and range of the given relation.

Solution

The graph is continuous to the right and left for all positive and negative real input or *x*-values. The domain is the set of real numbers, which is written as $x \in \mathbb{R}$.

The graph also shows that the output or *y*-values decrease infinitely for all numbers less than or equal to 6. The range can be expressed as the inequality $y \le 6$.

GRAPHING RELATIONS

When graphing relations, consider the following information:

Plot the data as points (x,y) on a Cartesian plane with two labelled and scaled axes. The data could also be entered on a TI-83 graphing calculator and graphed.

Determine whether the graph represents **discrete data** or **continuous data**. A graph displaying discrete data shows only points, since *x*- and *y*- values between the points are not possible. A graph displaying continuous data shows connected points that form a line or a curve, since an infinite number of real *x*- and *y*-values are possible.

Be aware of restrictions on the domain and range because of limiting factors within the context of a real-life situation.

Example

The given table compares the distance, *y* (in kilometres), that a person is from a lightning flash to the time, *x* (in seconds), that it takes the person to hear the thunder.

Time (s)	Distance (km)
3	1
6	2
9	3
12	4
15	5

Draw the graph that represents the given data within the restrictions of the domain and range.

Solution

Step 1
Plot the data as points on a Cartesian plane. The *x*-axis represents the time it takes to hear the thunder. The *y*-axis represents the distance the person is from the lightning. Plot the five ordered pairs from the table.

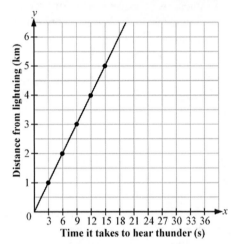

Relationship between Hearing Thunder and Seeing Lightning

Step 2
Determine whether the data is discrete or continuous.

The data is continuous because there are many possible values between the given points. A person could stand at any distance between 1 and 5 km away from a flash of lightning to hear the thunder in the given time.

Step 3
Determine the restrictions on the domain and range.

The closest a person could stand to see lightning is 0 km away. Thus, the line can be extended back to the origin. Also, the line can be extended upward past the point (5,15) to represent positions beyond 5 km. The range is $y \ge 0$, and the domain is $x \ge 0$.

INTERPRETING GRAPHS OF RELATIONS

A graph provides a picture of a relationship between two variables. To describe a situation that reflects each part of a graph, you must be aware of the rate of change in each section.

Example

The given graph portrays how a car's volume of fuel in liters varies with the time elapsed in hours during a trip.

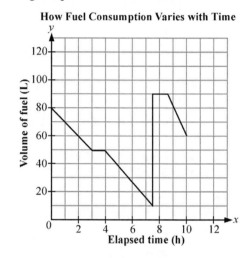

How Fuel Consumption Varies with Time

Describe the given graph in terms of the movement of the car and its fuel consumption.

Solution

To describe the graph, look at each of these sections:

Interval 1: 0–3 hours
The car moved at a constant speed, burning 10 L of fuel for every hour driven. The level of fuel in the tank dropped from 80 to 50 L.

Interval 2: 3–4 hours
The volume of fuel stayed fixed at 50 L, which means the car was not moving. The car was stopped for one hour.

Interval 3: 4–7.5 hours
The driver continued travelling at a constant speed, burning about 11.4 L of fuel for every hour driven. The level of fuel in the tank dropped from 50 to 10 L.

Interval 4: 7.5 hours
The fuel level rose suddenly from 10 L to 90 L, with no change in elapsed time. The car was filled up with gas.

Interval 5: 7.5–8.5 hours
The volume of fuel stayed at 90 L. The car was stopped for one hour.

Interval 6: 8.5–10 hours
The car continued at a constant speed, burning about 30 L of fuel over 2.5 hours. Finally, the car stopped at the end of the 10 hours.

Use the following information to answer the next question.

Aerial skiers realize that the vertical and horizontal distances they achieve depend upon their angle of trajectory when they leave the ramp.

The given graph represents the paths of an aerial skier for two jumps at different angles of trajectory. The range of the 45° trajectory is $0 \le y \le a$, and the range of the 55° trajectory is $0 \le y \le b$.

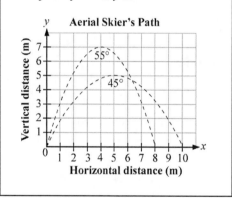

Aerial Skier's Path

Numerical Response

1. The difference between b and a is _____.

Use the following information to answer the next question.

Boon noticed that when he put a large jawbreaker in his mouth and sucked on it, it dissolved slowly at first and more quickly at the end. He decided to collect some data using his knowledge of geometry. The given table of values shows the volume of the jawbreaker, V, in cubic centimetres over time, t, in minutes.

Time (min)	Volume (cm³)
0	33.5
1	28.1
2	23.6
3	19.7
4	16.7
5	14.0

Written Response

2. State the restrictions on the domain (time) and range (volume) of the given data, and explain your answer.

Use the following information to answer the next question.

A graph of a function is given.

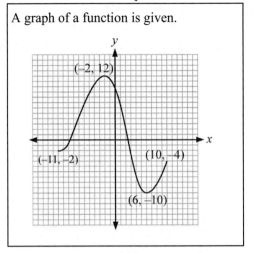

3. What are the domain and the range of the graph?

A. The domain is $\{-11 \le x \le 10\}$, and the range is $\{-10 \le y \le 12\}$.

B. The domain is $\{-10 \le x \le 12\}$, and the range is $\{-11 \le y \le 10\}$.

C. The domain is $\{-11 \le x \le 10\}$, and the range is $\{-4 \le y \le -2\}$.

D. The domain is $\{-2 \le x \le 6\}$, and the range is $\{-10 \le y \le 12\}$.

Use the following information to answer the next question.

A student dropped a ball from a height of 4.00 m and recorded the height to which it rebounded for the first eight bounces in the given table.

Bounces	Height (m)	Bounces	Height (m)
0	4.00	5	0.31
1	2.40	6	0.19
2	1.44	7	0.11
3	0.86	8	0.07
4	0.52		

4. Which of the following graphs models the height of the ball after successive bounces?

A. 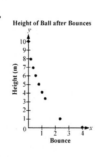 B.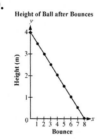

C. 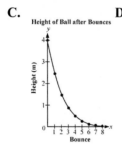 D.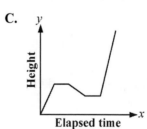

Use the following information to answer the next question.

A woman takes an elevator from the main floor of an office tower to the top floor. The elevator makes two stops on its way to the top.

5. Which of the following graphs **best** represents this scenario?

A.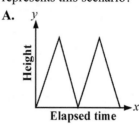

B.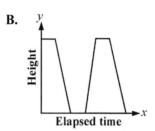

C.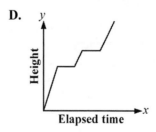

D.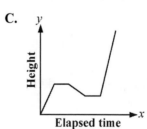

Use the following information to answer the next question.

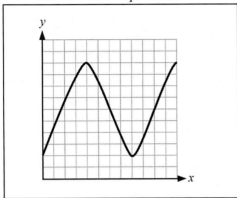

6. The given graph **best** represents which of the following situations?

   A. A basketball repeatedly bounces on the ground.

   B. The height of a chair on a ferris wheel changes as the wheel rotates.

   C. The distance between a commuter's home and work as she bicycles to work.

   D. The speed of a child starting on a skateboard, as she goes up and down one hill, and then up the next hill.

10RF1.2 Demonstrate an understanding of relations and functions.

UNDERSTANDING FUNCTIONS

A **function** is a special relation that is a set of ordered pairs (x, y) in which every x-value has exactly one corresponding y-value. In other words, a function is a rule that assigns only one output element for each input element.

Every function is a relation, but not every relation is a function.

To test whether a relation is a function, follow these steps:

- Examine numeric representations (ordered pairs, tables of values, mappings) to see if any x-value has more than one corresponding y-value. If it has more than one y-value, it is a relation, but **not** a function.
- Examine the graphical representation, and use the **vertical-line test**, which states, "if any vertical line drawn through a relation intersects the graph at more than one point, the relation is **not** a function."

Example

Represent the relation $y = 2x + 1$ using ordered pairs, mapping, and graphing, and determine whether or not it is a function.

Solution

Step 1
Represent the relation using ordered pairs.
$(-2, -3)$
$(-1, -1)$
$(0, 1)$
$(1, 3)$
$(2, 5)$

Step 2
Represent the relation using mapping.

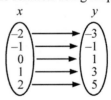

Step 3
Represent the relation using graphing.

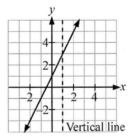

Step 4

Determine whether or not the relation is a function.

The relation $y = 2x + 1$ is a function, because every x-value has only one corresponding y-value. Also, any vertical line drawn through the graph passes through exactly one point.

Example

Represent the relation $x = y^2$ using ordered pairs, mapping, and graphing, and determine whether or not it is a function.

Solution

Step 1

Represent the relation using ordered pairs.

(4, 2)

(4, −2)

(1, 1)

(1, −1)

(0, 0)

Step 2

Represent the relation using mapping.

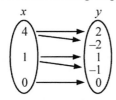

Step 3

Represent the relation using graphing.

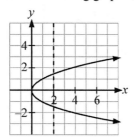

Step 4

Determine whether or not the relation is a function.

The relation $x = y^2$ is not a function, because there is at least one x-value that has more than one y-value. Also, at least one vertical line passes through more than one point on the graph.

Use the following information to answer the next question.

A student examined these four mappings, which represent various relations.

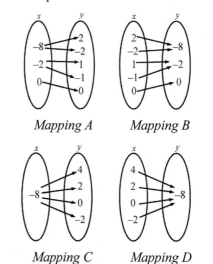

Mapping A   Mapping B

Mapping C   Mapping D

7.   How many of the given relations are also functions?

   A. 3   **B.** 2

   C. 1   **D.** 0

10RF1.3 Demonstrate an understanding of slope.

DETERMINING THE SLOPE OF A LINE

The **slope** of a line (or line segment) on a Cartesian plane is the rate at which the y-values change (Δy) with respect to the change in the x-values (Δx). The slope can also be defined as the ratio of vertical change, or **rise**, to the horizontal change, or **run**, between two points on the line. The slope of a line (or line segment) is usually represented by the lowercase letter m.

Slope(m) = rate of change

$$= \frac{\Delta y}{\Delta x}$$

$$= \frac{\text{rise}}{\text{run}}$$

Example

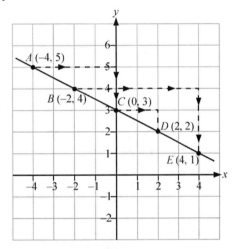

Determine the slope of the given line by analyzing the rate of change between several points on the graph.

Solution

Step 1
Calculate the slope from point A to point C.

Slope $= \dfrac{\text{rise}}{\text{run}}$

$$= \frac{y_C - y_A}{x_C - x_A}$$

$$= \frac{3 - 5}{0 - (-4)}$$

$$= -\frac{2}{4}$$

$$= -\frac{1}{2}$$

Step 2
Calculate the slope from point B to point E.

Slope $= \dfrac{\text{rise}}{\text{run}}$

$$= \frac{y_E - y_B}{x_E - x_B}$$

$$= \frac{1 - 4}{4 - (-2)}$$

$$= -\frac{3}{6}$$

$$= -\frac{1}{2}$$

Step 3
Calculate the slope from point C to point D.

Slope $= \dfrac{\text{rise}}{\text{run}}$

$$= \frac{y_D - y_C}{x_D - x_C}$$

$$= \frac{2 - 3}{2 - 0}$$

$$= -\frac{1}{2}$$

The rate of change between each of the points is $-\dfrac{1}{2}$. Therefore, the slope of the line is $-\dfrac{1}{2}$.

The slope of a line can be determined using any two points $(x_1,\ y_1)$ and $(x_2,\ y_2)$ on a line, as shown.

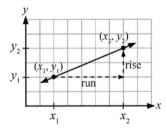

The rise is the difference between the y-values $(y_2 - y_1)$, and the run is the difference between the x-values $(x_2 - x_1)$. Thus, the slope, m, is:

$$m = \frac{\text{rise}}{\text{run}}$$
$$= \frac{y_2 - y_1}{x_2 - x_1}$$

This equation is referred to as the **slope formula**.

Example

A line passes through the points $P(3, 1)$ and $Q(-4, -3)$. Determine the slope of the line.

Solution

For $Q(-4, -3)$, let $x_2 = -4$ and $y_2 = -3$.

For $P(3, 1)$, let $x_1 = 3$ and $y_1 = 1$.

Substitute the values into the slope formula and solve for m.

$$m = \frac{y_2 - y_1}{x_2 - x_1}$$
$$= \frac{-3 - 1}{-4 - 3}$$
$$= \frac{-4}{-7}$$
$$= \frac{4}{7}$$

The slope of the line is $\frac{4}{7}$.

IDENTIFYING THE PROPERTIES OF SLOPE

There are several properties for the slope of a line that can be identified simply by looking at the graph of the line.

DIRECTION

You can determine if the slope of a line is positive or negative from the direction of the line from left to right on the graph.

A positive slope rises toward the right.

A negative slope falls toward the right.

SPECIAL LINES

A horizontal line, which is parallel to the x-axis, has a rise of 0. Therefore, the slope of a horizontal line is 0.

$$m = \frac{\text{rise}}{\text{run}}$$
$$= \frac{0}{\text{run}}$$
$$= 0$$

A vertical line, which is parallel to the y-axis, has run of 0. Therefore, the slope of a vertical line is undefined.

$$m = \frac{\text{rise}}{\text{run}}$$
$$= \frac{\text{rise}}{0}$$
$$= \text{undefined}$$

Example

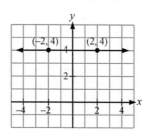

Determine the slope of the line passing through the points $(-2, 4)$ and $(2, 4)$ as shown.

Solution

Step 1
Label the coordinates of the points.

- For $(-2, 4)$, let $x_1 = -2$ and $y_1 = 4$.
- For $(2, 4)$, let $x_2 = 2$ and $y_2 = 4$.

Step 2

Determine the slope, by substituting the values into the slope formula.

$$m = \frac{y_2 - y_1}{x_2 - x_1}$$
$$= \frac{4 - 4}{2 - (-2)}$$
$$= \frac{0}{4}$$
$$= 0$$

The slope of the line is 0. This shows that this is a horizontal line.

SLOPES OF PARALLEL LINES

Parallel lines have the same slope. For example, the two lines in the given graph both have a slope of 2, because every run of 1 unit has a rise of 2 units.

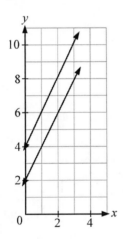

SLOPES OF PERPENDICULAR LINES

Perpendicular lines have slopes with opposite signs, since one line rises to the right while the other falls to the right. Their slopes are always negative reciprocals of one another, so that the product of their slopes is −1.

$$m_2 = -\frac{1}{m_1} \text{ or } m_1 m_2 = -1, \text{ where } m_1, m_2 \neq 0.$$

For example, if the slope of one line is $\frac{2}{3}$, the perpendicular line has a slope of $-\frac{3}{2}$. These two slopes multiplied together equal −1.

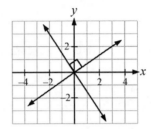

PROBLEM SOLVING WITH SLOPE

Concepts related to slope can be used to solve problems.

Example

Graph the line with a slope of $\frac{2}{3}$ and a *y*-intercept of -4.

Solution

Step 1

Determine two points on the line.

Plot the *y*-intercept $(0, -4)$ on a Cartesian plane. Then, use the slope to find another point on the line.

Since the slope is $\frac{2}{3}$, a rise of 2 followed by a run of 3 from the *y*-intercept will find the location of another point at $(3, -2)$.

Step 2

Draw a line passing through these two points.

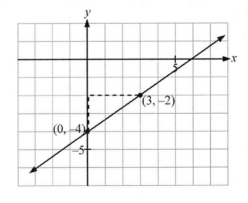

Example

Total Cost of Installation

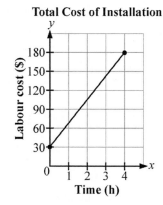

The graph shows the total labour cost of a plumber for the installation of a new water tank.

Determine the plumber's hourly rate of pay.

Solution

Step 1

Determine the slope of the linear relation. Choose two points on the graph to use in the slope formula. Two points that can be chosen are (0, 30) and (4, 180).

Step 2

Substitute the points into the slope formula, and solve for the slope.

$$m = \frac{y_2 - y_1}{x_2 - x_1}$$
$$= \frac{180 - 30}{4 - 0}$$
$$= \frac{150}{4}$$
$$= 37.5$$

Since the slope is 37.5, the plumber's hourly rate of pay is $37.50 /h.

Use the following information to answer the next question.

A ladder is 4.70 m long. It reaches a height of 4.40 m when leaned against a wall.

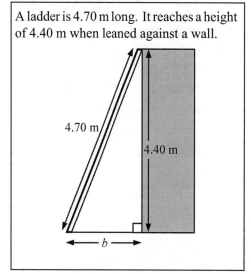

Numerical Response

8. To the nearest hundredth, the slope of the ladder against the wall is _____.

Use the following information to answer the next question.

The graph of a linear relation has a constant rate of change of $-\frac{1}{2}$.

9. Which of the following statements about the graph of this linear relation is **true**?
   A. The run is 2 units to the right, and the rise is 1 unit up.
   B. The run is 1 unit to the right, and the rise is 2 units up.
   C. The run is 1 unit to the right, and the rise is 2 units down.
   D. The run is 2 units to the right, and the rise is 1 unit down.

10. Which of the following statements about parallel lines is **true**?

   A. The slopes of parallel lines are negative reciprocals.

   B. Parallel lines share at least one common point.

   C. The slopes of parallel lines are equal.

   D. Parallel lines cannot be vertical.

11. A line segment that has an undefined slope

   A. is vertical

   B. is horizontal

   C. has an undefined length

   D. passes through the origin

Use the following information to answer the next question.

The given figure shows four lines, l_1, l_2, l_3, and l_4.

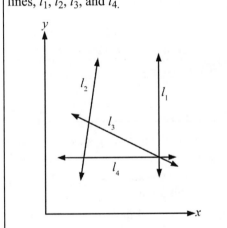

12. Which of the given lines has a negative slope?

   A. l_1 B. l_2

   C. l_3 D. l_4

13. If a line with a slope equal to -2 passes through the point $(1, -3)$, then what is the y-intercept of the line?

   A. 1   B. 2

   C. -1 D. -2

Use the following information to answer the next question.

A line passing through the points $A(2, 3)$ and $B(5, 5)$ is perpendicular to a line passing through the points $C(6, -1)$ and $D(5, k)$.

Numerical Response

14. The value of k, to the nearest tenth, is _____.

Use the following information to answer the next question.

A graph of a line is given.

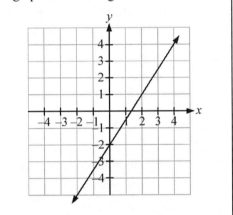

Numerical Response

15. Rounded to the nearest tenth, the slope of the given line is _____.

Use the following information to answer the next question.

Jamil's teacher asks him to graph the line that passes through the point $(-9, 8)$ and has a slope of $-\dfrac{4}{3}$. Jamil's partial solution is shown in the given graph.

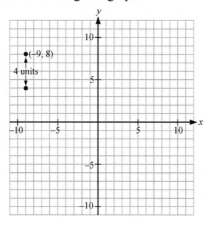

Written Response

16. Complete Jamil's solution by drawing the line with the given slope that passes through the given point.

10RF1.4 Describe and represent linear relations.

DETERMINING PROPERTIES OF LINEAR RELATIONS

Before identifying the properties of linear relations, it is important to first establish the independent and dependent variables in a given context.

IDENTIFYING VARIABLES OF A RELATION

The **independent variable**, x, of a relation that represents a given real-life situation is the variable that is manipulated or measured first.

The **dependent variable**, y, is the variable that responds to the corresponding values of the independent variable, and it is measured second. For example, if you conduct an experiment to see how long it will take for different volumes of water to boil on the stove, the independent variable would be the various volumes of water you measured first before boiling. The dependent variable is the time it takes for the various volumes of water to boil, and these times would be measured second.

PROPERTIES OF LINEAR CONTEXTS

Contexts in word problems describe linear relations if phrases are used that imply a constant rate of change, such as *so much per*, *changes by*, *decreases* or *increases by*, *so much for each*, and *rate of*.

Example

C_1: To rent a community hall, there is a flat fee of $100 and a $40 charge for every hour of use.

C_2: A bacteria sample containing 100 bacteria doubled in population every 2 hours.

Determine whether the two given contexts, C_1 and C_2, represent linear relations.

Solution

Context C_1 represents a linear relation between the independent variable of time and the dependent variable of cost, since the phrase "$40 for every hour" implies a constant rate of change.

Context C_2 is not a linear relation between the independent variable of time and the dependent variable of population, since the phrase "doubled in" does not imply a constant rate of change.

PROPERTIES OF LINEAR RELATIONS

Data in a table of values can define a **linear relation** or a **non-linear relation**, depending on the first differences. **First differences** are differences between successive y-values with evenly spaced x-values. If the differences between consecutive y-values are all the same, the relation is linear; if the differences between consecutive y-values are not the same, the relation is non-linear. Graphs of relations are linear if the points form a straight line and the rate of change is constant. Graphs of relations are non-linear if the points lie in a curve and the rate of change is not constant. Equations of relations are linear if the degree is 0 or 1, whereas equations of relations are non-linear if the degree is greater than 1 or the variable is an exponent.

These properties can be illustrated by analyzing the table of values and the graph of the equations $y = x + 5$ (a linear first-degree equation) and $y = x^2$ (a non-linear second-degree equation).

A table of values for $y = x + 5$ can be formed by substituting various x-values into the equation.

x	$y = x + 5$	First Differences
2	$y = 2 + 5 = 7$	
		$9 - 7 = 2$
4	$y = 4 + 5 = 9$	
		$11 - 9 = 2$
6	$y = 6 + 5 = 11$	
		$13 - 11 = 2$
8	$y = 8 + 5 = 13$	

Notice that the x-values are evenly spaced in increments of 2. The first difference is found by subtracting one y-value from the y-value that follows. The first differences in this table are all the same.

When the data is graphed, the points form a straight line with a constant rate of change or slope of 1.

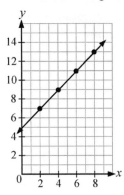

A table of values for $y = x^2$ can be formed by substituting various x-values into the equation.

x	$y = x^2$	First Differences
-3	$y = (-3)^2 = 9$	
		$4 - 9 = -5$
-2	$y = (-2)^2 = 4$	
		$1 - 4 = -3$
-1	$y = (-1)^2 = 1$	
		$0 - 1 = -1$
0	$y = 0^2 = 0$	
		$1 - 0 = 1$
1	$y = 1^2 = 1$	
		$4 - 1 = 3$
2	$y = 2^2 = 4$	
		$9 - 4 = 5$
3	$y = 3^2 = 9$	

Notice that the x-values are evenly spaced in increments of 1. The first differences in this case are all different.

When the data is graphed, the points form a curve that does not have a constant rate of change.

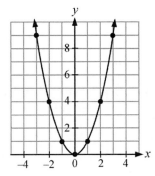

CONNECTIONS BETWEEN LINEAR REPRESENTATIONS

For any linear relation, the constant rate of change can be expressed as a particular phrase in the given context. It is also the value of the coefficient of the independent variable (x) in the corresponding equation. As well, it is the consistent first difference in a table of values (for unit intervals of x-values), and it is the slope of the graph of the given relation.

Example

The cost of producing a book of photos is $50.00 plus $5.00 per photo.

Identify the constant rate of change in the four representations of the given context.

Solution

Step 1

Identify the constant rate of change from a particular phrase in the given context.

The constant rate of change of 5 is represented in the phrase "$5.00 per photo."

Step 2

Identify the constant rate of change from the corresponding equation.

In the equation $C = 50 + 5b$, in which b is the independent variable, the coefficient 5 is the constant rate of change.

Step 3

Identify the constant rate of change from the first difference in the table of values.

b	$C = 50 + 5b$	First Difference
1	$C = 50 + 5(1)$ $= 55$	
2	$C = 50 + 5(2)$ $= 60$	$60 - 55 = 5$
3	$C = 50 + 5(3)$ $= 65$	$65 - 60 = 5$
4	$C = 50 + 5(4)$ $= 70$	$70 - 65 = 5$

The consistent first difference indicates that the constant rate of change is 5.

Step 4

Identify the constant rate of change from the slope of the graph of the given relation.

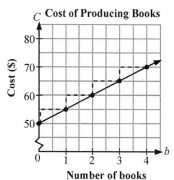

Notice that the line rises 5 units and runs 1 unit between each point $\left(\dfrac{5}{1} = 5\right)$. The slope indicates that the constant rate of change is 5.

Use the following information to answer the next question.

Geoff decided to go for a Sunday drive. At the start of his drive, he had 60 L of fuel in his truck's gas tank. As he drove, the fuel, F, in the tank decreased at a rate of 1 L / 10 km.

17. Which of the following graphs and equations could Geoff use to determine the number of kilometres, d, he could drive on 60 L of fuel?

A.

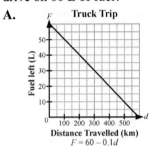

$F = 60 - 0.1d$

B.

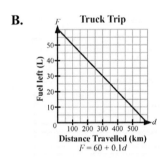

$F = 60 + 0.1d$

C.

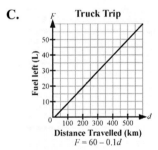

$F = 60 - 0.1d$

D.

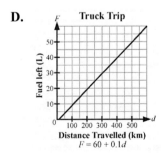

$F = 60 + 0.1d$

18. Which of the following tables represents a linear function?

A.

Time (s)	Speed (m/s)
0	2
1	4
2	8
3	16
4	32

B.

Time (s)	Speed (m/s)
0	20
1	32
2	38
3	50
4	56

C.

Time (s)	Speed (m/s)
0	35
1	32
2	28
3	20
4	8

D.

Table (s)	Speed (m/s)
0	28
1	23
2	18
3	13
4	8

Use the following information to answer the next question.

A student determined the volume, *V*, of various cubes in cubic centimetres where the length, *l*, of each side of the cube was given in centimetres. The student's data is shown in the given table.

Volume of Cube Related to Length of its Sides

l (cm)	*V* (cm^3)
2	8
3	27
4	64
5	125
6	216
7	343

19. The relationship between the length of a side, *l*, and the volume, *V*, of the cubes is a

   A. linear relationship because as *l* increases, *V* increases by a constant amount

   B. linear relationship because as *l* increases, *V* decreases by a constant amount

   C. non-linear relationship because as *l* increases, *V* does not increase by a constant amount

   D. non-linear relationship because as *l* decreases, *V* does not increase by a constant amount

Use the following information to answer the next question.

In a Canadian city, gas prices fell at a constant rate from the spring to the fall of a particular year.

20. If spring starts at the origin along the *x*-axis, which of the following graphs portrays this relationship?

A.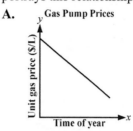

B.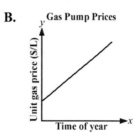

C.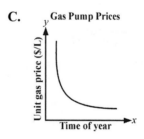

D.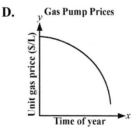

Use the following information to answer the next question.

John wanted to determine if there was any correlation between the number of car accidents and the age of the driver.

21. What is the independent variable in this relationship?

   A. Type of car

   B. Age of the driver

   C. Gender of the driver

   D. Number of accidents

Use the following information to answer the next question.

These equations are written on a piece of paper:

- $y = x$
- $y = x + 3$
- $y = x^2 + 3$
- $y = 3x + 3$
- $y = x^3 - 6$

Numerical Response

22. How many of the given equations represent graphs of linear relations? _____

10RF1.5 Determine the characteristics of the graphs of linear relations.

CHARACTERISTICS OF THE GRAPHS OF LINEAR RELATIONS

The graph of a linear relation is uniquely defined by its intercepts, slope, domain, and range.

DETERMINING INTERCEPTS AND SLOPE

When the graph of a continuous linear relation is given, the x-intercept, the y-intercept, and the slope can be calculated. The **x-intercept** is the x-value (a), or the ordered pair $(a, 0)$, that corresponds to the point where the line intersects the x-axis. The **y-intercept** is the y-value, b, or ordered pair $(0, b)$ that corresponds to the point where the line intersects the y-axis. The slope, m, can be determined by selecting two points (x_1, y_1) and (x_2, y_2) on the graph of the linear relation and then applying the slope formula, $m = \dfrac{y_2 - y_1}{x_2 - x_1}$.

Example

The graph of a linear relation is plotted on a Cartesian plane.

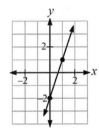

Determine the x-intercept, y-intercept, and slope of the graph of the linear relation.

Solution

Step 1

Find the y-intercept.

The line in the graph intersects the y-axis at the point $(0, -2)$.

Therefore, the y-intercept is -2 or $(0, -2)$.

Step 2

Find the slope of the line.

Select two points on the graph, such as $(0, -2)$ and $(1, 1)$, and apply the slope formula.

$$m = \frac{y_2 - y_1}{x_2 - x_1}$$
$$= \frac{1 - (-2)}{1 - 0}$$
$$= 3$$

Therefore, the slope of the line is 3.

Step 3

Find the x-intercept.

The x-intercept cannot be identified by inspecting where the line intersects the x-axis. However, the x-intercept $(a, 0)$ can be determined using the slope value, another point such as $(1, 1)$, and the slope formula.

$$m = \frac{y_2 - y_1}{x_2 - x_1}$$
$$3 = \frac{0 - 1}{a - 1}$$
$$3(a - 1) = -1$$
$$3a - 3 = -1$$
$$3a = 2$$
$$a = \frac{2}{3}$$

Therefore, the x-intercept is $\frac{2}{3}$ or $\left(\frac{2}{3}, 0\right)$.

DETERMINING THE DOMAIN AND RANGE

The domain and range of the graph of a continuous linear relation depend on the number of intercepts the graph has.

- A vertical line has only one x-intercept, a, with either no y-intercept or infinite y-intercepts (which is the y-axis). The domain for any vertical line is $x = a$ and the range is $y \in \mathbb{R}$.
- A horizontal line has only one y-intercept, b, with either no x-intercept or infinite x-intercepts (which is the x-axis). The domain for any horizontal line is $x \in \mathbb{R}$ and the range is $y = b$.
- A line with a positive or negative slope always has one x-intercept and one y-intercept. The domain for such a line is $x \in \mathbb{R}$ and the range is $y \in \mathbb{R}$.

Example

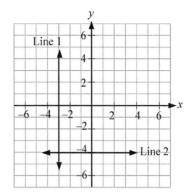

Determine the domain and range of lines 1 and 2 on the given Cartesian plane.

Solution

Line 1 is a vertical line that passes through the x-axis at the point $(-3, 0)$. Therefore, the x-intercept is -3. The domain of Line 1 is $x = -3$ and the range is $y \in \mathbb{R}$.

Line 2 is a horizontal line that passes through the y-axis at the point $(0, -4)$. Therefore, the y-intercept is -4. The domain of Line 2 is $x \in \mathbb{R}$ and the range is $y = -4$.

Many real-life problems representing linear relations can be solved by defining the intercepts, slope, domain, and range within the context.

Example

A parachutist jumps out of an airplane. At time $x = 0$ seconds, the parachutist is at 2 500 feet above the ground. At $x = 40$ seconds, the parachutist is at 2 200 feet above the ground, as illustrated.

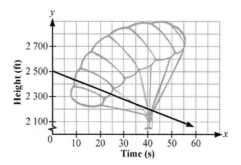

Determine the average rate of descent of the parachutist, the time required to reach the ground (nearest second), and the domain and range of the given graph.

Solution

Step 1

Identify properties of the line graph for the given problem.

The average rate of descent is the slope of the line graph. Two points on the line are given in the context of the problem, namely (0, 2 500) and (40, 2 200).

Step 2

Use the slope formula to determine the rate of change.

$$\text{Rate of change}(m) = \frac{y_2 - y_1}{x_2 - x_1}$$
$$= \frac{2\ 200 - 2\ 500}{40 - 0}$$
$$= \frac{-300}{40}$$
$$= -7.5 \text{ ft/s}$$

The parachutist is falling (negative implies downward motion) at an average rate of 7.5 feet per second.

Step 3

Determine the time, x, required for the parachutist to reach the ground. The point representing the parachutist touching down is the x-intercept $(x, 0)$, since the height at ground level is 0 ft. Substitute the point (0, 2 500) and the slope of -7.5 into the slope formula to find the value of x in the point $(x, 0)$, representing the x-intercept.

$$m = \frac{y_2 - y_1}{x_2 - x_1}$$
$$-7.5 = \frac{0 - 2\ 500}{x - 0}$$
$$-7.5 = \frac{-2\ 500}{x}$$
$$-7.5x = -2\ 500$$
$$x = \frac{-2\ 500}{-7.5}$$
$$\approx 333.33 \text{ s}$$

Therefore, the time required for the parachutist to reach the ground, to the nearest second, is 333 s.

Step 4

Identify the domain and range for this scenario. The domain for this context is related to the total time the parachutist was in the air, namely from 0 to 333 s (or $0 \le x \le 333$). The range for this context is related to the total height of the descent, namely from 2 500 to 0 ft (or $0 \le y \le 2\ 500$).

---

23. Which of the following figures could show the graph of a line that has a slope of $\frac{4}{3}$ and a y-intercept of -1?

A.

B.

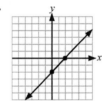

C.

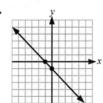

D.

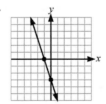

Use the following information to answer the next question.

The graph of the function $y = 3$ is shown.

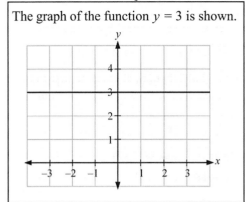

24. What are the domain (D) and range (R) of this linear function?

A. $D: x \in \mathbb{R}$
   $R: y \in \mathbb{R}$

B. $D: x = 3$
   $R: y \in \mathbb{R}$

C. $D: x \in \mathbb{R}$
   $R: y = 3$

D. $D: x \geq -4$
   $R: y = 3$

Use the following information to answer the next question.

The graph of a line is given.

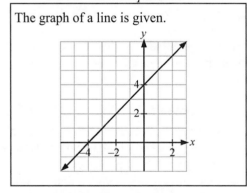

Numerical Response

25. If the slope is m and the y-intercept is b, then the sum of m and b is _____.

Use the following information to answer the next multipart question.

26. Stephan was selling tickets to a concert. After selling most of his tickets, he graphed a linear relation to illustrate the relationship between the number of tickets left to sell, y, and the amount of time, x, in minutes it takes to sell them.

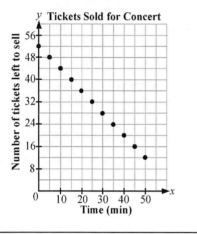

a) Which of the following statements correctly describes the graph of the linear relation?

A. Stephan started with 50 tickets and sold 4 tickets every 5 minutes.

B. Stephan started with 50 tickets and sold 2 tickets every 5 minutes.

C. Stephan started with 52 tickets and sold 4 tickets every 5 minutes.

D. Stephan started with 52 tickets and sold 2 tickets every 5 minutes.

b) If Stephan sold all his tickets at the rate illustrated in the graph, then the x-intercept would be

A. 52   B. 60

C. 65   D. 72

10RF1.6 Relate linear relations to their graphs.

Forms of Linear Equations and Graphing Lines

Linear relations can be expressed as equations in various forms, and the lines that represent them can be graphed using a variety of strategies.

FORMS OF EQUATIONS OF LINEAR RELATIONS

The equation of a line can be written in several forms:

- The **slope-intercept form** is written as $y = mx + b$, where m represents the slope, and b represents the y-intercept of the line.
- The **slope-point form** is written as $y - y_1 = m(x - x_1)$, where m represents the slope, and (x_1, y_1) represents a point on the line.
- The **general form** is written as $Ax + By + C = 0$, where A is a whole number, and B and C are integers.

Sometimes, it is necessary to convert linear equations into the slope-intercept form or into the general form.

Example

Rewrite the equation $4x + 2y + 8 = 0$ in the slope-intercept form $y = mx + b$.

Solution

Step 1

Subtract $4x$ and 8 from both sides of the equation to isolate the y-term.
$$4x + 2y + 8 = 0$$
$$4x - 4x + 2y + 8 - 8 = 0 - 4x - 8$$
$$2y = -4x - 8$$

Step 2

Divide both sides of the equation by 2 to isolate y.
$$\frac{2y}{2} = \frac{-4x}{2} - \frac{8}{2}$$
$$y = -2x - 4$$

Example

Rewrite the equation $y - 6 = \frac{2}{3}(x + 5)$ in the general form $Ax + By + C = 0$.

Solution

First, multiply both sides of the equation by 3 to remove the fraction, and then expand.

$$y - 6 = \frac{2}{3}(x + 5)$$
$$3(y - 6) = 3\left[\frac{2}{3}(x + 5)\right]$$
$$3y - 18 = 2(x + 5)$$
$$3y - 18 = 2x + 10$$

Next, since the coefficient of x is a whole number, set the left side of the equation equal to zero by subtracting $3y$ and adding 18 to both sides of the equation.
$$3y - 3y - 18 + 18 = 2x + 10$$
$$-3y + 18$$
$$0 = 2x - 3y$$
$$+10 + 18$$
$$0 = 2x - 3y + 28$$

If the coefficient of x was a negative number, then the right side of the equation would need to be set equal to zero.

GRAPHING LINES

There are several methods that can be used to graph a line by hand or view a line on a graphing calculator.

SLOPE-INTERCEPT METHOD (TECHNOLOGY)

To graph a linear equation on a TI-83 Plus graphing calculator, the equation of the line needs to be written in $y = mx + b$ form. For example, in order to graph the line $y - 2 = 3(x + 1)$, first convert it to the proper form by isolating y.
$$y - 2 = 3(x + 1)$$
$$y - 2 = 3x + 3$$
$$y = 3x + 5$$

Now, enter the equation into $\boxed{y=}$ as $y_1 = 3x + 5$, and display the result using the G-T(Mode) feature. From the table of values, note that the y-intercept of the given line is 5. From the graph, the rise is 3 and the run is 1; therefore, the slope is 3.

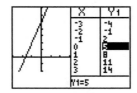

SLOPE-AND-POINT METHOD

Use this method when you are given an equation in the form of $y = mx + b$ or $y - y_1 = m(x - x_1)$. Start by plotting the y-intercept (b) as point $(0, b)$ on the y-axis or the point (x_1, y_1). Then, from the y-intercept or point, use the slope (m) to plot another point. This is done using the appropriate rise and run movements. Finish by drawing a line through the points using a straight edge.

Example

Graph $y = \dfrac{3}{4}x - 1$.

Solution

To graph $y = \dfrac{3}{4}x - 1$, plot the y-intercept,

$(0, -1)$. Then, use the slope of $\dfrac{3}{4}$ as $\dfrac{\text{rise}}{\text{run}}$, and

move 3 units down and 4 units left (or 3 up and 4 right) to plot a second point at $(-4, -4)$.

Draw a line through these points, as shown.

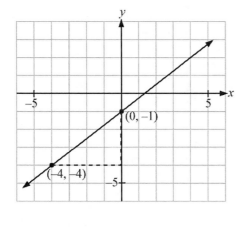

INTERCEPTS METHOD

Use this method when the equation of a line is in either slope-intercept or general form. To draw the line, first determine the x- and y-intercepts. In the equation, set x equal to zero when finding the y-intercept, and set y equal to zero when finding the x-intercept. Plot these two points, and then draw a line through them using a straight edge.

Example

Find the intercepts of the graph of the line $4x - y - 8 = 0$, and graph the line.

Solution

Step 1

Find the intercepts of the graph of the line $4x - y - 8 = 0$.

y-intercept	x-intercept
$4x - y - 8 = 0$ $4(0) - y - 8 = 0$ $y = -8$	$4x - y - 8 = 0$ $4x - (0) - 8 = 0$ $4x = 8$ $x = 2$

Step 2

Graph the line.

Plot the two points $(2, 0)$ and $(0, -8)$, and then draw a line through them.

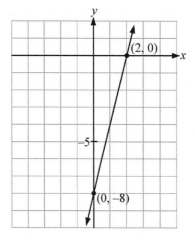

HORIZONTAL AND VERTICAL LINES

A horizontal line is written as $y = b$ or $By + C = 0$, where every point on the graph of this line has a y-coordinate of b or $\dfrac{-C}{B}$. For example, the equation $y = -3$ can easily be drawn by selecting two points with y-coordinates of -3, such as $(0, -3)$ and $(3, -3)$, and then drawing a horizontal line through them. The resulting graph would look like this:

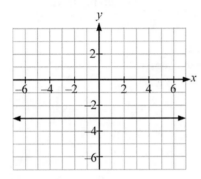

A vertical line is written as $x = a$ or $Ax + C = 0$, where every point on the graph of the line has an x-coordinate of a or $\dfrac{-C}{A}$. For example, the equation $2x - 6 = 0$ can easily be drawn by selecting two points with x-coordinates of $\dfrac{-(-6)}{2} = 3$, such as $(3, 0)$ and $(3, -3)$, and then drawing a vertical line through them. The resulting graph would look like this:

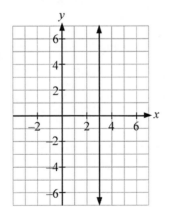

27. What is the standard form of the equation $y - \dfrac{2}{3} = \dfrac{3}{4}(x - 0)$?

   A. $9x - y + 8 = 0$

   B. $9x - 12y + 8 = 0$

   C. $9x + 12y - 8 = 0$

   D. $36x - 12y + 24 = 0$

28. Which graph represents the line that is parallel to $2x + y = 3$ and passes through point $(1, 3)$?

   A.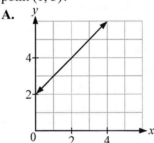

   B.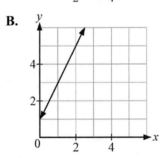

   C.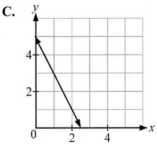

   D.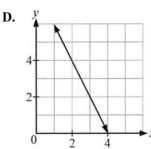

Use the following information to answer the next question.

The equations of four lines are given as follows:

I. $4x - 6y + 36 = 0$

II. $y - 7 = \frac{2}{3}(x + 3)$

III. $y = \frac{2}{3}x - 9$

IV. $6x - 9y + 81 = 0$

29. For the given equations, the set of equivalent lines is represented by lines

   A. I and II   **B.** II and III

   C. I and IV   **D.** II and IV

30. Which of the following graphs **best** represents the graph of the line $2x + 3y + 6 = 0$?

  A.

  B.

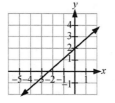

  C.

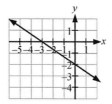

  D.

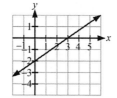

31. The equation $40x + 5y - 8 = 0$ can be written in the form $y = mx + b$. The value of b to the nearest tenth is _____.

10RF1.7 Determine the equation of a linear relation to solve problems.

DETERMINING THE EQUATION OF A LINE

The equation of a line can be determined using certain characteristics of the line:

- The graph of the equation
- The slope of the line
- At least one point on the line (such as the y-intercept)
- The equation of a parallel or perpendicular line

DETERMINING THE EQUATION OF A LINE USING A GRAPH

Given the graph of a line, the equation can be determined using a key point, such as the y-intercept, and another point on the line. The slope of the line can be determined from the information provided by these two points.

Example

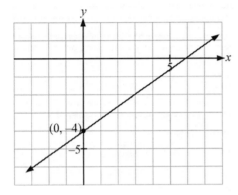

Write the equation for the line on the given graph.

Solution

From the graph, the y-intercept is $(0, -4)$. Thus, b in the equation for the line is -4.

Count the rise and the run to another clearly defined point to find the slope of the line.

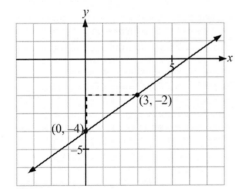

In this case, determine the slope from the y-intercept $(0, -4)$ to the point $(3, -2)$, where the rise is 2 and the run is 3.

$$m = \frac{\text{rise}}{\text{run}}$$

$$= \frac{2}{3}$$

Substitute the values for the y-intercept and the slope into the equation of the line in the form $y = mx + b$.

$$y = \frac{2}{3}x + (-4)$$

$$y = \frac{2}{3}x - 4$$

DETERMINING THE EQUATION OF A LINE USING THE SLOPE AND ONE POINT

When given one point on a line and the slope of the line, substitute the slope (m) and the x- and y-values of the point into the equation of the form $y - y_1 = m(x - x_1)$. If the point is the y-intercept, then substitute the slope (m) and the y-value of the y-intercept (b) into the equation of the form $y = mx + b$.

Example

A line with a slope of $\frac{3}{4}$ passes through the point $(-2, 5)$.

Write the equation for the line in the form $Ax + By + C = 0$.

Solution

Step 1

Substitute the slope and point values into the equation of a line of the form $y - y_1 = m(x - x_1)$:

$$y - y_1 = m(x - x_1)$$

$$y - 5 = \frac{3}{4}(x - (-2))$$

$$y - 5 = \frac{3}{4}(x + 2)$$

Step 2

Convert the equation into the form $Ax + By + C = 0$.

$$4(y - 5) = 4\left[\frac{3}{4}(x + 2)\right]$$

$$4(y - 5) = 3(x + 2)$$

$$4y - 20 = 3x + 6$$

$$0 = 3x - 4y + 26$$

$$3x - 4y + 26 = 0$$

DETERMINING THE EQUATION OF A LINE USING TWO POINTS

The equation of a line passing through the points (x_1, y_1) and (x_2, y_2) can be found using one of the following two methods:

Method 1

1. Find the slope (m) of the line using the slope formula.
    $$m = \frac{y_2 - y_1}{x_2 - x_1}$$

2. Substitute the slope and one of the points into the equation of the form $y - y_1 = m(x - x_1)$.

3. Convert the equation into the desired equation form.

Method 2:

1. Substitute the two points into the formula
    $$\frac{y - y_1}{x - x_1} = \frac{y_2 - y_1}{x_2 - x_1}.$$

2. Convert the equation into the desired equation form.

Example

Write the equation of the line that passes through the points $(3, -4)$ and $(1, 2)$ in the slope-intercept form.

Solution

Method 1

1. Determine the slope using the slope formula and the values of the two points.
    $$m = \frac{y_2 - y_1}{x_2 - x_1}$$
    $$m = \frac{2 - (-4)}{1 - 3}$$
    $$m = \frac{6}{-2}$$
    $$m = -3$$

2. Substitute the slope and the values for one of the points, such as $(3, -4)$ into the equation of the form $y - y_1 = m(x - x_1)$.
    $$y - y_1 = m(x - x_1)$$
    $$y - (-4) = -3(x - 3)$$
    $$y + 4 = -3(x - 3)$$

3. Convert the equation into the slope-intercept form.
    $$y + 4 - 4 = -3(x - 3) - 4$$
    $$y = -3x + 9 - 4$$
    $$y = -3x + 5$$

Method 2

1. Substitute the values of the points into the formula $\dfrac{y - y_1}{x - x_1} = \dfrac{y_2 - y_1}{x_2 - x_1}.$
    $$\frac{y - y_1}{x - x_1} = \frac{y_2 - y_1}{x_2 - x_1}$$
    $$\frac{y - (-4)}{x - 3} = \frac{2 - (-4)}{1 - 3}$$

2. Convert this equation into the slope-intercept form.
    $$\frac{y + 4}{x - 3} = \frac{6}{-2}$$
    $$-2(y + 4) = 6(x - 3)$$
    $$-2y - 8 = 6x - 18$$
    $$-2y - 8 + 8 = 6x - 18 + 8$$
    $$-2y = 6x - 10$$
    $$\frac{-2y}{-2} = \frac{6x}{-2} - \frac{10}{-2}$$
    $$y = -3x + 5$$

Determining the Equation of a Line Using One Point and the Equation of a Parallel or Perpendicular Line

When given a point on a line and the equation of a parallel or perpendicular line, use the following steps to determine the equation of the line:

1. Determine the slope of the parallel or perpendicular line.
2. Find the slope of the line using the properties of slopes for parallel or perpendicular lines.
3. Substitute the slope and the values of the point into the equation of the form
$y - y_1 = m(x - x_1)$.
4. Convert the equation into the desired equation form.

Example

A line passes through the point (3, 4) and is perpendicular to the line $8x - 4y + 15 = 0$.

What is the equation of the line in the form $Ax + By + C = 0$?

Solution

Step 1
Determine the slope of the line
$8x - 4y + 15 = 0$.
To determine the slope of the line, rewrite the equation in the slope-intercept form.
$$8x - 4y + 15 = 0$$
$$8x - 8x - 4y + 15 - 15 = 0 - 8x - 15$$
$$-4y = -8x - 15$$
$$\frac{-4y}{-4} = \frac{-8x}{-4} - \frac{15}{-4}$$
$$y = 2x + \frac{15}{4}$$

Since $m = 2$, the slope of the line $8x - 4y + 15 = 0$ is 2.

Step 2
Determine the slope of the line passing through the point (3, 4).
The slopes of perpendicular lines are negative reciprocals of each other. The negative reciprocal of 2 is $-\frac{1}{2}$, so the slope of the line is $-\frac{1}{2}$.

Step 3
Substitute the slope and the values of the point into the equation of the form
$y - y_1 = m(x - x_1)$.
$$y - y_1 = m(x - x_1)$$
$$y - 4 = -\frac{1}{2}(x - 3)$$

Step 4
Convert the equation into the form
$Ax + By + C = 0$.
$$y - 4 = -\frac{1}{2}(x - 3)$$
$$-2(y - 4) = -2\left[-\frac{1}{2}(x - 3)\right]$$
$$-2y + 8 = x - 3$$
$$-2y + 2y + 8 - 8 = x - 3 + 2y - 8$$
$$0 = x + 2y - 11$$
$$x + 2y - 11 = 0$$

Problem Solving with Equations of a Line

Some problems may involve circumstances that represent linear relations. These problems can be solved by finding and applying the equation that defines it.

Example

The heights of a hot air balloon, h, in metres, at various times of its descent, t, in minutes, are given in the following table of values.

Time (min)	Height (m)
0	320
1	280
2	240
3	200
4	160

Determine the equation that defines this linear relation, and find the time needed for the hot air balloon to touch the ground.

Solution

Step 1

Find the slope (the constant rate of change) from the first differences of the values in the table. For every increase of t by 1 unit, the first differences of h-values is a constant -40.

$280 - 320 = -40$
$240 - 280 = -40$
          etc.

Therefore, the slope of the corresponding line is -40 m/min.

Step 2

Identify the y-intercept for the relation.
The y-intercept of the relation is 320, since the height $h = 320$ when $t = 0$.

Step 3

Write the equation of the line in the form $y = mx + b$.
Substitute the values of the slope and y-intercept into the equation.
$h = mt + b$
$h = -40t + 320$

Step 4

Find the time, t, when the balloon touches the ground.
The balloon touches the ground when the height is 0 m, so substitute $h = 0$ into the equation.

$h = -40t + 320$
$0 = -40t + 320$
$0 - 320 = -40t + 320 - 320$
$-320 = -40t$
$\dfrac{-320}{-40} = \dfrac{-40t}{-40}$
$8 = t$
$t = 8$

Therefore, it takes 8 min for the hot air balloon to touch the ground.

Use the following information to answer the next question.

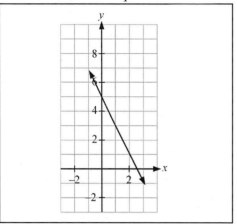

32. What is the **most likely** equation of this line?

A. $y - 2x - 4 = 0$

B. $y - 2x - 5 = 0$

C. $y = -2x + 5$

D. $y = -2x + 4$

Use the following information to answer the next question.

The slope of a line is $-\dfrac{3}{2}$, and the y-intercept is -3.

33. What is the equation of the line in general form?

A. $3x - 2y - 6 = 0$

B. $3x - 2y + 6 = 0$

C. $3x + 2y - 6 = 0$

D. $3x + 2y + 6 = 0$

34. A vertical line runs through the point $(3, 6)$. What is the equation of the line?

A. $x = 3$ B. $x = 6$

C. $y = 3$ D. $y = 6$

35. What is the equation of the line passing through the points $(-3, 2)$ and $(1, 5)$?

    A. $4x - 3y + 21 = 0$

    B. $3x - 4y + 17 = 0$

    C. $5x + 3y + 2 = 0$

    D. $2x + 5y + 3 = 0$

Use the following information to answer the next question.

> The vertices of triangle PQR are $P(-6, -4)$, $Q(6, 2)$, and $R(-2, 8)$.

36. What is the equation of the line that is parallel to side PQ and passes through point R?

    A. $y = \dfrac{1}{2}x - 1$

    B. $y = \dfrac{1}{2}x + 9$

    C. $y = -2x + 4$

    D. $y = -\dfrac{1}{6}x + \dfrac{23}{3}$

Use the following information to answer the next question.

> A line passes through the point $(-3, 4.5)$ and has a slope of 2.5.

Numerical Response

37. When the equation of this line is written in the form $y = mx + b$, the value of b is _____. (Record your answer to the nearest tenth.)

Use the following information to answer the next multipart question.

38. The data shows the cost of renting a Jet Ski at a local lake.

Time (h)	1	2	3	4	5	6	7
Cost ($)	28	36	44	52	60	68	76

Written Response

a) Graph the relation, and determine the equation of the line.

Show your work.

b) If it cost Tammy $104 to rent a Jet Ski over 2 days, then how long did she use the Jet Ski?

10RF1.8 Represent a linear function, using function notation.

USING FUNCTION NOTATION

The ordered pairs (x, y) that satisfy the equation $y = 2x + 3$ form a function. An equation that is a function can be named using **function notation**. For example, the equation $y = 2x + 3$ can be written in function notation as $f(x) = 2x + 3$.

The symbol $f(x)$ is read as "the value of f at x" or "f of x." Function notation describes the output or range value, $f(x)$, as a result of an input or domain value of x into a **function machine**, defined by f.

Input   Output

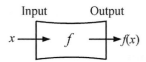

For example, $f(5)$ means substituting the input value of 5 into the function machine defined by f to produce the resulting output value $f(5)$.

Input	Function (f)	Output [$f(5)$]
5→	$2x + 3$→	$2(5) + 3 = 13$

Similarly, an input value, x, can be found for a given output value, such as $f(x) = 15$.

Input	Function (f)	Output [$f(x) = 15$]
x→	$2x + 3$→	$2x + 3 = 15$ $2x + 3 - 3 = 15 - 3$ $2x = 12$ $x = 6$

Thus, the input value of 6 produces the given output value of 15.

Example

The relationship between the total cost, C (in dollars), with respect to the distance, d (in kilometres), travelled by a truck to deliver furniture to a particular customer can be represented by the following equation:
$C = 1.00d + 80$

Rewrite the equation in function notation, graph the function, and then determine the distance traveled by the truck if the cost was $280.

Solution

Since d is the input or independent variable and C is the output or dependent variable, the equation rewritten in function notation is $C(d) = 1.00d + 80$.

To graph this function, create a table of values by determining several output values, $C(d)$, for several input values, d.

d	$C(d)$
0	$C(0) = 1.00(0) + 80$ $= 80$
20	$C(20) = 1.00(20) + 80$ $= 100$
40	$C(40) = 1.00(40) + 80$ $= 120$
60	$C(60) = 1.00(60) + 80$ $= 140$
80	$C(80) = 1.00(80) + 80$ $= 160$
100	$C(100) = 1.00(100) + 80$ $= 180$

The graph of this linear function can be drawn as shown.

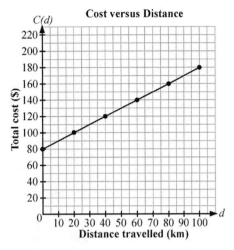

Use the function $C(d) = 1.00d + 80$ to determine the distance, d, that the truck travelled if the cost, $C(d)$, is \$280.

$$C(d) = 1.00d + 80$$
$$280 = 1.00d + 80$$
$$280 - 80 = 1.00d + 80 - 80$$
$$200 = 1.00d$$
$$d = 200$$

The truck travelled 200 km to result in a cost of \$280.

Use the following information to answer the next question.

This graph depicts the relationship between the speed of a car, $v(t)$, in kilometres per hour and the time travelled, t, in hours.

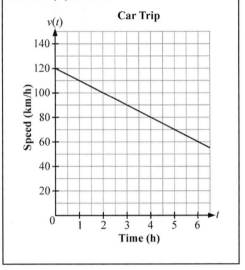

39. Which of the following functions correctly represents the given graph?
   A. $v(t) = 120 + 2t$
   B. $v(t) = 120 - 6t$
   C. $v(t) = 120 - 10t$
   D. $v(t) = 120 + 10t$

Numerical Response

40. For the linear function $f(x) = -20x + 5$, the sum of $f(-2)$ and $f(-5)$ is _____.

Numerical Response

41. Given the function $h(x) = -\dfrac{3}{4}x + \dfrac{25}{4}$ and that $h(x) = -\dfrac{47}{10}$, the value of x is _____. (Record your answer to the nearest tenth.)

10RF1.9 Solve problems that involve systems of linear equations in two variables, graphically and algebraically.

Solving Systems of Two Linear Equations

A collection of linear equations involving the same set of variables is called a **system of linear equations**. The solution to a system of two linear equations that are not parallel can be determined graphically or algebraically with or without technology.

Using the Graphing Method

Two lines that are not parallel and distinct will eventually intersect at one point.
The **point of intersection** occurs where the two lines have the same x- and y-values. It is also the solution of the system of the two equations, since the values satisfy both equations.

Example

Find the point of intersection of the linear relations $y = x + 4$ and $y = -x + 3$ using graphing.

Solution

The point of intersection can be determined using either graph paper or technology.

Using Graph Paper
The most common way to graph the two linear relations is to use the x- and y-intercepts.

The two lines graphed on grid paper are shown in the given diagram.

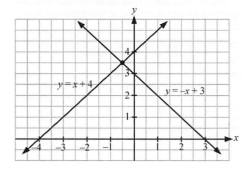

The point of intersection of the two lines is $(-0.5, 3.5)$.

Using Technology
A more precise way of finding solutions graphically is to use either a graphing calculator or a computer. These solutions are more precise than using graph paper, but exact solutions must be determined algebraically.

A TI-83 Plus graphing calculator can be used to determine the point of intersection as follows.

Enter the equations into the calculator as shown in the following diagram.

Using the INTERSECTION feature, the point of intersection can be determined as shown.

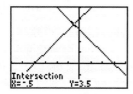

An appropriate window setting is $x:[-6, 4, 1]$, $y:[-2, 5, 1]$.

The solution to the system of linear equations is $(-0.5, 3.5)$.

Understanding Contexts

Two linear equations can represent two different conditions for the same real-life context. The point of intersection of the graphs of the two lines represents the situation in which both conditions are the same. Points below or above the point of intersection also provide valuable information regarding the differences in the conditions of the real-life context.

Example

A movie rental company has two monthly plans:

A. A flat fee of $40/month is charged for unlimited rentals.
B. A fixed fee of $8 is charged, plus $4 for every movie rented.

Under which conditions is one plan a better choice than the other?

Solution

Step 1

Analyze these two plans by drawing their representative lines.

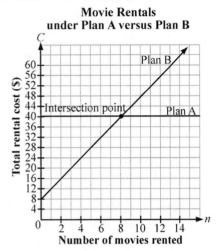

Movie Rentals under Plan A versus Plan B

The intersection point of the two lines is (8, 40). This point represents the point where both plans have the same total cost. When eight movies are rented, the cost is $40 under plan A and $40 under plan B.

Step 2

Examine points to the left of the intersection point, and determine which plan is better for the customer.

Since the points for plan B are below the points for plan A (from $n = 0$ to $n = 8$), it indicates that plan B is less expensive than plan A.

For example, at $n = 4$, the total cost is $24 for plan B and $40 for plan A. Plan B is a better choice when renting fewer than eight movies.

Step 3

Examine points to the right of the intersection point, and determine which plan is better for the customer.

Since the points for plan A are lower than the points for plan B (from $n = 8$ and up), it indicates that plan A is less expensive than plan B when renting more than eight movies. For example, at $n = 12$, the total cost is $40 under plan A and $56 under plan B.

THE ALGEBRAIC METHOD OF SUBSTITUTION

To solve a system of two linear equations using the method of substitution, follow these steps:

1. Label the equations 1 and 2.
2. Choose the simplest equation and isolate one of the variables.
3. Substitute this rearranged equation into the equation that was not changed. Use the rearranged equation in place of the variable that was isolated.
4. Solve for the remaining variable in the equation that was not changed.
5. Use this calculated value of the variable to determine the value of the other variable by substituting its value back into one of the original equations.

Example

A system of linear equations is given.
$$y - 4x + 1 = 0$$
$$4x - 5y + 3 = 0$$

Using the method of substitution, solve the given system of linear equations.

Solution

Step 1

Label the equations.

① $y - 4x + 1 = 0$
② $4x - 5y + 3 = 0$

Step 2

Isolate variable y in equation 1 since the coefficient of y is 1.

Thus, equation 1 becomes $y = 4x - 1$

Step 3

Substitute $4x - 1$ for y into equation 2.

② $4x - 5y + 3 = 0$
$4x - 5(4x - 1) + 3 = 0$

Step 4

Solve for the variable x.
$$4x - 5(4x - 1) + 3 = 0$$
$$4x - 20x + 5 + 3 = 0$$
$$-16x + 8 = 0$$
$$8 = 16x$$
$$\frac{8}{16} = x$$
$$x = \frac{1}{2}$$

Step 5

Substitute $\frac{1}{2}$ for x in either the first or second equation or in the equation $y = 4x - 1$ to determine the values for y.

$$y = 4x - 1$$
$$y = 4\left(\frac{1}{2}\right) - 1$$
$$y = 2 - 1$$
$$y = 1$$

The solution is $x = \frac{1}{2}$ and $y = 1$.

Step 6

To verify the solution, substitute the values for both variables into the original equations.

Equation ①
$$y - 4x + 1 = 0$$
$$(1) - 4\left(\frac{1}{2}\right) + 1 = 0$$
$$1 - 2 + 1 = 0$$
$$0 = 0$$

Equation ②
$$4x - 5y + 3 = 0$$
$$4\left(\frac{1}{2}\right) - 5(1) + 3 = 0$$
$$2 - 5 + 3 = 0$$
$$0 = 0$$

The solution to the given system of linear equations is $x = \frac{1}{2}$ and $y = 1$ or $\left(\frac{1}{2}, 1\right)$.

THE ALGEBRAIC METHOD OF ELIMINATION

The algebraic method of elimination involves eliminating one of the variables in an equation. Some suggested steps for using this method are outlined in the following example.

Example

Solve the following system of equations:
$$3x - 4y = 20$$
$$x + 3y = -2$$

Solution

Step 1
Label the equations.
① $\quad 3x - 4y = 20$
② $\quad x + 3y = -2$

Step 2
Multiply both sides of equation 2 by 3.
① $\quad 3x - 4y = 20$
② $\quad 3x + 9y = -6$

Step 3
Subtract the two equations, and solve for y.
$$3x - 4y = 20$$
$$\underline{3x + 9y = -6}$$
$$0 - 13y = 26$$
$$-13y = 26$$
$$y = -2$$

Step 4
Substitute -2 for y in one of the original equations (in this case, equation 2), and solve for x.
$$x + 3y = -2$$
$$x + 3(-2) = -2$$
$$x - 6 = -2$$
$$x = 4$$

Step 5
The solution is $x = 4$ and $y = -2$, or $(4, -2)$.

NUMBER OF SOLUTIONS OF TWO LINEAR EQUATIONS

A system of two linear equations can have one solution if the graphs are **intersecting lines**, no solution if the graphs are **parallel lines**, and infinite solutions if the graphs are **coincident lines**.
Each system has a unique relationship between the slopes and y-intercepts of the graphs of the two lines.

Intersecting lines have these characteristics:

- One solution
- Different slopes
- Different or same y-intercepts

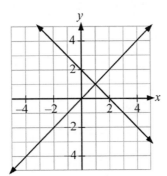

Parallel lines have these characteristics:

- No solution
- Same slope
- Different y-intercepts

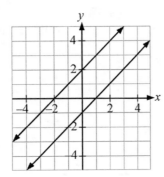

Coincident lines have these characteristics:

- Infinite solutions
- Same slope
- Same y-intercept

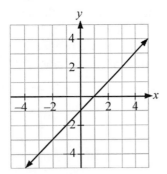

To predict the number of solutions for a linear system of equations, write the equations in the slope-intercept form and then compare the slopes (m) and y-intercepts (b).

Example

System 1	**System 2**
$4x + 2y - 6 = 0$	$3x - 2y - 5 = 0$
$2x + y - 3 = 0$	$y + 2 = \dfrac{3}{2}(x - 1)$

How many solutions does each linear system have?

Solution

Rewrite each equation in the form $y = mx + b$, and then compare the values of m and b to determine the number of solutions for each system.

Step 1
Rewrite the equations in system 1.
$$4x + 2y - 6 = 0$$
$$2y = -4x + 6$$
$$y = -2x + 3$$
$$2x + y - 3 = 0$$
$$y = -2x + 3$$

Step 2
Rewrite the equations in system 2.
$$3x - 2y - 5 = 0$$
$$-2y = -3x + 5$$
$$y = \frac{3}{2}x - \frac{5}{2}$$
$$y + 2 = \frac{3}{2}(x - 1)$$
$$y = \frac{3}{2}x - \frac{3}{2} - 2$$
$$y = \frac{3}{2}x - \frac{7}{2}$$

Step 3

Compare the values of m and b to determine the number of solutions for each system.

In system 1, both equations have the same slope ($m = -2$) and same y-intercept ($b = 3$). Therefore, the system has infinite solutions.

In system 2, both equations have the same slope $\left(m = \dfrac{3}{2}\right)$ but different y-intercepts $\left(b_1 = -\dfrac{5}{2},\right.$ $\left. b_2 = -\dfrac{7}{2}\right)$.

Therefore, the system has no solution.

PROBLEM SOLVING USING SYSTEMS OF TWO LINEAR EQUATIONS

Follow these steps when solving problems that arise from realistic situations represented by a linear system of two equations:

- Assign a different variable to each of the unknown quantities.
- Set up a system of two linear equations, and solve the system using either an algebraic or graphical method.
- Clearly state the solution to the given problem.

Example

Four cabbages and five heads of lettuce cost $8.40, whereas six cabbages and two heads of lettuce cost $8.20.

Determine the price of one cabbage and one head of lettuce.

Solution

Step 1

Determine the system of equations.

- Let the price in dollars of one cabbage = x.
- Let the price in dollars of one head of lettuce = y.

Using the information given in the problem, the following system of equations can be formed:

① $4x + 5y = 8.40$
② $6x + 2y = 8.20$

Step 2

Multiply equation 1 by 2 and equation 2 by 5 to obtain a common coefficient for y.

③ $8x + 10y = 16.80$ (Equation 1 multiplied by 2)

④ $30x + 10y = 41.00$ (Equation 2 multiplied by 5)

Step 3

Subtract equation 4 from equation 3, and then solve for x.

$$-22x + 0y = -24.20$$
$$x = \dfrac{-24.20}{-22}$$
$$x = 1.10$$

Step 4

Substitute 1.10 for x into equation 1, and then solve for y.

$$4(1.10) + 5y = 8.40$$
$$4.40 + 5y = 8.40$$
$$5y = 4.00$$
$$y = 0.80$$

The price of one cabbage is $1.10, and the price of one head of lettuce is $0.80.

---

42. The perimeter of a rectangle is 22 cm. If the length of the rectangle is 1 cm more than its width, the width of the rectangle is

    A. 5 cm   **B.** 6 cm

    C. 7 cm   **D.** 8 cm

Use the following information to answer the next question.

The sum of the present ages of Samantha and Jocelyn is 22 years. In four years, Samantha will be twice as old as Jocelyn.

43. If x represents the present age of Samantha and y represents the present age of Jocelyn, then the system of linear equations that could be solved in order to determine the present age of each girl is

    A. $x + y = 22$ and $x - 2y = 4$

    B. $x + y = 22$ and $x = 2(y - 4)$

    C. $x + y = 22$ and $x = 2(y + 4)$

    D. $x + y = 22$ and $2x - y = -4$

Use the following information to answer the next question.

The ordered pair (x, y) is the solution to the system of linear equations $8x + 3y = -41$ and $6x - 5y = -9$.

44. What is the value of x?

A. 4   **B.** $\dfrac{-89}{29}$

C. -4 **D.** $\dfrac{-159}{29}$

Use the following information to answer the next question.

The solution to the system of linear equations $x - \dfrac{1}{3}y = 2$ and $3x + 2y - 24 = 0$ is obtained using the method of substitution.

45. A possible substitution that could be made to solve this system is to replace

A. x with $\dfrac{y+2}{2}$

B. x with $1 + 2y$

C. y with $1 - 2x$

D. y with $\dfrac{24 - 3x}{2}$

Use the following information to answer the next question.

Breanna and Jacob decided to jog around a track. Jacob left the starting point first, running at a constant speed of 4 m/s. Breanna waited 3 s and then left from the same starting point, running at a constant speed of 5 m/s. The given graph shows their progress around the track.
The intersection point of the lines that represents the two given linear relations is _____*i*_____, and at 10 s, _____*ii*_____ is ahead by _____*iii*_____ m.

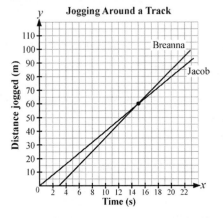

46. Which of the following tables completes the given statement?

A.
i	*ii*	*iii*
(15, 60)	Jacob	5

B.
i	*ii*	*iii*
(15, 60)	Breanna	10

C.
i	*ii*	*iii*
(60, 15)	Jacob	5

D.
i	*ii*	*iii*
(60, 15)	Breanna	10

Use the following information to answer the next question.

A company wants to rent a hall for a holiday party.

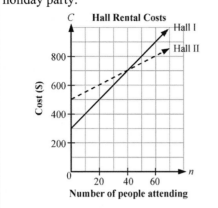

47. Which of the following statements is **true**?

   A. The equation for Hall I is $C = 500 + 5n$, and it is the better value if 40 or less people attend.

   B. The equation for Hall II is $C = 500 - 5n$, and it is the better value if 40 or less people attend.

   C. The equation for Hall I is $C = 300 + 10n$, and it is the better value if 40 or less people attend.

   D. The equation for Hall II is $C = 300 - 10n$, and it is the better value if 40 or less people attend.

48. Which of the following systems of equations has the solution $x = -5$ and $y = -2$?

   A. $2x + 3y = 9$ and $7x - 5y = 2$

   B. $-3x + 5y = 5$ and $x - 3y = 1$

   C. $4x - 3y = 9$ and $x - y = -3$

   D. $2x - y = -5$ and $7x + 3y = 4$

Use the following information to answer the next question.

A student decides to solve a given system of two linear equations by using a graphical approach. The graph of the first linear equation is shown.

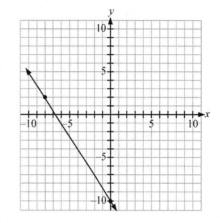

49. If the equation of the second linear equation is $2x - y = 3$, then the solution to the system of equations is

   A. $\begin{array}{l} x = -6 \\ y = -1 \end{array}$

   B. $\begin{array}{l} x = -4 \\ y = -4 \end{array}$

   C. $\begin{array}{l} x = -2 \\ y = -7 \end{array}$

   D. $\begin{array}{l} x = -1 \\ y = -5 \end{array}$

Numerical Response

50. In the system of two linear equations $2x + 5y = 12$ and $y - x = 2$, the value of $x + y$ (to the nearest tenth) is _____.

Numerical Response

51. For the system of linear equations $12x + Ky = -9$ and $-16x - 20y = 12$ to have an infinite number of solutions, what is the value of K? _____

Use the following information to answer the next question.

At a particular theatre, adult tickets cost $12.50 each and student tickets cost $8 each. At a certain show, only adult and student tickets were sold.

If twice as many student tickets as adult tickets were sold and the total sales were $2 280, then how many adult and how many student tickets were sold?

Written Response

52. Set up a system of two linear equations involving two variables, and then use this system to solve the problem above.

ANSWERS AND SOLUTIONS
RELATIONS AND FUNCTIONS

1. 2	12. C	23. A	33. D	44. C
2. WR	13. C	24. C	34. A	45. D
3. A	14. 0.5	25. 5	35. B	46. A
4. A	15. 1.5	26. a) C	36. B	47. C
5. D	16. WR	26. b) C	37. 12.0	48. B
6. B	17. A	27. B	38. WR	49. C
7. B	18. D	28. C	39. C	50. 2.6
8. 2.66	19. C	29. D	40. 150	51. 15
9. D	20. A	30. C	41. 14.6	52. WR
10. C	21. B	31. 1.6	42. A	
11. A	22. 3	32. C	43. A	

1. 2

The upper limit of the range of the 45° trajectory, *a*, is 5 m.

The upper limit of the range of the 55° trajectory, *b*, is 7 m.

Determine the difference between *b* and *a*.

$b - a$

$7 - 5 = 2$

2. WR

The jawbreaker is largest when Boon first puts it in his mouth at $t = 0$ min. This value is 33.5 cm³. The jawbreaker is smallest when it is completely dissolved. This value is 0 cm³. Realistically, the final change would occur some time after 5 min. For the given situation, suppose that the time required to completely dissolve the jawbreaker is about 15 min. This value can be called t_f (final time). Therefore, the restrictions of the domain (time) and range (volume) are as follows:

- Domain: 0 to tf min or $0 \le t \le 15$
- Range: 0 to 33.5 cm3 or $0 \le V \le 33.5$

3. A

The domain and range can be visually represented on the graph as shown.

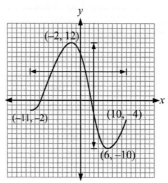

Step 1

Determine the domain of the graph. The domain of a function is equal to all the values of *x* for which *x* is defined. From the graph, *x*-values lie between −11 and +10 because the farthest point to the left of the *y*-axis is (−11, −2) and the farthest point to the right of the *y*-axis is (10, −4). The domain of the function is $\{-11 \le x \le 10\}$.

Step 2

Determine the range of the graph. The range of a function is equal to all the values of *y* for which *y* is defined. From the graph, *y*-values lie between +12 and −10 because the farthest point above the *x*-axis is (−2, 12) and the farthest point below the *x*-axis is (6, −10). The range of the function is $\{-10 \le y \le 12\}$.

4. A

The data will present a graph where the points are not joined. This means that the data is discrete.

This graph best represents the ball's rebound heights after eight bounces.

Height of Ball after Bounces

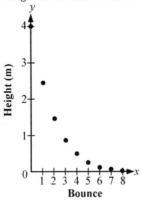

5. D

You must assume that a height of 0 is the main floor and the maximum height is the top floor of the office tower.

Alternative A: In this graph, the height goes from the main floor to the top floor, back to the main level, back up, and then returns to the main floor. This is not the situation described.

Alternative B: In this graph, the height that the elevator starts at is the top floor, which is not described in the given information.

Alternative C: In this graph, the height increases, remains constant for a time, then decreases before going up again. This could be the situation, but it is unlikely that the second stop would be at a lower floor.

Alternative D: The height of the elevator continues to increase in this graph, with two flat spots that represent the two stops. This graph best represents the scenario described.

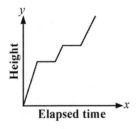

6. B

Alternative A: The graph would start as it does, but it would go down first to indicate the bounce before the rebound. This answer is not correct.

Alternative B: The graph shows the chair going up in the air, peaking, returning to the ground level, and then peaking again.

Alternative C: The graph shows the commuter going to work from some other place than home, returning to that place, and then going back to work. This is not the correct answer.

Alternative D: The graph shows the skateboard starting in motion, not at rest. This answer is not correct.

7. B

In order to be a function, any x-value cannot have more than one corresponding y-value.

In mapping A, the value $x = -8$ has two output values of -2 and 2. The relation that this mapping represents is not a function.

In mapping B, the value of $x = 2$ has a single output value of -8. All the other x-values in this mapping also have single y-values. The relation that this mapping represents is a function.

In mapping C, the value $x = -8$ has four output values of 4, 2, 0, and -2. The relation that this mapping represents is not a function.

In mapping D, the values of $x = 4$, $x = 2$, $x = 0$, and $x = -2$ all have a single output value of -8. The relation that this mapping represents is a function.

Two of the given relations are also functions.

8. 2.66

Placing the ladder against the wall creates a right-angled triangle. The lengths of two sides are given.

Step 1

Use the Pythagorean theorem, $a^2 + b^2 = c^2$, to determine the distance of the base of the ladder from the wall.

Let $a = 4.40$ m and $c = 4.70$ m.

$$a^2 + b^2 = c^2$$
$$(4.40)^2 + b^2 = (4.70)^2$$

Step 2

Solve this equation to find the value of b.

$$(4.40)^2 + b^2 = (4.70)^2$$
$$19.36 + b^2 = 22.09$$
$$b^2 = 22.09 - 19.36$$
$$b^2 = 2.73$$
$$b = \sqrt{2.73}$$
$$b \approx 1.652\,27 \text{ m}$$

Step 3

Find the slope of the ladder using the slope formula, $m = \dfrac{\text{rise}}{\text{run}}$.

$$m = \frac{\text{rise}}{\text{run}}$$
$$= \frac{4.40 \text{ m}}{1.652\,27 \text{ m}}$$
$$\approx 2.663$$

To the nearest hundredth, the slope is 2.66.

9. D

A rate of change of $-\dfrac{1}{2}$ can be written as $\dfrac{-1}{2}$.

Since the rate of change is defined as rise divided by run, the rise is -1 while the run is 2.

The run is 2 units to the right, and the rise is 1 unit down.

10. C

Parallel lines have the same slope, $m_1 = m_2$.

Parallel lines have a distinct set of points that make up each line, which means they share no common points.

11. A

The slope formula is $m = \dfrac{\text{rise}}{\text{run}}$. A vertical line has no run and only rise. The formula becomes $m = \dfrac{\text{rise}}{\text{run}} = \dfrac{\text{rise}}{0}$. Division by 0 is undefined.

A vertical line segment has an undefined slope.

12. C

The line l_3 falls from left to right thus its slope is negative.

13. C

The y-intercept of a line intersects the y-axis at the point $(0, b)$.

Substitute the given value of the slope(2) and coordinates of the point $(1, -3)$ into the slope formula, and solve for b.

$$m = \frac{y_2 - y_1}{x_2 - x_1}$$
$$m = \frac{y_2 - y_1}{x_2 - x_1}$$
$$-2 = \frac{b - (-3)}{0 - 1}$$
$$-2 = \frac{b + 3}{-1}$$
$$-1(-2) = -1\left(\frac{b + 3}{-1}\right)$$
$$2 = b + 3$$
$$-3 + 2 = b + 3 - 3$$
$$-1 = b$$

The y-intercept of the line is -1.

14. 0.5

Step 1

Using the slope formula, determine the slope of the line that passes through the points $A(2, 3)$ and $B(5, 5)$.

$$m = \frac{y_2 - y_1}{x_2 - x_1}$$
$$= \frac{5 - 3}{5 - 2}$$
$$= \frac{2}{3}$$

Step 2

For the line that passes through the points C and D, use the slope formula to find the value of the coordinate k.

The slopes of perpendicular lines are negative reciprocals of each other. Because line $\overline{AB}$ has a slope of $\frac{2}{3}$, any line perpendicular to $\overline{AB}$ has a slope of $-\frac{3}{2}$.

$$m = \frac{y_2 - y_1}{x_2 - x_1}$$
$$-\frac{3}{2} = \frac{k - (-1)}{5 - 6}$$
$$-\frac{3}{2} = \frac{k + 1}{-1}$$
$$(-3)(-1) = 2(k + 2)$$
$$3 = 2k + 2$$
$$1 = 2k$$
$$\frac{1}{2} = k$$
$$k = 0.5$$

The value of k is 0.5.

15. 1.5

Step 1

Choose any two points on the line.
Let $(x_1, y_1) = (0, -2)$ and $(x_2, y_2) = (2, 1)$.

Step 2

Calculate the slope of the line using the slope formula.

$$m = \frac{\text{rise}}{\text{run}}$$
$$= \frac{y_2 - y_1}{x_2 - x_1}$$
$$= \frac{1 - (-2)}{2 - 0}$$
$$= \frac{1 + 2}{2}$$
$$= \frac{3}{2}$$

The slope of the line is $\frac{3}{2}$ or 1.5.

16. WR

The slope of the line means that from the given point $(-9, 8)$, another point on the line will be 4 units down and 3 units to the right. This point will be at $(-6, 4)$. Plot this point, and then draw a line through the two points.

This graph shows the required line passing through the given point with the given slope.

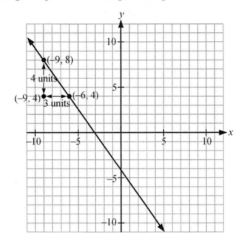

17. A

Step 1

Determine the initial value.
The initial value is 60, since 60 L is the amount of fuel Geoff has in his tank at the start of his trip.

Step 2

Determine the rate of change.
Since the amount of fuel decreases, the rate of change is negative. The constant rate of change is -1 L per 10 km, which can be written as $\frac{-1 \text{ L}}{10 \text{ km}}$ or -0.10 L / km.

Step 3

Determine the equation using the form $y = mx + b$, and write the equation in terms of the given variables, where the coefficient of d represents the rate of change.

$$y = mx + b$$
$$= -0.1x + 60$$
$$= 60 - 0.1x$$
$$F = 60 - 0.1d$$

Step 4

Determine the graph that Geoff could use.

The graph that enables Geoff to determine the value of d when $F(d) = 0$ should have an initial value of 60 (the F-intercept) and portray a negative rate of change of $-1\text{L}/10\text{ km}$. A line that has a negative rate of change falls from left to right.

The given graph and equation represent the number of kilometres that Geoff could drive on 60 L of gas.

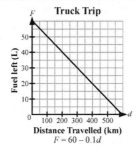

Truck Trip

$F = 60 - 0.1d$

18. D

For a linear function, the value of the first differences must be constant.

Step 1

Check the first differences in table A.

$4 - 2 = 2$

$8 - 4 = 4$

Since $2 \neq 4$, the first differences are not constant.

Step 2

Check the first differences in table B.

$32 - 20 = 12$

$38 - 32 = 6$

Since $12 \neq 6$, the first differences are not constant.

Step 3

Check the first differences in table C.

$35 - 32 = 3$

$32 - 28 = 4$

Since $4 \neq 3$, the first differences are not constant.

Step 4

Check the first differences in table D.

$28 - 23 = 5$

$23 - 18 = 5$

$18 - 13 = 5$

$13 - 8 = 5$

Since the first differences are the same, the data in table D represents a linear function.

19. C

This is a non-linear relationship because for every constant increase in the length of each side, l, the value, V, does not increase by a constant amount.

$27 - 8 = 19$

$64 - 27 = 37$

$125 - 64 = 61$

$216 - 125 = 91$

$343 - 216 = 127$

Since the first differences are not constant, the relationship is non-linear.

20. A

Since gas prices decreased at a constant rate from the spring to the fall, the relationship between gas prices and time of year is linear. The graph portraying this relationship is a line segment that falls from the left to the right.

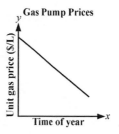

Gas Pump Prices

21. B

The relationship is looking at age and the number of accidents. Therefore, alternatives A and C are immediately eliminated. John is looking at how age (independent variable) affects the number of accidents (dependent variable).

22. 3

Any equation where the degree of each variable is one will graph a linear relation (a straight line).

The equations $y = x^2 + 3$ and $y = x^3 - 6$ are of the second and third degree, so they will graph non-linear curves. The remaining three equations have graphs of linear relations.

23. A

The given line has a y-intercept of –1.

The line passes through a point with coordinates (0, –1).

The slope of the line:

$$\text{slope} = \frac{\text{rise}}{\text{run}} = \frac{4}{3}$$

The graph of the line passes through the points (0, –1) and (3, 3).

Thus, the correct graph is shown in alternative A.

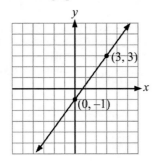

24. C

Step 1

Determine the domain of the function.

The line $y = 3$ is a horizontal line that passes through the y-axis at the point (0, 3).

Therefore, the y-intercept is 3. Since the line extends indefinitely to the left and right, the

domain is $x \in \mathbb{R}$.

Step 2

Determine the range of the function.

Since all y-values of the points on the line would be 3, the range is $y = 3$.

25. 5

Step 1

Determine the value of b.

From the graph, the line crosses the y-axis at (0, 4).

Therefore, the y-intercept is b = 4.

Step 2

Find the slope, m, of the line.

Two methods can be used to find the slope.

Method 1—Graphically

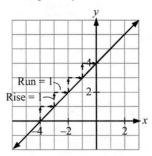

To find the slope, m, pick any point on the line. Count how many units of rise there are (1) and how many units of run there are (1) until the next point.

$$m = \frac{\text{rise}}{\text{run}}$$
$$= \frac{1}{1}$$
$$= 1$$

Method 2—Using the slope formula

Pick two points on the graph, such as (1, 5) and (0, 4). Substitute these values into the formula, and solve.

$$m = \frac{\text{rise}}{\text{run}}$$
$$= \frac{y_2 - y_1}{x_2 - x_1}$$
$$m = \frac{5 - 4}{1 - 0}$$
$$= \frac{1}{1}$$
$$= 1$$

Step 3

Determine the sum of $m + b$.

$m + b = 1 + 4 = 5$

26. a) C

Step 1

Determine the number of tickets Stephan started with.

The point (0, 52) is located on the y-axis, so the number of tickets that Stephan started with was 52.

Step 2

Determine the rate that Stephan sold his tickets.

The next point to the right is (5, 48). This means he had 48 tickets left to sell after 5 minutes. This pattern continues in a linear manner.

Therefore, Stephan started with 52 tickets and sold 4 tickets every 5 minutes.

b) C

There are two methods you could use to find the *x*-intercept.

Method 1—Graphically

Apply the rate of 4 tickets per 5 minutes as a rise of –4 and a run of 5 to the final point (50, 12), until you arrive at the *x*-axis.

After 3 steps, the *x*-intercept would be (65, 0).

Method 2—Using the slope formula

Use a point, such as (50, 12), and the slope value of $-\dfrac{4}{5}$ to find the *x*-intercept $(x, 0)$

$$m = \frac{y_2 - y_1}{x_2 - x_1}$$

$$-\frac{4}{5} = \frac{0 - 12}{x - 50}$$

$$-\frac{4}{5} = \frac{-12}{x - 50}$$

$$-4(x - 50) = 5(-12)$$

$$-4x + 200 = -60$$

$$-4x = \frac{-260}{-4}$$

$$x = 65$$

The *x*-intercept would be 65.

27. B

The equation is currently in point-slope form.

Step 1

Simplify the right side.

$$y - \frac{2}{3} = \frac{3}{4}(x - 0)$$

$$y - \frac{2}{3} = \frac{3}{4}x$$

Step 2

Multiply each term by 12, the lowest common denominator, to eliminate the fractional coefficients.

$$12y - 8 = 9x$$

$$12y - 12y - 8 + 8 = 9x - 12y + 8$$

$$0 = 9x - 12y + 8$$

$$9x - 12y + 8 = 0$$

Therefore, the equation in standard form is $9x - 12y + 8 = 0$.

28. C

First eliminate alternative D since it does not go through (1, 3).

Rewrite the equation in slope y-intercept form.

$$2x + y = 3$$

$$y = -2x + 3$$

The slope of the line = –2.

The line you are to find must also have a slope of –2 since it is parallel to the line $2x + y = 3$.

Eliminate alternatives A and B with their positive sloping lines.

The graph in alternative C has a line that passes through the points (1, 3) and has a slope of –2.

29. D

In order to determine which lines are equivalent, convert all the equations into the form $y = mx + b$.

Step 1

Convert line I.

$$4x - 6y + 36 = 0$$

$$-6y = -4x - 36$$

$$\frac{-6y}{-6} = \frac{-4x - 36}{-6}$$

$$y = \frac{2}{3}x + 6$$

Step 2

Convert line II.

$$y - 7 = \frac{2}{3}(x + 3)$$

$$y - 7 = \frac{2}{3}x + 2$$

$$y = \frac{2}{3}x + 2 + 7$$

$$y = \frac{2}{3}x + 9$$

Step 3

Line III is already in the desired form.

$$y = \frac{2}{3}x - 9$$

Step 2

Convert line IV.

$$6x - 9 + 81 = 0$$

$$-9y = -6x - 81$$

$$\frac{-9y}{-9} = \frac{-6x - 81}{-9}$$

$$y = \frac{2}{3}x + 9$$

Since the equations in the $y = mx + b$ forms are the same for lines II and IV, the set of equivalent lines is represented by lines II and IV.

30. C

The given line is

$$2x + 3y + 6 = 0$$
$$3y = -2x - 6$$
$$y = \frac{-2x - 6}{3}$$
$$y = -\frac{2}{3}x - 2$$

The slope is $-\frac{2}{3}$ and the y-intercept is -2.

Therefore, the given line has a negative slope and intersects the y-axis at $(0, -2)$. The required graph is shown in alternative C.

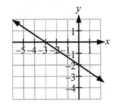

31. 1.6

$$0 = 40x + 5y - 8$$
$$5y = -40x + 8$$
$$y = \frac{1}{5}(-40x + 8)$$
$$y = -8x + \frac{8}{5}$$

The equation $y = -8x + \frac{8}{5}$ is in the form

$y = mx + b$. Therefore, $b = \frac{8}{5} = 1.6$.

32. C

The slope, $m = \dfrac{\text{rise}}{\text{run}} = \dfrac{-2}{1} = -2$. The y-intercept is 5. Substitute these values into the slope y-intercept form of the equation of the line.
$$y = -2x + 5$$

33. D

Step 1
Determine the equation of the line in the slope-intercept form, $y = mx + b$.

The slope (m) is $-\frac{3}{2}$ and the y-intercept (b) is -3.

Substitute these values into the equation of the line in slope-intercept form.

$$y = -\frac{3}{2}x - 3$$

Step 2
Rewrite the equation in the form $Ax + By + C = 0$

$$y = -\frac{3}{2}x - 3$$
$$2(y) = 2\left(-\frac{3}{2}x - 3\right)$$
$$2y = -3x - 6$$
$$3x + 2y + 6 = 0$$

The equation of the line in general form is $3x + 2y + 6 = 0$.

34. A

A vertical line has the equation $x = c$, in which c is the x-coordinate of every point on the line. Since the line passes through the point $(3, 6)$, the equation of the line is $x = 3$.

35. B

The two points are $(x_1, y_1) = (-3, 2)$ and $(x_2, y_2) = (1, 5)$.

Method 1
Determine the slope of the line.

The equation for the slope of a line is $m = \dfrac{y_2 - y_1}{x_2 - x_1}$, where m is the slope.

$$m = \frac{5 - 2}{1 - (-3)}$$
$$= \frac{3}{4}$$

Choose one of the points, $(-3, 2)$ for example, and substitute its values and the slope value into the slope-point formula.

$$y - y_1 = m(x - x_1)$$
$$y - 2 = \frac{3}{4}(x + 3)$$

Convert to the general form $Ax + By + C = 0$.

$$4(y - 2) = 4\left[\frac{3}{4}(x + 3)\right]$$
$$4(y - 2) = 3(x + 3)$$
$$4y - 8 = 3x + 9$$
$$3x - 4y + 17 = 0$$

Method 2—Graphically

Substitute the values of the points into the formula

$$\frac{y - y_1}{x - x_1} = \frac{y_2 - y_1}{x_2 - x_1}.$$

$$\frac{y - y_1}{x - x_1} = \frac{y_2 - y_1}{x_2 - x_1}$$

$$\frac{y - 2}{x - (-3)} = \frac{5 - 2}{1 - (-3)}$$

Simplify the equation.

$$\frac{y - 2}{x - (-3)} = \frac{5 - 2}{1 - (-3)}$$

$$\frac{y - 2}{x - (-3)} = \frac{3}{4}$$

$$4(y - 2) = 3(x + 3)$$

$$4y - 8 = 3x + 9$$

$$0 = 3x - 4y + 7$$

Therefore, the equation of the line is
$3x - 4y + 7 = 0$

36. B

Step 1

Determine the slope of line segment PQ, using the slope formula.

$$m = \frac{y_2 - y_1}{x_2 - x_1}$$

$$m = \frac{2 - (-4)}{6 - (-6)}$$

$$m = \frac{6}{12}$$

$$m = \frac{1}{2}$$

Step 2

Determine the equation of the line passing through point R. Recall that the slopes of parallel lines are equal. Therefore, the slope of the line segment PQ is equal to the slope of the line passing through point R, namely $\frac{1}{2}$.

Substitute the point $R(-2, 8)$ and the slope value of $\frac{1}{2}$ into the slope-point form of a line,

$$y - y_1 = m(x - x_1)$$

$$y - 8 = \frac{1}{2}(x - (-2))$$

$$y - 8 = \frac{1}{2}(x + 2)$$

Step 3

Convert the equation of the line to the form $y = mx + b$.

$$y - 8 = \frac{1}{2}(x + 2)$$

$$y - 8 = \frac{1}{2}x + 1$$

$$y = \frac{1}{2}x + 9$$

37. 12.0

When given one point and the slope, use the form $y - y_1 = m(x - x_1)$.

Step 1

Substitute the values of the point $(-3, 4.5)$ and the slope 2.5 into the formula.

$$y - y_1 = m(x - x_1)$$

$$y - 4.5 = 2.5(x - (-3))$$

$$y - 4.5 = 2.5(x + 3)$$

Step 2

Simplify to the equation of a line of the form $y = mx + b$.

$$y - 4.5 = 2.5(x + 3)$$

$$y - 4.5 = 2.5x + 7.5$$

$$y = 2.5x + 12.0$$

To the nearest tenth, the value of b is 12.0.

38. a) WR

Step 1

Create the graph.

The independent variable is time, so it must go on the x-axis. The cost must go on the y-axis. Add a title describing the context of the problem. Use the data in the table, and plot the points on the graph. Draw a line to join the points.

Step 2

Find the equation of the line. Determine the slope of the line by selecting two data points, such as (1, 28) and (2, 36). Substitute them into the slope formula.

$$m = \frac{y_2 - y_1}{x_2 - x_1}$$
$$m = \frac{36 - 28}{2 - 1}$$
$$m = 8$$

Step 3

Determine the equation in slope-intercept form, $y = mx + b$.

Since the y-intercept (b) is 20 and the slope (m) is 8, the equation in slope-intercept form is $y = 8x + 20$.

b) WR

Use the equation to find the time x when the cost is $y = 104$.

Step 1

Substitute the known values into the equation
$$y = 8x + 20$$
$$104 = 8x + 20$$

Step 2

Use the additive inverse to remove the constant.
$$104 = 8x + 20$$
$$104 - 20 = 8x$$
$$84 = 8x$$

Step 3

Solve for x.
$$84 = 8x$$
$$\frac{84}{8} = x$$
$$10.5 = x$$

Tammy used the Jet Ski for a total time of 10.5 h.

39. C

Step 1

Determine the y-intercept of the line. Looking at the graph, the line crosses the y-axis at 120 km/h. Therefore, the y-intercept is 120.

Step 2

Determine the slope of the line using the slope formula $m = \frac{y_2 - y_1}{x_2 - x_1}$.

The slope of the line can be found by choosing two points, such as (0, 120) and (2, 100), and substituting their values into the slope formula.

$$m = \frac{y_2 - y_1}{x_2 - x_1}$$
$$= \frac{100 - 120}{2 - 0}$$
$$= -\frac{20}{2}$$
$$= -10$$

Step 3

Substitute the value of the slope and y-intercept into the form $y = mx + b$ to create the equation of the line.

$$y = mx + b$$
$$y = -10 + 120$$

Step 4

Write the equation in functional notation. Since the speed of the car, $v(t)$, is dependent on the time travelled, t, the equation can be rewritten in functional notation as $v(t) = -10t + 120$ or $v(t) = 120 - 10t$.

40. 150

Step 1

Evaluate $f(-2)$ in $f(x) = -20x + 5$ by substituting –2 for x.
$$f(x) = -20x + 5$$
$$f(-2) = -20(-2) + 5$$
$$= 40 + 5$$
$$= 45$$

Step 2

Evaluate $f(-5)$ in $f(x) = -20x + 5$ by substituting –5 for x.
$$f(x) = -20x + 5$$
$$f(-5) = -20(-5) + 5$$
$$= 100 + 5$$
$$= 105$$

Step 3

Calculate the sum of $f(-2)$ and $f(-5)$.
$$f(-2) + f(-5) = 45 + 105$$
$$= 150$$

41. 14.6

Step 1

Since $h(x) = -\dfrac{47}{10}$, substitute $-\dfrac{47}{10}$ for $h(x)$ in the function $h(x) = -\dfrac{3}{4}x + \dfrac{25}{4}$.

$$h(x) = -\frac{3}{4}x + \frac{25}{4}$$

$$-\frac{47}{10} = -\frac{3}{4}x + \frac{25}{4}$$

Step 2

Solve for x.

$$-\frac{47}{10} = -\frac{3}{4}x + \frac{25}{4}$$

$$20\left(-\frac{47}{10}\right) = 20\left[-\frac{3}{4}x + \frac{25}{4}\right]$$

$$-94 = -15x + 125$$

$$-125 - 94 = -15x + 125 - 125$$

$$-219 = -15x$$

$$\frac{-219}{-15} = x$$

$$x = 14.6$$

42. A

Let the length and width of the rectangle be L cm and W cm, respectively.

Perimeter of the rectangle $= 2(L + W) = 22$ cm

① $L + W = \dfrac{22}{2} = 11$ cm...

② $\quad\quad L - W = 1$ cm...

Adding equations ① and ②,

$$L + W + L - W = 11 + 1$$

$$2L = 12$$

$$L = 6 \text{ cm}$$

$$W = 6 - 1 = 5 \text{ cm}$$

The width of the rectangle is 5 cm.

43. A

Step 1

Write an equation to express the sum of their ages.

$$x + y = 22$$

Step 2

Write the equation to express their ages in four years.

- $x + 4 \rightarrow$ Samantha's age in 4 years
- $y + 4 \rightarrow$ Jocelyn's age in 4 years

Samantha is twice as old as Jocelyn in 4 years.

$$x + 4 = 2(y + 4)$$

Expand.

$$x + 4 = 2y + 8$$

Subtract 4 and $2y$ from both sides.

$$x + 4 = 2y + 8$$

$$x - 2y + 4 - 4 = 2y - 2y + 8 - 4$$

$$x - 2y = 4$$

The system is as shown:

① $\quad x + y = 22$

② $\quad x - 2y = 4$

44. C

Step 1

Label the equations, and choose which variable is to be eliminated.

① $8x + 3y = -41$

② $6x - 5y = -9$

Eliminate the y-value so that the x-value can be found.

Step 2

Eliminate y by addition.

Multiply equation ① by 5 and equation ② by 3.

$5 \times$ ① $8x + 3y = -41$

$\quad\quad 40x + 15y = -205$

$3 \times$ ② $6x - 5y = -9$

$\quad\quad 18x - 15y = -27$

- Let $40x + 15y = -205$ represent equation ③.
- Let $18x - 15y = -27$ represent equation ④.

Step 3

Add equations ③ and ④ to eliminate y.

③ $\quad 40x + 15y = -205$

④ $\quad \underline{18x - 15y = -27}$

$\quad\quad 58x + 0y = -232$

Step 4

Solve for x.

$$58x + 0y = -232$$

$$58x = -232$$

$$x = -4$$

45. D

Isolate the equation $3x + 2y - 24 = 0$ for y.

$$3x + 2y - 24 = 0$$

$$2y = 24 - 3x$$

$$y = \frac{24 - 3x}{2}$$

Thus, y could be replaced with $\dfrac{24 - 3x}{2}$.

46. A

Step 1

Determine the intersection point of the two lines.
According to the graph, the two lines intersect at the point (15, 60).
Remember to write the x-coordinate first in the ordered pair.

Step 2

Determine who is in the lead at 10 s.
According to the graph, Jacob has jogged 40 m, and Breanna has jogged 35 m. Therefore, Jacob is ahead of Breanna.

Step 3

Determine how far Jacob is ahead of Breanna.
At 10 s, Jacob is 5 m(40 − 35) ahead of Breanna.

47. C

The line for Hall I has a y-intercept of 300 and the slope is $\dfrac{100}{10} = 10$. The equation of the line is $C = 300 + 10$ n.

Looking at the line for Hall II, the y-intercept is 500 and the slope is $\dfrac{100}{20} = 5$. The equation of the line is $C = 500 + 5$ n.

When $n < 40$, the line for Hall II is lower, so it is the better deal.

48. B

To solve, substitute −5 for x and −2 for y into each of the given equations for each alternative.

Consider the equations $-3x + 5y = 5$ and $x - 3y = 1$:

Step 1

Label the equations.
① $-3x + 5y = 5$
② $x - 3y \quad = 1$

Step 2

Substitute −5 for x and −2 for y into equation ① .
$$-3x + 5y = 5$$
$$-3(-5) + 5(-2) = 5$$
$$15 - 10 = 5$$
$$5 = 5$$
Left side = Right side

Step 3

Substitute −5 for x and −2 for y into equation ② .
$$x - 3y = 1$$
$$-5 - 3(-2) = 1$$
$$-5 + 6 = 1$$
$$1 = 1$$
Left side = Right side

Hence, $x = -5$ and $y = -2$ is the solution of the system of equations $-3x + 5y = 5$ and $x - 3y = 1$.

49. C

Step 1

Sketch the line represented by the equation $2x - y = 3$ by determining the x-intercept and y-intercept for $2x - y = 3$.

For $2x - y = 3$, the x-intercept is determined by setting $y = 0$.
$$2x - (0) = 3$$
$$2x = 3$$
$$x = \frac{3}{2}$$

Since the x-intercept is $\dfrac{3}{2}$ or 1.5, (1.5, 0) is a point on the graph.

The y-intercept is determined by setting $x = 0$.
$$2(0) - y = 3$$
$$y = -3$$

Since the y-intercept is −3, (0, −3) is a point on the graph.

Step 2

Graph a line through (1.5, 0) and (0, −3) for the equation $2x - y = 3$ on the same grid with the line shown.

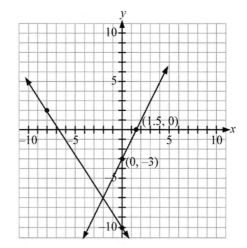

Step 3

Determine the solution to the system of equations by identifying the point of intersection.

The point of intersection is at an x-value of approximately −2 and a y-value of −7.

50. 2.6

① $2x + 5y = 12$
② $y - x = 2$

From equation ② , $y = x + 2$ ③ .
Substitute $x + 2$ for y in equation ① .

$$2x + 5y = 12$$
$$2x + 5(x + 2) = 12$$
$$2x + 5x + 10 = 12$$
$$7x = 12 - 10$$
$$7x = 2$$
$$x = \frac{2}{7}$$

Substituting $\frac{2}{7}$ for x in equation ③ gives

$$y = \frac{2}{7} + 2 = \frac{2 + 14}{7} = \frac{16}{7}$$
$$\therefore x = \frac{2}{7}, \ y = \frac{16}{7}$$

To verify this result, substitute the values of x and y in the left-hand side of each equation. If the left-hand side of the equations equals their right-hand sides, then the obtained solution is correct.

Substitute $x = \frac{2}{7}$ and $y = \frac{16}{7}$ in the left hand side of the equation $2x + 5y = 12$.
Left-hand side $= 2x + 5y$

$$= 2\left(\frac{2}{7}\right) + 5\left(\frac{16}{7}\right)$$
$$= \frac{4}{7} + \frac{80}{7}$$
$$= \frac{84}{7}$$
$$= 12 = \text{Right-hand side}$$

Substitute $x = \frac{2}{7}$ and $y = \frac{16}{7}$ in the left-hand side of the equation $y - x = 2$.
Left-hand side $= y - x$

$$= \frac{16}{7} - \frac{2}{7}$$
$$= \frac{16 - 2}{7}$$
$$= \frac{14}{7}$$
$$= 2 = \text{Right-hand side}$$

Thus, the solution $x = \frac{2}{7}$ and $y = \frac{16}{7}$ of the given system of linear equation is verified.

The value of $x + y$ to the nearest tenth is
$$\frac{2}{7} + \frac{16}{7} = \frac{18}{7} = 2.6.$$

51. 15

To have an infinite number of solutions, the equations must be equivalent.

For the equation $-16x - 20y = 12$, divide both sides by -4 to get $4x + 5y = -3$.

For the equation $12x + Ky = -9$, divide both sides by 3 to get $4x + \frac{K}{3}y = -3$.

The coefficients for x are both 4, and the constant terms are equal. Therefore, the coefficients of y must also be equal.

Thus, $\frac{K}{3} = 5$.

Multiply both sides by 3.
$K = 15$

For the given system of linear equations to have an infinite number of solutions, the value of K is 15.

52. WR

Let $x =$ the number of adult tickets sold.
Let $y =$ the number of student tickets sold.

Thus, ① $12.50x + 8y = 2\ 280$ and ② $2x = y$.

Equation ① can be rewritten as
$125x + 80y = 22\ 800$ when each term is multiplied by 10.
Equation ② can be rewritten as $2x - y = 0$.

Equations ① and ② can be solved by using the method of elimination as shown:

$$\begin{array}{r} ①\quad 125x + 80y = 22\ 800 \\ 80 \times \ ②\quad \underline{160x - 80y = 0} \\ ① + 80 \times ②\qquad 285x = 22\ 800 \\ x = 80 \end{array}$$

The value of y can be determined by substituting 80 for x in either equation ① or ② . Using equation ② , the result is as follows:

$$2x - y = 0$$
$$2(80) - y = 0$$
$$160 - y = 0$$
$$160 = y$$

There were 80 adult tickets and 160 student tickets sold.

UNIT TEST — RELATIONS AND FUNCTIONS

Use the following information to answer the next question.

In the given graph, the ellipse has a width of 20 units and a center at (2, 3). The domain of the ellipse can be expressed as $a \leq x \leq b$.

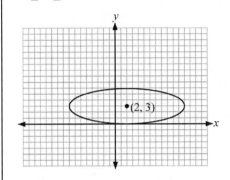

Numerical Response

1. The value of *b* is _____.

Use the following information to answer the next question.

A volleyball player's movements during the events of one play are represented in the following graph. The graph shows the relationship between distance, *d*, in metres of the player from the net and the time, *t*, in seconds during the play.

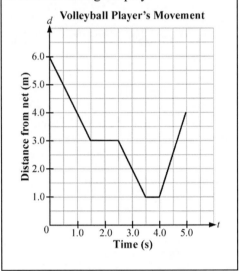

Written Response

2. Describe the volleyball player's movement over the duration of the five-second play mentioning speed, direction, and distance from the net.

Use the following information to answer the next question.

A relation is defined by this table of values.

x	y
−6	−2
−3	−1
−1	0
2	−1
5	−2

3. According to the table, the range of the given relation is

   A. {−6, −3, −1, 2, 5}

   B. {−2, −1, 0}

   C. $−6 \le x \le 5$

   D. $−2 \le y \le 0$

Use the following information to answer the next question.

A model rocket was launched from a platform and its height, h, in metres above the ground with respect to time, t, in seconds, was recorded. Some of the data obtained is shown in the following table.

Time (s)	Height (m)
0	0
1	148
3	410
8	880
14	1 140
20	1 030
25	660
29	148
30	0

4. Which of the following graphs **best** represents the data shown in the table?

   A.   B.

   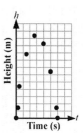 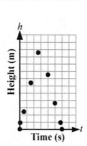

   C.   D.

   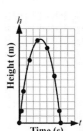 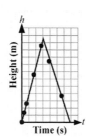

Use the following information to answer the next question.

Each day after work, Steve goes for a walk from his home. The diagram represents Steve's walk on a particular day.

Steve's Walk from Home

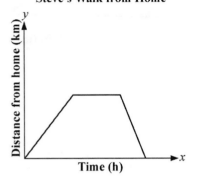

5. Which of the following statements **best** describes Steve's walk from home on that day?

   A. Steve walks at a constant rate, stops for a period of time, and then walks home at a constant rate.

   B. Steve walks at an increasing rate, then walks at a constant rate, and finally walks at a decreasing rate until he returns home.

   C. Steve walks at a fast constant rate, then walks at a slower rate, turns around, and finally walks back home at a fast constant rate.

   D. Steve starts out slowly, increases his speed, walks at a constant rate, and finally decreases his speed until he comes to a stop at home.

Use the following information to answer the next question.

While skateboarding, Dan goes down and then up the side of a halfpipe.

6. Which of the following graphs **best** shows the relationship between his speed and the elapsed time?

   A.

   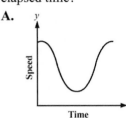

   B.

   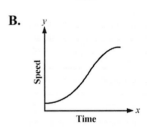

   C.

   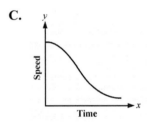

   D.

   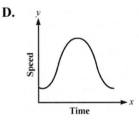

7. Which of the following graphs represents a function?

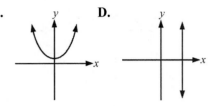

A.   B.

C.   D.

Use the following information to answer the next question.

To hire a cab, Carla has to pay a fixed charge plus an additional constant rate for every kilometre driven.

8. If the cab driver charges $23 for 10 km and $33 for 15 km, what is the fixed charge to hire this cab?

   A. $1   B. $2

   C. $3   D. $4

Use the following information to answer the next question.

The given linear graph passes through points A, B, and C.

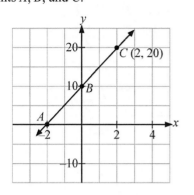

9. Which of the following equations expresses the constant rate of change of the linear graph?

   A. $\dfrac{10}{2} = 5$

   B. $\dfrac{20}{2} = 10$

   C. $\dfrac{10}{-2} = -5$

   D. $\dfrac{20}{-2} = -10$

10. If the line through $(0, 4)$ and $(5, 2)$ is perpendicular to the line through $(-2, 0)$ and $(-3, y)$, then y equals

   A. $\dfrac{5}{2}$ B. $\dfrac{2}{5}$

   C. $-\dfrac{2}{5}$ D. $-\dfrac{5}{2}$

Use the following information to answer the next question.

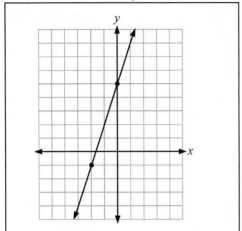

11. The slope of a line parallel to the line given in the graph is

A. 3   **B.** −3

C. $\dfrac{1}{3}$ **D.** $-\dfrac{1}{3}$

Use the following information to answer the next question.

A line segment passes through the point (2, −3).

12. If the line segment is horizontal, which of the following points is also on this line segment?

A. (2, 4)   **B.** (8, −3)

C. (−2, 3)   **D.** (−3, 2)

13. What is the slope of a line passing through the points (−2, 3) and (1, 5)?

A. $\dfrac{1}{3}$ **B.** $\dfrac{2}{3}$

C. $\dfrac{1}{2}$ **D.** $\dfrac{3}{2}$

14. Which of the following graphs represents a line with a rate of change of $\dfrac{3}{2}$ and that passes through the point (−3, −1)?

A.

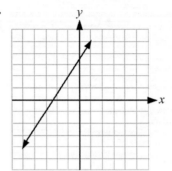

B.

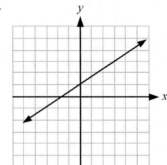

C.

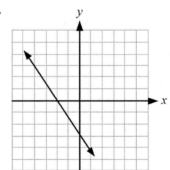

D.

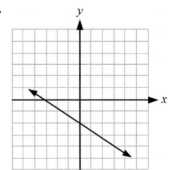

On a warm April day, the height of a snow bank decreases at a constant rate of change of 2 cm / h.

15. Which of the following graphs illustrates the relationship between the height of the snow bank and the time?

A.

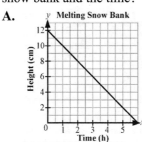

B.

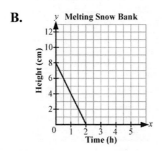

C.

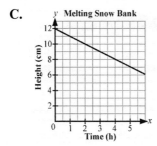

D.

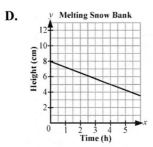

A particular line has a slope of $-\dfrac{3}{4}$. A line that is parallel to the first line has a slope of $\dfrac{K}{10}$.

16. The value of K is

A. $-\dfrac{40}{3}$ **B.** $-\dfrac{15}{2}$

C. $\dfrac{40}{3}$ **D.** $\dfrac{15}{2}$

In an investigation, Mavis is trying to find out whether or not the age of a person affects his or her ability to float in water.

17. Which of the following statements about her investigation is **true**?

A. The person's age is the dependent variable.

B. The person's height is the independent variable.

C. The person's ability to float is the dependent variable.

D. The person's ability to float is the independent variable.

Use the following information to answer the next question.

As the price of oil steadily increases, the Alberta government receives corresponding increases in oil royalties.

18. Which of the following graphs illustrates this relationship?

A.

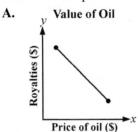

B.

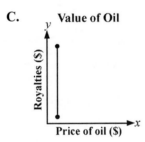

C.

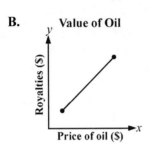

D.

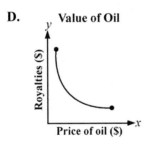

Use the following information to answer the next question.

Four different storage tanks like the one shown in the given diagram were opened at the bottom to allow grain to be removed. For each tank, an equation giving the height, h, in metres of the grain in the tank after t minutes is given.

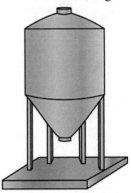

Tank I: $h = 8(0.80)^t, 0 \leq t \leq 8$

Tank II: $h = 8 - 0.80t, 0 \leq t \leq 8$

Tank III: $h = 0.016t^2 - 0.8t + 8, 0 \leq t \leq 8$

Tank IV: $h = -0.02(t + 2)^2 + 8, 0 \leq t \leq 8$

Numerical Response

19. The number of tanks that allow the grain in the tank to decrease non-linearly is

_____.

Use the following information to answer the next question.

Landon carried out an investigation of the cooling of a cup of coffee. The given data portrays the relationship between the temperature in degrees Celsius and the time, *t*, in minutes.

Time (min)	Temperature (°C)
0	65.6
1	62.4
2	59.2
3	56.4
4	53.7
5	51.2
6	48.7

Written Response

20. Determine whether the relationship between the temperature of the coffee and time of cooling is linear or non-linear, and justify your answer.

21. Which of the following graphs represents the line that has an *x*-intercept of 1 and a slope of $\frac{1}{2}$?

A.
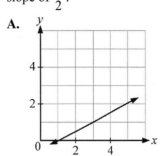

B.
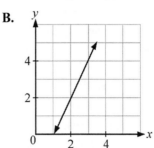

C.
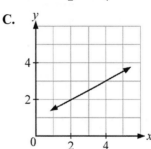

D.
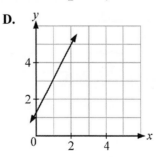

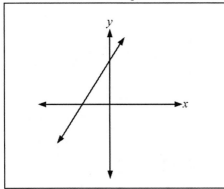

22. What are the coordinates of this graph's *y*-intercept?

   A. (3, 0)   **B.** (0, 3)

   C. (−2, 0)   **D.** (0, −2)

Use the following information to answer the next question.

Manuela described four linear relations based on the number of intercepts they had.

1. The line has infinite intercepts. One of the intercepts is (2, 0).
2. The line has one *x*-intercept and one *y*-intercept.
3. The line's only intercept is the origin.
4. The line has infinite intercepts. One of the intercepts is (0, −4).

Numerical Response

23. How many of the lines have a domain of $x \in \mathbb{R}$? _____

24. The equation $y = \dfrac{4}{5}x - 7$ in standard form is

   A. $4x - 5y + 7 = 0$

   B. $4x - 5y - 7 = 0$

   C. $4x - 5y + 35 = 0$

   D. $4x - 5y - 35 = 0$

Use the following information to answer the next question.

The equations of four lines are given.

I. $8x - 4y + 3 = 0$
II. $3x - 4y + 36 = 0$
III. $9x - 12y + 2 = 0$
IV. $5x - 12y + 9 = 0$

25. Among the given lines, a set of parallel lines is represented by lines

   A. I and II   **B.** I and IV

   C. II and III   **D.** III and IV

26. Which of the following graphs represents the equation $2x - y - 5 = 0$?

   A.   **B.**

 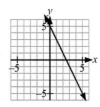

   C.   **D.**

27. Which of the following graphs best represents the line $3x + 4y = 12$?

A.

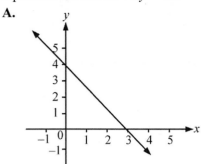

B.

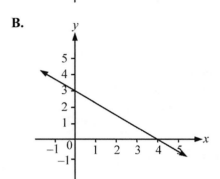

C.

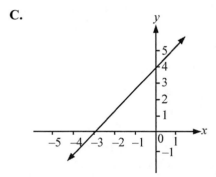

D.

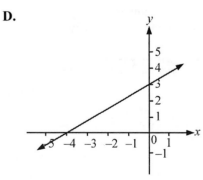

Use the following information to answer the next question.

When the graph of $Ax + By - 9 = 0$ is graphed, it forms a horizontal line passing through the y-axis at $(0, 2)$.

Numerical Response

28. To the nearest tenth, the value of B is

_____.

Use the following information to answer the next question.

A line on a graph is shown.

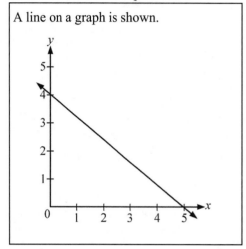

29. The equation of the given line is
   A. $2x + 3y - 10 = 0$
   B. $2x - 3y - 25 = 0$
   C. $4x + 5y - 20 = 0$
   D. $5x - 4y - 15 = 0$

Use the following information to answer the next question.

The cost of buying jerseys for a basketball team is shown in the graph.

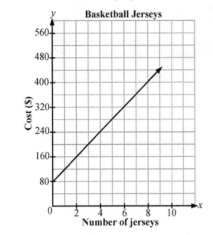

30. What is the cost of buying 25 jerseys?
- **A.** $1 000
- **B.** $1 080
- **C.** $1 200
- **D.** $2 000

31. What is the equation of a line with an x-intercept of 4 and a y-intercept of 12?
- **A.** $y = 3x + 12$
- **B.** $y = 12x + 3$
- **C.** $y = -3x + 12$
- **D.** $y = -12x - 3$

Use the following information to answer the next question.

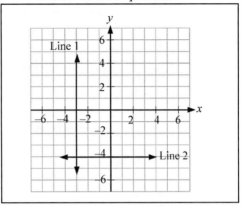

32. The equations of line 1 and line 2 are, respectively,
- **A.** $x = 3$ and $y = -4$
- **B.** $x = -4$ and $y = -3$
- **C.** $x = -3$ and $y = -4$
- **D.** $x = -3$ and $y = 4$

33. What is the equation of the line that passes through the points $(-4, 5)$ and $(2, -3)$?
- **A.** $4x - 3y - 17 = 0$
- **B.** $4x - 3y - 11 = 0$
- **C.** $4x + 3y - 5 = 0$
- **D.** $4x + 3y + 1 = 0$

Use the following information to answer the next question.

A line has a y-intercept of -2 and is parallel to the line $8x - 12y + 15 = 0$.

Numerical Response

34. When the equation of the parallel line is written in the form $Ax + By + C = 0$, where $A > 0$, then the value of $A - C$ is _____.

The slope of a given line is 2, and the *y*-intercept is 3.

Written Response

35. After writing the equation of the given line in slope-intercept form and general form, graph the linear relation. Then, compare the characteristics of this graph with the graph of $y = 3$.

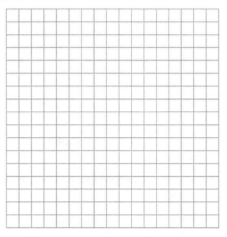

In a robotics lab, students analyzed the relationship between the horizontal position, *x*, and the vertical position, $f(x)$, in centimeters, of a robot's movement. The linear graph portraying the robot's movement is shown.

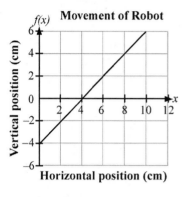

Movement of Robot

36. What is the function representing the graph of this linear relation?

   A. $f(x) = 4x$

   B. $f(x) = 4x - 4$

   C. $f(x) = 1x - 4$

   D. $f(x) = -1x + 4$

Numerical Response

37. For the linear function $f(x) = -\dfrac{3}{2}x + 7$, the value of $f\left(-\dfrac{3}{2}\right)$ is _____. (Record your answer to the nearest hundredth.)

The function $g(x) = ax - 6$, and $g(4) = 124$.

Numerical Response

38. To the nearest tenth, the value of *a* is

_____.

Use the following information to answer the next question.

Two brothers left different stores at the same time and headed home at different rates. Alex started 1 000 m away from home and walked home at a rate of 100 m/min. Ben started 700 m away from home and walked home at a rate of 50 m/min. The two lines show the relationship between their distance, *d*, from home in metres and their time walked, *t*, in minutes.

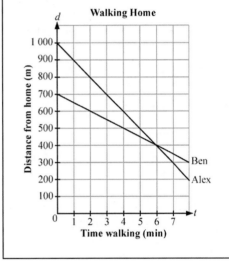

39. Which of the following statements is a correct interpretation of the intersection point?

A. Alex and Ben are walking together when they are 400 m from home.

B. Alex and Ben are walking together when they are 200 m from home.

C. After 6 minutes, the two boys have walked a distance of 400 m.

D. After 6 minutes, the two boys arrive at home together.

Use the following information to answer the next question.

A ski rental shop has two different monthly plans for renting skis. Plan A charges a flat fee of $30 per month for unlimited rentals. Plan B charges $9 per month plus $3 per ski rental. A snapshot from a graphing calculator showing the lines representing each respective plan and the point of intersection of the two plans is given.

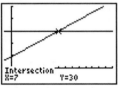

40. Which of the following statements is **true**?

A. Plan B is cheaper for monthly ski rentals.

B. Plan A is cheaper for monthly ski rentals.

C. Plan B is more economical when renting skis less than seven times a month.

D. Plan B is more economical when renting skis more than seven times a month.

Use the following information to answer the next question.

Two students showed their partial solutions in solving this system of equations.
$$4x + y = -14$$
$$3x + 2y = -8$$

Minesh's Partial Solution

1. Multiply the first equation by 3.
2. Multiply the second equation by 4.
3. Subtract the second equation from the first equation.
$$12x + 3y = -42$$
$$\underline{12x + 8y = -32}$$
$$-5y = -10$$
4. Solve for y.
5. Then, solve for x.

Cameron's Partial Solution

1. Rearrange the first equation in the form $y = -4x - 14$.
2. Rearrange the second equation in the form $y = -\frac{3}{2}x - 4$.
3. Graph both equations using technology.
4. Determine the point of intersection of the two lines.

41. Which of the following statements about these partial solutions is **true**?

A. Minesh and Cameron each made an error that will lead to a wrong answer.

B. Minesh's partial solution is wrong, and Cameron's partial solution is correct.

C. Cameron's partial solution is wrong, and Minesh's partial solution is correct.

D. Minesh's partial solution and Cameron's partial solution will both lead to the same correct answer.

42. The solution for the system of equations $7x + 2y = 49$ and $2y - x = 9$ is
A. $x = 1$ and $y = 4$
B. $x = 5$ and $y = 7$
C. $x = -2$ and $y = 3$
D. $x = -9$ and $y = 2$

Use the following information to answer the next question.

The ordered pair $(K, -3)$ is the solution to the system of equations $8x + 3y = -41$ and $6x - 5y = -9$.

43. What is the value of K?

A. 1
B. $\frac{4}{25}$

C. -4
D. $\frac{-25}{4}$

Use the following information to answer the next question.

The given system of linear equations can be solved using the elimination method. To eliminate y by addition, the first equation is multiplied by 3.
$$-3x - 4y = -2$$
$$5x + 6y = 4$$

44. The second equation must be multiplied by
A. -4
B. -2
C. 2
D. 4

Use the following information to answer the next question.

The number obtained by reversing the order of the digits of a two-digit number is 18 more than the original number. The sum of the digits of the original number is 8.

45. Based on the information in the given description, what is the original number?
A. 17
B. 35
C. 53
D. 71

Use the following information to answer the next question.

Harold invested his savings of $5 000, part at 4% per annum and the other part at 6% per annum. At the end of one year, the interest from the amount invested at 4% was $50 more than the interest from the amount invested at 6%.

46. If x represents the amount of money invested at 4% and y represents the amount of money invested at 6%, which of the following systems of equations could be solved to determine the amount of money invested at each rate?

　A. $x + y = 5\ 000$ and $4x = 6y + 5\ 000$

　B. $x + y = 5\ 000$ and $6y - 4x = 5\ 000$

　C. $4x + 6y = 5\ 000$ and $x = y - 50$

　D. $4x + 6y = 5\ 000$ and $x - 50 = y$

Use the following information to answer the next question.

A system of linear equations is given.
$11y = -ax + 4$
$3y = -45x + 13$

Numerical Response

47. To the nearest whole number, what is the value of a if the system has no solutions? _____

Use the following information to answer the next question.

Aelyn is asked to solve a linear system of equations. She uses a graphical approach to solve the given system. One of the equations that Aelyn graphs correctly is shown below.

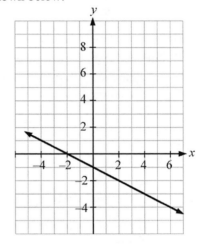

Numerical Response

48. If the other equation in the system is $y = 2x + 9$, then the solution to the system is the point $(-a, b)$. The value of $a + b$ is _____.

Use the following information to answer the next question.

Walter is researching the cost of renting a car for one week because he is getting his car repainted. Company I charges $75 per week plus $0.20 for each kilometre driven. Company II charges $100 per week plus $0.10 for each kilometer driven.

Written Response

49. Write an equation of the line formed by each relation, and solve graphically. Explain the conditions under which each plan is better.

Use the following information to answer the next multipart question.

50. An otter dives into a river.
The position, d, in centimetres, of the top of the otter's head with respect to the surface of the river at time, t, in seconds, is illustrated in the given graph.

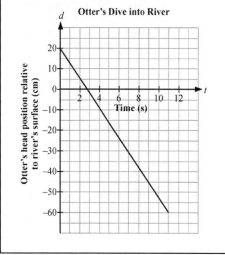

a) If the rate of descent of the otter's head is 7.2 cm/s, then at what time, t, did the top of its head disappear below the waterline?

A. 2.60 s   **B.** 2.78 s

C. 2.85 s   **D.** 2.90 s

b) If the range of the otter's total dive is $-88 \leq d \leq 20$ and the rate of descent of the otter's head is 7.2 cm / s, what is the domain?

A. $0 \leq t \leq 12$ **B.** $0 \leq t \leq 15$

C. $0 \leq t \leq 20$ **D.** $0 \leq t \leq 24$

Use the following information to answer the next multipart question.

51. The given table shows the relationship between pounds and kilograms.

Kilograms (x)	10	15	20	25
Pounds (y)	22	33	44	55

a) Which of the following equations can be used to convert kilograms to pounds?

A. $y = x + 2.2$ **B.** $x = y + 2.2$

C. $y = 2.2x$ **D.** $x = 2.2y$

b) Which of the following graphs represents the data given in the table?

A.

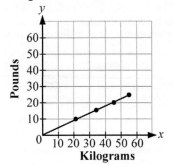

B.

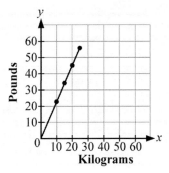

C.

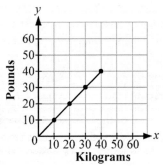

D.

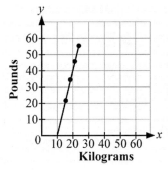

ANSWERS AND SOLUTIONS—UNIT TEST

1. 12	12. B	23. 3	34. 8	45. B
2. WR	13. B	24. D	35. WR	46. A
3. B	14. A	25. C	36. C	47. 165
4. C	15. A	26. A	37. 9.25	48. 5
5. A	16. B	27. B	38. 32.5	49. WR
6. D	17. C	28. 4.5	39. A	50. a) B
7. C	18. B	29. C	40. C	50. b) B
8. C	19. 3	30. B	41. D	51. a) C
9. A	20. WR	31. C	42. B	51. b) B
10. D	21. A	32. C	43. C	
11. A	22. B	33. D	44. C	

1. 12

The domain of a graph is defined by all the values for which x is defined. The graph shows that the ellipse has a centre at (2, 3). The x-coordinate of the centre is $x = 2$.

The width of the ellipse is 20 units; therefore, the domain extends 10 units to the left of the centre and 10 units to the right of the centre.

The left limit, a, of the domain is $2 - 10 = -8$, and the right limit, b, is $2+10 = 12$. When expressed in set notation, the domain of the ellipse is $-8 \leq x \leq 12$. Therefore, the value of b is 12.

2. WR

Step 1
Consider the interval from 0 s to 1.5 s. For this interval, the rise is $3 - 6 = -3$ and the run is $1.5 - 0 = 1.5$. In other words, for the first 1.5 s, the rate of change is $-3 \div 1.5 = -2$, which represents a constant rate of change of -2 m/s. The volleyball player moves from 6 m to 3 m from the net at a constant rate of 2 m/s from 0 to 1.5 s.

Step 2
Consider the interval from 1.5 s to 2.5 s. The volleyball player's distance from the net does not change. The player stays at a distance of 3 m from the net.

Step 3
Consider the interval from 2.5 s to 3.5 s. From 2.5 s to 3.5 s, the rise is $1 - 3 = -2$, and the run is $1(3.5 - 2.5)$; thus, from 2.5 s to 3.5 s, the rate of change is $-2 \div 1 = -2$, which represents a constant rate of change of -2 m/s. The volleyball player moves from 3 m to 1 m from the net at a constant rate of 2 m/s from 2.5 s to 3.5 s.

Step 4
Consider the interval from 3.5 s to 4.0 s. From 3.5 s to 4.0 s, the volleyball player's distance from the net does not change. The player stays at a distance of 1.0 m from the net.

Step 5
Consider the interval from 4.0 s to 5.0 s. The rise is $4.0 - 1.0 = 3$, and the run is $5.0 - 4.0 = 1$. In other words, from 4.0 s to 5.0 s, the rate of change is $3 \div 1 = 3$, which represents a constant rate of change of 3 m/s. The volleyball player moves from 1 m to 4 m from the net at a constant rate of 3 m/s from 4 s to 5 s.

3. B

The range of a relation is the set of all output y-values and can be expressed as a list. According to the table provided, the range of this relation is $\{-2, -1, 0\}$.

4. C
Step 1
The shape of the graph can be determined by sketching by hand or by using technology. Using a TI-83 Plus graphing calculator, enter the data as lists L1 and L2 in the STAT EDIT mode. Then, use ZOOM STAT to get the following graph:

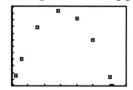

Step 2

Determine the shape of the curve.

The shape of the graph models a curve. Since the model rocket has heights at real number values of t between the restricted domain values of 0 s to 30 s while the rocket is in the air, the data is continuous and should have the points connected as a solid curved line.

This graph best represents the data in this context.

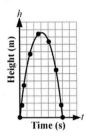

5. A

Steve walks at a constant rate away from his home, since the distance from home increases at a constant rate. Then Steve stops, since his distance from home does not change. Finally, Steve returns home at a constant rate, since his distance from home decreases at a constant rate.

6. D

Since he is already skateboarding, his speed cannot start at zero. He gains speed as he goes down the halfpipe. The graph must progress in the positive direction. After peaking, he then slows down as he goes up the other side of the halfpipe. The graph has to then move in a negative direction, ending with a slower speed as he continues skateboarding.

The following graph shows this situation the best.

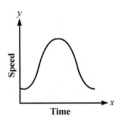

7. C

According to the vertical line test, if two points on a graph can be joined by a vertical line, the graph does not represent a function.

Graph A: For some values of x in the domain, there are two y-values. A vertical line intersects the graph at two points. This graph is not a function.

Graph B: For some values of x in the domain of this circle, a vertical line intersects the graph at two points. This graph is not a function.

Graph C: For each x-value in the domain, there is only one y-value. This graph is a function.

Graph D: For the only x-value, there are an infinite number of y-values. This graph is not a function.

The graph in alternative C represents a function.

8. C

Step 1

Determine the constant rate of change, m.

$$\text{Constant rate of change } (m) = \frac{\text{rise}}{\text{run}}$$

The rise is the change in charge.
$33 - 23 = 10$

The run is the change in distance.
$15 - 10 = 5$

$$\text{Constant rate of change } (m) = \frac{\$10}{5 \text{ km}} \text{ or } \$2/\text{km}$$

Step 2

Determine the fixed charge.

The initial value is the charge, C, at the start of the ride when the distance driven is 0 km. Use one of the other charge values and the value of m to find c.

$$m = \frac{\text{rise}}{\text{run}}$$

$$2 = \frac{23 - c}{10 - 0}$$

$$2 = \frac{23 - c}{10}$$

$$10(2) = 10\left(\frac{23 - c}{10}\right)$$

$$20 = 23 - c$$

$$c + 20 - 20 = 23 - c + c - 20$$

$$c = 3$$

The fixed charge, or initial value, is $3.

9. A

Step 1

Determine the rate of change from points A to C.

run = 4 units right $(2 - (-2) = 4)$

rise = 20 units up $(20 - 0 = 20)$

$$\text{rate of change} = \frac{\text{rise}}{\text{run}}$$
$$= \frac{20}{4}$$
$$= \frac{10}{2}$$
$$= 5$$

Step 2

Determine the rate of change from points B to C.

run = 2 units right $(2 - 0 = 2)$

rise = 10 units up $(20 - 10 = 10)$

$$\text{rate of change} = \frac{\text{rise}}{\text{run}}$$
$$= \frac{10}{2}$$
$$= 5$$

The correct equation for the constant rate of change is $\frac{10}{2} = 5$.

10. D

Step 1

Use the slope formula, $m = \frac{y_2 - y_1}{x_2 - x_1}$, to determine the slope of the line through $(0, 4)$ and $(5, 2)$.

$$m = \frac{y_2 - y_1}{x_2 - x_1}$$
$$= \frac{2 - 4}{5 - 0}$$
$$= \frac{-2}{5}$$

Step 2

Find the slope of the line perpendicular to the line with a slope of $m = -\frac{2}{5}$.

Perpendicular lines have slopes that are negative reciprocals of each other (when they are multiplied together, the result is -1).

$$\frac{5}{2} \times \frac{-2}{5} = -1$$

Therefore, the slope of the line that is perpendicular to this line is $\frac{5}{2}$.

Step 3

Use the slope formula to find the value of y.

Substitute the coordinates of the points $(-2, 0)$ and $(-3, y)$, and the value of the slope, $\frac{5}{2}$, into the slope formula and solve for y.

$$m = \frac{y_2 - y_1}{x_2 - x_1}$$
$$\frac{5}{2} = \frac{y - 0}{-3 - (-2)}$$
$$\frac{5}{2} = \frac{y}{-1}$$
$$5(-1) = 2(y)$$
$$-5 = 2y$$
$$-\frac{5}{2} = \frac{2y}{2}$$
$$-\frac{5}{2} = y$$

Therefore, the value of y in the point $(-3, y)$ is $y = -\frac{5}{2}$.

11. A

Parallel lines have equal slopes.

Choose any two points on the given line and then use these two points in order to determine the slope of the line.

The points $(0, 5)$ and $(-2, -1)$ are on the given line.

Thus, the slope of the line can be found by using the formula slope.

$$m = \frac{y_2 - y_1}{x_2 - x_1}$$
$$m = \frac{-1 - 5}{-2 - 0}$$
$$m = \frac{-6}{-2}$$
$$m = 3$$

The slope of the given line is 3, therefore, the slope of a line parallel to this line is also 3.

12. B

A horizontal line has a slope of zero, since the rise = 0. For the rise to be equal to 0 between two points, the y-coordinates have to be the same. Thus, if $(2, -3)$ is on the line, the other point must also have a y-coordinate of -3. The point $(8, -3)$ has the correct y-coordinate.

13. B

The points on the line are $(x_1, y_1) = (-2, 3)$ and $(x_2, y_2) = (1, 5)$.

Use the slope formula, $m = \dfrac{y_2 - y_1}{x_2 - x_1}$, where m is the slope, to determine the slope of the line.

$$m = \frac{y_2 - y_1}{x_2 - x_1}$$
$$= \frac{5 - 3}{1 - (-2)}$$
$$= \frac{2}{3}$$

14. A

The rate of change is given as $\dfrac{3}{2}$, which is a positive value. The graph of the line must rise toward the right. Only the graphs in alternatives A and B fulfill this requirement. Now, determine which of these two graphs passes through the point $(-3, -1)$.

Only the graph in alternative A passes through this point with the given rate of change.

15. A

The rate of change of the height of the snow bank with respect to time is 2 cm/h. This means that for a run of 1 unit horizontally to the right, there is a fall of 2 units vertically down (-2), and the graph has a rate of change of -2.

Step 1
Check the rate of change in graph A.
$$m = \frac{\text{rise}}{\text{run}}$$
$$= \frac{-2}{1}$$
$$= -2$$
This graph has a rate of change of -2.

Step 2
Check the rate of change in graph B.
$$m = \frac{\text{rise}}{\text{run}}$$
$$= \frac{-4}{1}$$
$$= -4$$
This graph has a rate of change of -4.

Step 3
Check the rate of change in graph C.
$$m = \frac{\text{rise}}{\text{run}}$$
$$= \frac{-1}{1}$$
$$= -1$$
This graph has a rate of change of -1.

Step 4
Check the rate of change in graph D.
$$m = \frac{\text{rise}}{\text{run}}$$
$$= \frac{-3}{4}$$
$$= -\frac{3}{4}$$

This graph has a rate of change of $-\dfrac{3}{4}$.

Only graph A has a rate of change of -2.

16. B

Step 1
Determine the relationship between the slopes of two lines that are parallel.
Since the lines are parallel, they have the same slope.

Therefore, $-\dfrac{3}{4} = \dfrac{K}{10}$

Step 2
Solve for K.
$$-30 = 4K$$
$$-\frac{30}{4} = \frac{4K}{4}$$
$$-\frac{15}{2} = K$$

17. C

Alternative A: The person's age is not dependent on his or her ability to float; therefore, it is the independent variable.

Alternative B: Height is not part of the relationship.

Alternative C: The person's ability to float cannot be controlled; therefore, it is the dependent variable. This statement is true.

Alternative D: The person's ability to float cannot be controlled; therefore, it is the dependent variable.

18. **B**

Since the increase is constant for both variables, the graph required needs to be linear, a straight line. Also, since both variables are increasing, the required graph needs to increase from left to right. This graph satisfies these requirements.

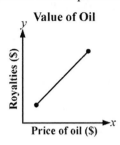

Value of Oil

19. **3**

For equations of relations to be linear, each variable must be a degree of 1.

The equation representing the flow of grain in tank I has the t-variable in the exponent position, which defines a non-linear relation.

The equation representing the flow of grain in tank II has each variable in a degree of 1, which defines a linear relation.

The equations representing the flow of grain in tanks III and IV have t-variables in a degree of 2, which defines non-linear relations.

Therefore, there are three tanks that allow the grain to flow non-linearly.

20. **WR**

To determine whether the relationship between the cooling time in minutes and the temperature in degrees Celsius is linear, you must find the first differences.

Time (min)	Temperature (°C)	First Differences
0	65.6	
1	62.4	$62.4 - 65.6$ $= -3.2$
2	59.2	$59.2 - 62.4$ $= -3.2$
3	56.4	$56.4 - 59.2$ $= -2.8$
4	53.7	$53.7 - 56.4$ $= -2.7$
5	51.2	$51.2 - 53.7$ $= -2.5$
6	48.7	$48.7 - 51.2$ $= -2.5$

In a linear relationship, the first differences are the same. Since the first differences are not the same, this relationship is non-linear.

21. **A**

First, eliminate the alternatives that do not have an x-intercept of 1. That is, the lines do not cross the x-axis at 1: alternatives C and D.

Since the line has an x-intercept of 1, it passes through the point $(1, 0)$. Use the slope to rise 1 unit and run 2 units to plot the next point on the line $(3, 1)$.

The line passes through the points $(1, 0)$ and $(3, 1)$.

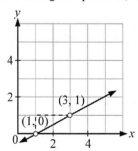

22. **B**

The y-intercept of a linear relation is located at the point where the graph crosses the y-axis and the x-value is 0. The y-value on this graph is positive. Of the given points, the only point that satisfies these two conditions is $(0, 3)$.

23. 3

For a line to have infinite intercepts, it must lie on the x-and y-axes.

- Line 1 has infinite intercepts. One of the intercepts is (2, 0). This line is on the x-axis, which has a domain of $x \in \mathbb{R}$.
- Line 2 has one x-intercept and one y-intercept, which means that it rises to the left or right. The domain of such a line is $x \in \mathbb{R}$.
- Line 3 has one intercept at the origin, which means that it rises to the left or right. The domain of this line is also $x \in \mathbb{R}$.
- Line 4 has infinite intercepts. One of the intercepts is (0, −4). This line is on the y-axis, which has a domain of $x = 0$.

Three of the lines have a domain of $x \in \mathbb{R}$.

24. D

The equation $y = \dfrac{4}{5}x - 7$ is in slope y-intercept form. Standard form has all the terms equal to zero ($Ax + By + C = 0$). The coefficient of x must be positive.
$$y = \frac{4}{5}x - 7$$

Multiply each of the terms by 5 to eliminate the fractional coefficient.
$$5y = 4x - 35$$

Use inverse operations to move $5y$ to the other side of the equation.
$$5y - 5y = 4x - 5y - 35$$
$$0 = 4x - 5y - 35$$
$$4x - 5y - 35 = 0$$

25. C

Parallel lines have the same slopes. In order to determine which lines have the same slope, m, convert all equations into the form $y = mx + b$.

Step 1
Determine the slope of line I.
$$8x - 4y + 3 = 0$$
$$-4y = -8x - 3$$
$$y = \frac{-8x - 3}{-4}$$
$$y = 2x + \frac{3}{4}$$
The slope is 2.

Step 2
Determine the slope of line II.
$$3x - 4y + 36 = 0$$
$$4y = 3x + 36$$
$$y = \frac{3x + 36}{4}$$
$$y = \frac{3}{4}x + 9$$
The slope is $\dfrac{3}{4}$.

Step 3
Determine the slope of line III.
$$9x - 12y + 2 = 0$$
$$12y = 9x + 2$$
$$y = \frac{9x + 2}{12}$$
$$y = \frac{3}{4}x + \frac{1}{6}$$
The slope is $\dfrac{3}{4}$.

Step 4
Determine the slope of line IV.
$$5x - 12y + 9 = 0$$
$$-12y = -5x - 9$$
$$y = \frac{-5x - 9}{-12}$$
$$y = \frac{5}{12}x + \frac{3}{4}$$
The slope is $\dfrac{5}{12}$.

Lines II and III have the same slope. Therefore, they are parallel.

26. A

Step 1
Rewrite the equation in $y = mx + b$ form.
$$2x - y - 5 = 0$$
$$-y = -2x + 5$$
$$y = 2x - 5$$

Step 2
Determine the appropriate graph.
According to the equation, the slope is 2 and the y-intercept is −5.

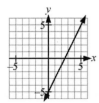

27. B

The given line is:
$3x + 4y = 12$

- The x-intercept of the graph of this line can be determined by substituting 0 for y. Thus, $3x = 12$ which implies $x = 4$.
- The y-intercept of the graph of this line can be determined by substituting 0 for x. Thus, $4y = 12$ which implies $y = 3$.

Therefore, the given line intersects the x-axis at $(4, 0)$ and the y-axis at $(0, 3)$. The required graph is:

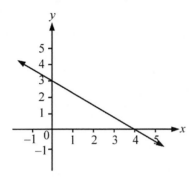

28. 4.5

A horizontal line has a slope of $m = 0$.
This horizontal line also has a y-intercept of $(0, 2)$ or $b = 2$.

Step 1
To relate the values of A and B to the slope and y-intercept values, rewrite the equation in $y = mx + b$ form.
$Ax + By - 9 = 0$
$$By = -Ax + 9$$
$$y = \frac{-Ax + 9}{B}$$
$$y = \frac{-A}{B}x + \frac{9}{B}$$

Step 2
Determine B by equating it to the y-intercept $b = 2$.
$$b = \frac{9}{B}$$
$$2 = \frac{9}{B}$$
$$2B = 9$$
$$B = \frac{9}{2}$$

To the nearest tenth, the value of B is 4.5.

29. C

Step 1
The given line intersects the x-axis at $(5, 0)$ and the y-axis at $(0, 4)$. Substitute these values into the slope formula, $m = \dfrac{y_2 - y_1}{x_2 - x_1}$, to find the slope of this line.
$$m = \frac{y_2 - y_1}{x_2 - x_1}$$
$$= \frac{4 - 0}{0 - 5}$$
$$= -\frac{4}{5}$$

Step 2
Substitute the slope of the line, $-\dfrac{4}{5}$, and the y-intercept, 4, into the equation of the form $y = mx + b$.
$$y = mx + b$$
$$y = -\frac{4}{5}x + 4$$

Step 3
Rewrite the equation in the general form $Ax + By + C = 0$.
$$y = -\frac{4}{5}x + 4$$
$$5y = -4x + 20$$
$$4x + 5y - 20 = 0$$
The equation of the line is $4x + 5y - 20 = 0$.

30. B

Step 1
Find the slope of the line by choosing two points, and substituting their values into the slope formula, $m = \dfrac{y_2 - y_1}{x_2 - x_1}$.
One option is to choose the points $(0, 80)$ and $(9, 440)$.
$$m = \frac{y_2 - y_1}{x_2 - x_1}$$
$$= \frac{440 - 80}{9 - 0}$$
$$= \frac{360}{9}$$
$$= 40$$

Step 2
Determine the equation of the line in the slope-intercept form, $y = mx + b$.
The y-intercept is $b = 80$, and the slope is $m = 40$.
$$y = mx + b$$
$$y = 40x + 80$$

Step 3

Use the equation to determine the cost, y, to buy 25 jerseys.

Substitute 25 for x, and solve for y.

$y = 40x + 80$
$y = 40(25) + 80$
$y = 1\ 000 + 80$
$y = 1\ 080$

The cost to buy 25 jerseys is $1 080.

31. C

Step 1

Determine the slope of the line by substituting the coordinates of the y-intercept $(0,\ 12)$ and x-intercept $(4,\ 0)$ into the slope formula, $m = \dfrac{y_2 - y_1}{x_2 - x_1}$.

$m = \dfrac{y_2 - y_1}{x_2 - x_1}$

$= \dfrac{0 - 12}{4 - 0}$

$= \dfrac{-12}{4}$

$= -3$

Step 2

Substitute the value of the slope -3 for m and the value of the y-intercept 12 for b into the slope-intercept form, $y = mx + b$.

$y = mx + b$
$y = -3x + 12$

32. C

Line 1 is a vertical line and thus its equation is $x = -3$.

Line 2 is a horizontal line and thus its equation is $y = -4$.

33. D

There are two methods that can be used to determine the equation of the line in the point-slope form.

Method 1

Determine the slope, m, of the line by substituting the values of the points $(-4,\ 5)$ and $(2,\ -3)$ into the slope formula, $m = \dfrac{y_x - y_1}{x_2 - x_1}$.

$m = \dfrac{y_2 - y_1}{x_2 - x_1}$

$= \dfrac{-3 - 5}{2 - (-4)}$

$= \dfrac{-8}{6}$

$= -\dfrac{4}{3}$

Substitute the slope of $-\dfrac{4}{3}$ and one of the points, such as $(2,\ -3)$, into the point-slope form, $y - y_1 = m(x - x_1)$.

$y - y_1 = m(x - x_1)$

$y - (-3) = -\dfrac{4}{3}(x - 2)$

$y + 3 = -\dfrac{4}{3}(x - 2)$

Convert the equation into general form, $Ax + By + C = 0$.

$y + 3 = -\dfrac{4}{3}(x - 2)$

$3(y + 3) = 3\left[\dfrac{-4}{3}(x - 2)\right]$

$3y + 9 = -4(x - 2)$
$3y + 9 = -4x + 8$
$4x + 3y + 1 = 0$

Method 2
Substitute the values of the points $(-4, 5)$ and $(2, -3)$ into the formula $\dfrac{y - y_1}{x - x_1} = \dfrac{y_2 - y_1}{x_2 - x_1}$.

$$\frac{y - y_1}{x - x_1} = \frac{y_2 - y_1}{x_2 - x_1}$$
$$\frac{y - (-3)}{x - 2} = \frac{5 - (-3)}{-4 - 2}$$

Simplify the equation.
$$\frac{y - (-3)}{x - 2} = \frac{5 - (-3)}{-4 - 2}$$
$$\frac{y + 3}{x - 2} = \frac{8}{-6}$$
$$y + 3 = -\frac{4}{3}(x - 2)$$

Convert the equation into general form,
$Ax + By + C = 0$.
$$y + 3 = -\frac{4}{3}(x - 2)$$
$$3(y + 3) = 3\left[\frac{-4}{3}(x - 2)\right]$$
$$3y + 9 = -4(x - 2)$$
$$3y + 9 = -4x + 8$$
$$4x + 3y + 1 = 0$$

34. 8

Step 1
The given line is $8x - 12y + 15 = 0$. Convert the line into $y = mx + b$ form by isolating y.
$$12y = 8x + 15$$
$$y = \frac{8x + 15}{12}$$
$$y = \frac{2}{3}x + \frac{5}{4}$$

Step 2
Determine the slope and y-intercept of the given line $y = \frac{2}{3}x + \frac{5}{4}$.

Since the equation of a line is given in the form $y = mx + b$, the slope of the line is $m = \frac{2}{3}$, and the y-intercept is $b = \frac{5}{4}$.

Step 3
Determine the equation of the parallel line with a y-intercept of -2 in the form $y = mx + b$.

Any line parallel to $y = \frac{2}{3}x + \frac{5}{4}$ must have the same slope; that is, $m = \frac{2}{3}$. The equation of the line with a slope of $\frac{2}{3}$ and a y-intercept of -2, in the form of $y = mx + b$, is $y = \frac{2}{3}x - 2$.

Step 4
Convert the equation to the general form
$Ax + By + C = 0$.
$$y = \frac{2}{3}x - 2$$
$$3(y) = 3\left(\frac{2}{3}x - 2\right)$$
$$3y = 2x - 6$$
$$0 = 2x - 3y - 6$$

Step 5
Determine the value of $A - C$.
In the form $Ax + By + C = 0$, the equation $2x - 3y - 6 = 0$ has the values of $A = 2$, $B = -3$, and $C = -6$.
$$A - C = 2 - (-6)$$
$$= 8$$

35. WR

Step 1
Determine the equation of the line in slope-intercept form, $y = mx + b$, where m is the slope and b is the y-intercept.
Substitute 2 for m and 3 for b.
$$y = mx + b$$
$$y = 2x + 3$$

Step 2
Rewrite the equation $y = 2x + 3$ in general form, $Ax + By + C = 0$.
$$y = 2x + 3$$
$$y - y = 2x - y + 3$$
$$0 = 2x - y + 3$$

Step 3
Create a table of values.

x	$y = 2x + 3$
3	−3
−2	−1
−1	1
0	3
1	5
2	7
3	9

Step 4
Sketch the graphs of the equations $y = 2x + 3$ and $y = 3$.

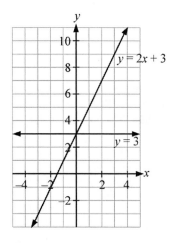

Step 5
Compare the characteristics of $y = 2x + 3$ and $y = 3$.
The graph of $y = 2x + 3$ is a line with a positive slope of 2. It intersects the y-axis at 3. The line $y = 3$ intersects the y-axis at the same point (3), but it is a horizontal line.

36. C

Step 1
Determine the y-intercept
According to the graph, the line passes the y-axis at −4. Therefore, the y-intercept is −4.

Step 2
Find the slope of the line.
Choose two points, such as $(0, -4)$ and the x-intercept $(4, 0)$, and substitute their values into the slope formula, $m = \dfrac{y_2 - y_1}{x_2 - x_1}$.

$$m = \frac{y_2 - y_1}{x_2 - x_1}$$
$$= \frac{0 - (-4)}{4 - 0}$$
$$= \frac{4}{4}$$
$$= 1$$

Step 3
Substitute the value of the slope and y-intercept into the $y = mx + b$ form.
$$y = mx + b$$
$$y = (1)x + (-4)$$
$$y = 1x - 4$$
Since the vertical position, $f(x)$, is dependent on the horizontal position, x, the equation can be rewritten in functional notation as $f(x) = 1x - 4$.

37. 9.25

Step 1
Substitute $-\dfrac{3}{2}$ for x into the function
$f(x) = -\dfrac{3}{2}x + 7$.

$$f(x) = -\frac{3}{2}x + 7$$
$$f\left(-\frac{3}{2}\right) = -\frac{3}{2}\left(-\frac{3}{2}\right) + 7$$

Step 2
Evaluate $f\left(-\dfrac{3}{2}\right)$.
$$f\left(-\frac{3}{2}\right) = \frac{9}{4} + 7$$
$$= 2.25 + 7$$
$$= 9.25$$

To the nearest hundredth, $f\left(-\dfrac{3}{2}\right)$ is 9.25.

38. 32.5

Step 1
Since $g(4) = 124$, substitute 4 for x and 124 for $g(x)$, in the equation $g(x) = ax - 6$.
$$g(x) = ax - 6$$
$$124 = a(4) - 6$$

Step 2
Solve for a.
$$124 = a(4) - 6$$
$$124 + 6 = 4a - 6 + 6$$
$$130 = 4a$$
$$\frac{130}{4} = a$$
$$32.5 = a$$

39. A

On the graph, the lines intersect at the point (6, 400). This point represents a walking time of 6 min and a distance from home of 400 m. Since the point represents both lines, Alex and Ben are walking together when they are 400 m from home.

40. C

The intersection point of the two plans is located at (7, 30). The y-coordinates of the points on the line representing plan B are lower than the corresponding y-coordinates on the line representing plan A when x is between 0 and 7. Therefore, plan B is more economical if skis are rented less than seven times per month.

41. D

In solving the system of equations, Minesh chose the method of elimination, while Cameron chose the method of graphing with technology. No mistake was made in either partial solution, so both will yield the same correct answer.

42. B

The given system of equations is
① $7x + 2y = 49$
② $2y - x = 9$

Rewrite equation ② as $x = 2y - 9$.

Substitute this value of x into equation ① and simplify.
$$7(2y - 9) + 2y = 49$$
$$14y - 63 + 2y = 49$$
$$16y = 49 + 63$$
$$16y = 112$$
$$y = \frac{112}{16} = 7$$

Substituting 7 for y into $x = 2y - 9$ gives
$$x = 2y - 9$$
$$= 2(7) - 9$$
$$= 14 - 9$$
$$= 5$$

Thus, $x = 5$ and $y = 7$ is the required solution.

43. C

The point $(K, -3)$ must satisfy both equations.

Step 1
Substitute K for x and -3 for y into the equation $8x + 3y = -41$.
$$8x + 3y = -41$$
$$8(K) + 3(-3) = -41$$

Step 2
Solve for K.
$$8(K) + 3(-3) = -41$$
$$8K - 9 = -41$$
$$8K = -32$$
$$K = -4$$

Step 3
Check the solution of $K = -4$ by substituting -4 for x and -3 for y into the equation $6x - 5y = -9$.
$$6x - 5y = -9$$
$$6(-4) - 5(-3) = -9$$
$$-24 - (-15) = -9$$
$$-24 + 15 = -9$$
$$-9 = -9$$

The value of K works, so $K = -4$.
The equation $6x - 5y = -9$ could also have been used to determine the value for K.

44. C

Step 1
Label the equations.
① $3x - 4y = -2$
② $5x + 6y = 4$

Step 2
Multiply equation ① by 3.
$3 \times$ ① $-9x - 12y = -6$

Step 3
Determine the value by which the second equation must be multiplied.
In order to use addition to eliminate y, the coefficient of y in equation ② must be 12.
This can be obtained by multiplying equation ② by 2.

45. B

- Let the digit in the unit's place be x.
- Let the digit in the ten's place be y.

Thus, the original number $= 10y + x$.

The number obtained upon reversing the order of the digits $= 10x + y$.

According to the condition given in the question:
$(10x + y) - (10y + x) = 18$
$10x + y - 10y - x = 18$
$9x - 9y = 18$
$9(x - y) = 18$
$x - y = \dfrac{18}{9}$
$x - y = 2$

  ① $x = y + 2$
  ② $y + x = 8$

Substituting the value of x from equation ① in equation ② ,
$y + (y + 2) = 8$
$2y + 2 = 8$
$2y = 8 - 2$
$2y = 6$
$y = \dfrac{6}{2}$
$y = 3$

Substituting this value of y in equation ① ,
$x = y + 2 = 3 + 2 = 5$
$(10y + x) = 35$

The original number is 35.

46. A

Step 1

Determine the first equation.

If x represents one portion of the total amount of invested money and y represents the other portion, the equation can be written as $5\ 000$ being equal to the sum of x and y.

  ① $x + y = 50$

Step 2

Determine the second equation.

$0.04x =$ interest earned on the amount invested at 4%

$0.06y =$ interest earned on the amount invested at 6%

Since the interest earned on the x-amount of invested money is \$50 more than the interest earned on the y-amount of invested money, the equation can be written as the x-amount multiplied by its interest rate being equal to the y-amount multiplied by its interest rate plus 50.

  ② $0.04x = 0.06y + 50$

Step 3

Multiply the second equation by 100.
      ② $0.04x = 0.06y + 50$
$100 \times$ ② $4x = 6y + 5\ 000$
The system of equations is $x + y = 50$ and $4x = 6y + 50$.

47. 165

In order to have no solution, the lines must be parallel; they must have the same slope.

Step 1

Rewrite the equation $3y = -45x + 13$ in the slope-intercept form $y = mx + b$.
$3y = -45x + 13$
$y = \dfrac{-45x + 13}{3}$
$y = -15x + \dfrac{13}{3}$

For the line represented by this equation, the slope is -15.

Step 2

Rewrite the equation $11y = -ax + 4$ in the slope-intercept form $y = mx + b$.
$11y = -ax + 4$
$y = \dfrac{-ax + 4}{11}$
$y = -\dfrac{a}{11}x + \dfrac{4}{11}$

For the line represented by this equation, the slope is $\dfrac{-a}{11}$.

Step 3

Equate the slope from $y = -15x + \dfrac{13}{3}$ and the slope from $y = -\dfrac{a}{11}x + \dfrac{4}{11}$.

$-\dfrac{a}{11} = -15$
$-a = -165$
$a = 165$

If the system has no solutions, the value of a is 165.

48. 5

The equation is given in slope y-intercept form $y = mx + b$.

Use the y-intercept to plot $(0, 9)$. Use the slope (2) to determine the second and third points, such as $(-1, 7)$ and $(-2, 5)$. Join the points and extend the line through that of the first equation.

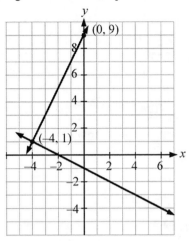

The intersection point or solution is $(-4, 1)$.

Therefore, the value of $a + b$ is $4 + 1 = 5$.

49. WR

The equation for each company can be written in slope y-intercept form ($y = mx + b$). The y-intercept is the weekly charge, and the slope is the rate per kilometre.

Step 1
Determine the equation of the line for company I. Since the y-intercept is 75 and the slope is 0.2, substitute 75 for b and 0.2 for m in the equation $y = mx + b$.
$$y = mx + b$$
$$= 0.2x + 75$$

Step 2
Determine the equation of the line for company II. Since the y-intercept is 100 and the slope is 0.10, substitute 100 for b and 0.1 for m in the equation $y = mx + b$.
$$y = mx + b$$
$$= 0.1x + 100$$

Step 3
Graph each relation.
First, plot the y-intercept. Then, use the slope or substitute values into the equation to determine other points on the line.

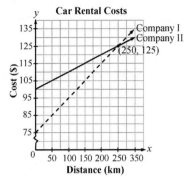

Step 4
Determine the conditions under which each plan is better.

Company I is the better value if Walter travels less than 250 km. Company II is the better value if Walter travels more than 250 km.

50. a) B

Step 1
Determine the d-intercept.
The top of the otter's head is 20 cm above the surface of the river (when $t = 0$ seconds, the value of d is 20 cm). This represents the d-intercept of the line.

Step 2
Substitute the d-intercept $(0, 20)$ and the rate of descent or slope of -7.2 into the slope formula,
$$m = \frac{y_2 - y_1}{x_2 - x_1},$$ to find the value of t in the point
$(t, 0)$ representing the time when the top of the otter's head disappeared below the waterline $(d = 0 \text{ cm})$.
$$m = \frac{y_2 - y_1}{x_2 - x_1}$$
$$-7.2 = \frac{0 - 20}{t - 0}$$
$$-7.2 = \frac{-20}{t}$$
$$-7.2t = -20$$
$$t = \frac{-20}{-7.2}$$
$$t \approx 2.7778$$

Therefore, the time when the top of the otter's head disappeared below the waterline is 2.78 s.

b) B

Step 1

According to the graph, the left limit of the domain is $t = 0$. This corresponds to the y-intercept, where the upper range value is d = 20. To find the right limit of the domain, find the time, t, when the otter's head is 88 cm, the lower value of the range, below the river's surface. Substitute the y-intercept (0, 20) and the slope, –7.2, into the slope formula to find the value of t when $d = –88$.

$$m = \frac{y_2 - y_1}{x_2 - x_1}$$

$$-7.2 = \frac{(-88) - 20}{t - 0}$$

Step 2

Solve for t.

$$-7.2 = \frac{(-88) - 20}{t - 0}$$

$$-7.2 = \frac{-108}{t}$$

$$-7.2t = -108$$

$$t = \frac{-108}{-7.2}$$

$$t = 15$$

Therefore, the right limit of the domain is $t = 15$, and the domain of the total dive is $0 \leq t \leq 15$.

51. a) C

The constant rate of change is the ratio of the change in y-values (rise) to the change in x-values (run).

Step 1

Determine the change in y-values. From the table, calculate the change in y-values.

$$44 - 33 = 33 - 22$$
$$11 = 11$$

Step 2

Determine the change in x-values. From the table, calculate the change in x-values.

$$20 - 15 = 15 - 10$$
$$5 = 5$$

Step 3

Determine the constant rate of change using the formula $m = \frac{\Delta y}{\Delta x}$, where m is the constant rate of change.

Substitute 5 for Δx and 11 for Δy.

$$m = \frac{\Delta y}{\Delta x}$$

$$= \frac{11}{5}$$

$$= 2.2 \text{ lb/kg}$$

Step 4

Write the constant rate of change in the form of an equation. The relationship between pounds (y) and kilograms (x) is y = 2.2x, where the coefficient of x is the constant rate of change. Therefore, the equation that can be used to convert kilograms to pounds is $y = 2.2x$.

51. b) B

The graph of the relationship between kilograms (x) and pounds (y) must have x- and y-values that are the same as those given in the table.

When pounds equal 0, so do kilograms. Since the graph must go through the origin, graph D can be eliminated.

The first x-value in the table is 10. Since graph A has the first x-value at 22, graph A can be eliminated.

The first y-value in the table is 22. Since the first y-value in graph C is 10, graph C can be eliminated.

In graph B, the first x-value is 10, the first y-value is 22, the graph goes through the origin, and the slope is 2.2.

Therefore, graph B represents the data given in the table.

KEY Strategies for Success on Tests

KEY STRATEGIES FOR SUCCESS ON TESTS

This section is all about the skills and strategies you need to be successful on tests. It is designed for you to use together with your classroom learning and assignments.

FINDING OUT ABOUT THE TESTS

Here are some questions you may wish to discuss with your teacher to help you prepare for quizzes and tests:

• What will this test assess, or cover?

• How much time do I have to write the test?

• How important is this test to my final grade?

• Are there any materials provided for the test?

• What materials do I need to bring to write the test?

• What kind of questions are on the test? Will they be multiple choice? Short answer?

Having a good understanding of effective test-taking skills can help you do well on tests. Being familiar with different types of questions may also help you.

THINGS TO CONSIDER WHEN TAKING A TEST

It is normal to feel anxious before you write a test. You can manage this anxiety by using the following strategies:

- Think positive thoughts. Imagine yourself doing well on the test.

- Make a conscious effort to relax by taking several slow, deep, controlled breaths. Concentrate on the air going in and out of your body.

- Before you begin the test, ask questions if you are unsure of anything.

- Jot down key words or phrases from any instructions your teacher gives you.

- Look over the entire test to find out the number and kinds of questions on the test.

- Read each question closely, and reread if necessary.

- Pay close attention to key vocabulary words. Sometimes, these words are **bolded** or *italicized*, and they are usually important words in the question.

- If you are putting your answers on an answer sheet, mark your answers carefully. Always print clearly. If you wish to change an answer, erase the mark completely, and ensure that your final answer is darker than the one you have erased.

- Use highlighting to note directions, key words, and vocabulary that you find confusing or that are important to answering the question.

- Double-check to make sure you have answered everything before handing in your test.

- When taking tests, students often overlook the easy words. Failure to pay close attention to these words can result in an incorrect answer. One way to avoid this is to be aware of these words and to underline, circle, or highlight them while you are taking the test.

- Even though some words are easy to understand, they can change the meaning of the entire question, so it is important that you pay attention to them. Here are some examples.

all	always	most likely	probably	best	not
difference	usually	except	most	unlikely	likely

Example

1. Which of the following equations is incorrect?

    A. $3 + 2 = 5$

    B. $4 - 3 = 1$

    C. $5 \times 4 = 15$

    D. $6 \times 3 = 18$

HELPFUL STRATEGIES FOR ANSWERING MULTIPLE-CHOICE QUESTIONS

A multiple-choice question gives you some information and then asks you to select an answer from four choices. Each question has one correct answer. The other choices are distractors, which are incorrect.

The following strategies can help you when answering multiple-choice questions:

- Quickly skim through the entire test. Find out how many questions there are, and plan your time accordingly.

- Read and reread questions carefully. Underline key words, and try to think of an answer before looking at the choices.

- If there is a graphic, look at the graphic, read the question, and go back to the graphic. Then, you may want to underline the important information from the question.

- Carefully read the choices. Read the question first and then each choice that goes with it.

- When choosing an answer, try to eliminate those choices that are clearly wrong or do not make sense.

- Some questions may ask you to select the best answer. These questions will always include words like *best*, *most appropriate*, or *most likely*. All of the choices will be correct to some degree, but one of the choices will be better than the others in some way. Carefully read all four choices before choosing the answer you think is the best.

- If you do not know the answer, or if the question does not make sense to you, it is better to guess than to leave it blank.

- Do not spend too much time on any one question. Make a mark (*) beside a difficult question, and come back to it later. If you are leaving a question to come back to later, make sure you also leave the space on the answer sheet, if you are using one.

- Remember to go back to the difficult questions at the end of the test; sometimes, clues are given throughout the test that will provide you with answers.

- Note any negative words like *no* or *not*, and be sure your answer fits the question.

- Before changing an answer, be sure you have a very good reason to do so.

- Do not look for patterns on your answer sheet, if you are using one.

HELPFUL STRATEGIES FOR ANSWERING WRITTEN-RESPONSE QUESTIONS

A written response requires you to respond to a question or directive indicated by words such as *explain*, *predict*, *list*, *describe*, *show your work*, *solve*, or *calculate*. The following strategies can help you when answering written-response questions:

• Read and reread the question carefully.

• Recognize and pay close attention to directing words such as *explain*, *show your work*, and *describe*.

• Underline key words and phrases that indicate what is required in your answer, such as *explain*, *estimate*, *answer*, *calculate*, or *show your work*.

• Write down rough, point-form notes regarding the information you want to include in your answer.

• Think about what you want to say, and organize information and ideas in a coherent and concise manner within the time limit you have for the question.

• Be sure to answer every part of the question that is asked.

• Include as much information as you can when you are asked to explain your thinking.

• Include a picture or diagram if it will help to explain your thinking.

• Try to put your final answer to a problem in a complete sentence to be sure it is reasonable.

• Reread your response to ensure you have answered the question.

• Ask yourself if your answer makes sense.

• Ask yourself if your answer sounds right.

• Use appropriate subject vocabulary and terms in your response.

ABOUT MATHEMATICS TESTS

WHAT YOU NEED TO KNOW ABOUT MATHEMATICS TESTS

To do well on a mathematics test, you need to understand and apply your knowledge of mathematical concepts. Reading skills can also make a difference in how well you perform. Reading skills can help you follow instructions and find key words, as well as read graphs, diagrams, and tables. They can also help you solve mathematics problems.

Mathematics tests usually have two types of questions: questions that ask for understanding of mathematics ideas and questions that test how well you can solve mathematics problems.

HOW YOU CAN PREPARE FOR MATHEMATICS TESTS

The following strategies are particular to preparing for and writing mathematics tests:

- Know how to use your calculator, and, if it is allowed, use your own for the test.

- Note taking is a good way to review and study important information from your class notes and textbook.

- Sketch a picture of the problem, procedure, or term. Drawing is helpful for learning and remembering concepts.

- Check your answer to practice questions by working backward to the beginning. You can find the beginning by going step by step in reverse order.

- Use the following steps when answering questions with graphics (pictures, diagrams, tables, or graphs):

  1. Read the title of the graphic and any key words.

  2. Read the test question carefully to figure out what information you need to find in the graphic.

  3. Go back to the graphic to find the information you need.

  4. Decide which operation is needed.

- Always pay close attention when pressing the keys on your calculator. Repeat the procedure a second time to be sure you pressed the correct keys.

TEST PREPARATION COUNTDOWN

If you develop a plan for studying and test preparation, you will perform well on tests.

Here is a general plan to follow seven days before you write a test.

COUNTDOWN: 7 DAYS BEFORE THE TEST

1. Create your own personal test preparation plan.

2. Review the following information:

   – Areas to be included on the test

   – Types of test items

   – General and specific test tips

3. Start preparing for the test at least seven days before the test. Develop your test preparation plan,
   and set time aside to prepare and study.

COUNTDOWN: 6, 5, 4, 3, 2 DAYS BEFORE THE TEST

1. Review old homework assignments, quizzes, and tests.

2. Rework problems on quizzes and tests to make sure you still know how to solve them.

3. Correct any errors made on quizzes and tests.

4. Review key concepts, processes, formulas, and vocabulary.

5. Create practice test questions for yourself, and answer them. Work out many sample problems.

COUNTDOWN: THE NIGHT BEFORE THE TEST

1. Use the night before the test for final preparation, which includes reviewing and gathering materials needed for the test before going to bed.

2. Most importantly, get a good night's rest, and know you have done everything possible to do well on the test.

TEST DAY

1. Eat a healthy and nutritious breakfast.

2. Ensure you have all the necessary materials.

3. Think positive thoughts, such as "I can do this," "I am ready," and "I know I can do well."

4. Arrive at your school early, so you are not rushing, which can cause you anxiety and stress.

SUMMARY OF HOW TO BE SUCCESSFUL DURING A TEST

You may find some of the following strategies useful for writing a test:

- Take two or three deep breaths to help you relax.

- Read the directions carefully, and underline, circle, or highlight any important words.

- Look over the entire test to understand what you will need to do.

- Budget your time.

- Begin with an easy question or a question you know you can answer correctly rather than follow the numerical question order of the test.

- If you cannot remember how to answer a question, try repeating the deep breathing and physical relaxation activities. Then, move on to visualization and positive self-talk to get yourself going.

- When answering questions with graphics (pictures, diagrams, tables, or graphs), look at the question carefully, and use the following steps:

  1. Read the title of the graphic and any key words.

  2. Read the test question carefully to figure out what information you need to find in the graphic.

  3. Go back to the graphic to find the information you need.

- Write down anything you remember about the subject on the reverse side of your test paper. This activity sometimes helps to remind you that you do know something and are capable of writing the test.

- Look over your test when you have finished, and double-check your answers to be sure you did not forget anything.

Practice Tests

PRACTICE TEST 1

1. Which of the following sets of numbers has a greatest common factor of 14 and a least common multiple of 840?

    A. 40, 84, and 280

    B. 84, 140, and 280

    C. 84, 210, and 280

    D. 126, 210, and 420

2. When $-1.5\sqrt[3]{160}$ is converted into an entire radical, the resulting expression is

    A. $\sqrt[3]{360}$ B. $\sqrt[3]{-360}$

    C. $\sqrt[3]{540}$ D. $\sqrt[3]{-540}$

Use the following information to answer the next question.

Four students made statements pertaining to rational and irrational numbers.

- Nicole: The number 14 641 is a perfect fourth power.

- Kevin: $\sqrt{1.7424}$ is a rational number.

- Chelsea: $3\sqrt[3]{3}$ is larger than $\sqrt[3]{80}$.

- Tanner: $\sqrt[4]{-16}$ simplifies to -2.

3. The student who made an incorrect statement is

    A. Kevin   B. Nicole

    C. Tanner   D. Chelsea

4. The simplified form of the expression $\dfrac{(-2x^{-3})^{-3}}{(-2x^{-2})^{-4}}$ is

    A. $-\dfrac{1}{2x^{17}}$ B. $-2x$

    C. $\dfrac{1}{2x^{17}}$ D. $2x$

5. When the expression $\dfrac{\sqrt[4]{a^{11}}}{\sqrt[4]{a^{-5}}}$, $a > 0$ is converted to a^n, the value of n is

    A. 6   B. 4

    C. $\dfrac{3}{2}$ D. $\dfrac{2}{3}$

Numerical Response

6. When the expression $\left(-\dfrac{3}{10}\right)^{-\frac{10}{3}}$ is evaluated to the nearest tenth, the resulting value is _____.

Use the following information to answer the next question.

A culture of bacteria triples every 5 min. At 4:27 P.M., the population is 50 000.

The equation $P_t = P_0(3)^{\frac{t}{5}}$ can be used to determine the population P_t after t minutes when P_0 is the initial population.

Written Response

7. Determine the population 27 min earlier, at 4:00 P.M.

8. If $(3x - 4)(4x - 1) = 12x^2 + bx + 4$, what is the value of b?

    A. -16 B. -19

    C. -27 D. -33

9. Expanding the expression
$(x - 3)(x^2 + 2x - 4)$ results in which of
the following polynomials?

A. $x^3 + x^2 - 10x + 7$

B. $x^3 - x^2 - 10x + 12$

C. $x^3 + 5x^2 + 10x - 7$

D. $x^3 - 5x^2 + 10x - 12$

Numerical Response

10. The expression $9x^2 - 25$ can be written in
factor form as $(Ax + B)(Ax - B)$.
The value of $A + B$ is _____.

11. If $x - k$ is a factor of $x^2 + x - 30$, then the
value of k is

A. 3   B. 5

C. 6   D. 10

12. Which of the following expressions is a
factor of the trinomial $2x^2 + x - 28$?

A. $2x + 1$ B. $2x - 7$

C. $x + 7$ D. $x - 4$

13. Which of the following imperial units is
the **most appropriate** for measuring the
height of a flag pole?

A. Inch   B. Foot

C. Mile   D. Yard

*Use the following information to
answer the next question.*

Ravi measured the lengths of four
different pipes.

• Pipe 1 is 153 in. long.
• Pipe 2 is 3.6 m long.
• Pipe 3 is 4 yd long.
• Pipe 4 is 3 000 mm long.

Numerical Response

14. If the pipes are placed in ascending order
of their lengths, the order is _____,
_____, _____, and _____.

*Use the following information to
answer the next question.*

A right cone has a radius of 8 ft and a
height of 15 ft.

15. What is the surface area of the lateral face
of the cone?

A. 120π ft^2

B. 128π ft^2

C. 136π ft^2

D. 200π ft^2

*Use the following information to
answer the next question.*

The manager of a theatre is considering
two containers for peanuts. One is a right
rectangular prism, and the other is a right
cylinder.

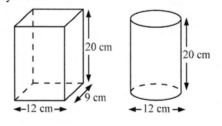

16. What is the volume of the container that
holds more peanuts?

A. 2 160 cm^3

B. 2 262 cm^3

C. 3 770 cm^3

D. 9 048 cm^3

Use the following information to answer the next question.

The garbage bin shown is built with a cylindrical bottom and a hemispherical top.

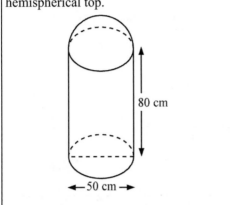

80 cm

←50 cm→

17. To the nearest whole cubic centimetre, what is the volume of garbage that the garbage bin can hold if it is completely filled?

   A. 189 805 cm^3 **B.** 236 529 cm^3

   C. 418 879 cm^3 **D.** 668 043 cm^3

Use the following information to answer the next question.

A right square pyramid with given dimensions is shown.

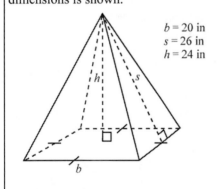

$b = 20$ in
$s = 26$ in
$h = 24$ in

Numerical Response

18. To the nearest square inch, the surface area of the right square pyramid is _____ in^2.

Use the following information to answer the next question.

A triangle is given.

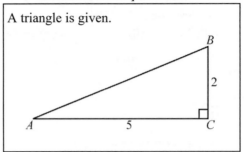

19. Given $\triangle ABC$, what is the measure of angle A?

   A. 21.8°   **B.** 23.6°

   C. 66.4°   **D.** 68.2°

Use the following information to answer the next question.

From an altitude of 2 000 metres, the pilot of a fighter jet spots a target on the ground at an angle of depression of 41°.

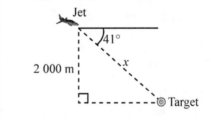

Jet

41°

2 000 m

x

Target

20. Which of the following equations could be used to determine the distance, x, from the fighter jet to the target?

   A. $\cos 41° = \dfrac{x}{2\ 000}$

   B. $\cos 41° = \dfrac{2\ 000}{x}$

   C. $\sin 41° = \dfrac{x}{2\ 000}$

   D. $\sin 41° = \dfrac{2\ 000}{x}$

Jordan is building a roof truss as shown in the following diagram.

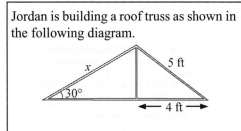

Numerical Response

21. The length of the side labelled *x*, to the nearest foot, is _____ ft.

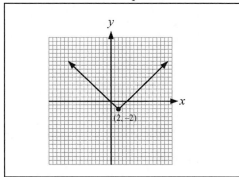

22. The domain and range of the graph of the relation are

   A. $x \in \mathbb{R}$ and $y \in \mathbb{R}$

   B. $x \in \mathbb{R}$ and $y \geq -2$

   C. $x \geq 2$ and $y \geq -2$

   D. $x \geq -2$ and $y \in \mathbb{R}$

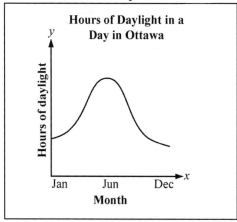

23. The given graph shows the relationship between the

   A. number of days that receive precipitation in a month and the time of day in the city of Ottawa

   B. day of the month and the amount of precipitation that falls each day in the city of Ottawa

   C. day of the month and the amount of sunlight each day receives in the city of Ottawa

   D. number of hours of daylight in a day and the time of year in the city of Ottawa

Use the following information to answer the next question.

> Representations of four different relations are given.
>
> Relation I
> {(2, −3), (−4, 2), (1, −3)}
>
> Relation II
> $4x − 3y + 7 = 0$
>
> Relation III
>
> | x | y |
> |---|---|
> | −1 | 5 |
> | 1 | 3 |
> | 3 | −1 |
> | −1 | 2 |
>
> Relation IV
>
>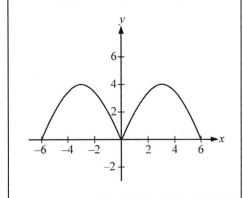

24. How many of the given relations are also functions?

   A. 1   **B.** 2

   C. 3   **D.** 4

25. The slope of the line passing through points (4, 6) and (2, 12) is

   A. -3   **B.** -2

   C. 2   **D.** 3

Use the following information to answer the next question.

> A glass box in a laboratory contains 150 fruit flies. After 25 days, the population of the fruit flies increases to 340.

26. The constant rate of change of the fruit fly population during this period is

   A. 7.6 flies/day   **B.** 8.6 flies/day

   C. 9.6 flies/day   **D.** 10.6 flies/day

27. Which of the following pairs of slopes represents two parallel lines?

   A. $-\dfrac{1}{2}$ and $\dfrac{1}{2}$

   B. $\dfrac{2}{5}$ and $\dfrac{10}{25}$

   C. $\dfrac{2}{1}$ and $\dfrac{1}{2}$

   D. $-\dfrac{2}{5}$ and $\dfrac{25}{10}$

28. Which of these graphs has a slope of $\dfrac{-2}{3}$ and a *y*-intercept of 2?

   A.   **B.**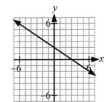

   C. 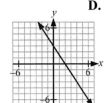   **D.**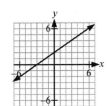

Use the following information to answer the next question.

The area, *A*, of a square is related to the length of its side, *s*.

s

Claire created the given table of values for several side length measurements.

Side Length (cm)	Area (cm²)
0	0
1	1
2	4
3	9
4	16
5	25
6	36

29. According to the pattern of data in the table, which of the following statements describing the relationship between the area of a square and its side length is **true**?

   A. The area, *A*, increases linearly as *s* increases, since the first differences are constant.

   B. The area, *A*, increases linearly as *s* increases, since the first differences are not constant.

   C. The area, *A*, increases non-linearly as *s* increases, since the first differences are constant.

   D. The area, *A*, increases non-linearly as *s* increases, since the first differences are not constant.

Use the following information to answer the next question.

A list of equations is given.

$$y = \frac{x}{y} \qquad\qquad y = -5x + 2$$

$$x = -2 \qquad\qquad 3x - 2y + 7 = 0$$

$$y = x(x + 3) \qquad\qquad 4x^2 - 3y + 6 = 0$$

$$y = 3(x - 2)$$

30. How many equations in this list represent linear relations?

   A. 2   **B.** 3

   C. 4   **D.** 5

31. Which of the following graphs does **not** have a range of $y \in \mathbb{R}$?

   A.   **B.**

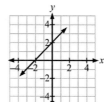 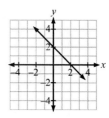

   C.   **D.**

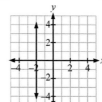 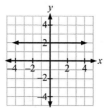

Use the following information to answer the next question.

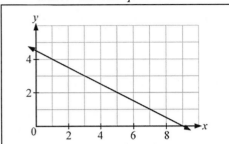

Numerical Response

32. To the nearest tenth, the sum of the *x*-intercept and *y*-intercept of the graph is _____.

33. The equation of the line $4y - 2x - 6 = 0$ can be expressed in slope *y*-intercept form as

A. $y = \dfrac{x}{2} - \dfrac{3}{2}$

B. $y = \dfrac{x}{2} + \dfrac{3}{2}$

C. $y = -\dfrac{x}{2} - \dfrac{3}{2}$

D. $y = -\dfrac{x}{2} + \dfrac{3}{2}$

34. What is the equation of the horizontal line passing through $(3, 1)$?

A. $x = 3$ **B.** $y = 1$

C. $x = -3$ **D.** $y = -1$

35. What is the equation of a line that passes through the point $(2, -1)$ and has a slope of $-\dfrac{4}{5}$?

A. $4x - 5y - 3 = 0$

B. $4x - 5y + 3 = 0$

C. $4x + 5y + 3 = 0$

D. $4x + 5y - 3 = 0$

Use the following information to answer the next question.

> A linear function is given.
> $$f(x) = \dfrac{ax}{4} + \dfrac{11}{4}$$

36. If $f(1) = 2$, what is the value of *a*?

A. -9 **B.** -3

C. 1 **D.** 3

37. The linear function $4x - 5y + 20 = 0$ expressed in function notation is

A. $f(x) = 4x - 5y + 20$

B. $f(x) = -\dfrac{4}{5}x + 20$

C. $f(x) = \dfrac{5}{4}y - 5$

D. $f(x) = \dfrac{4}{5}x + 4$

38. A bag of flour weighs 52.50 kg and a bag of wheat weighs 43.25 kg. If 13 bags of flour and wheat have a total weight of 590 kg, how many bags are there of flour and wheat respectively?

A. 4 and 9   **B.** 8 and 5

C. 3 and 10   **D.** 10 and 3

Use the following information to answer the next question.

> The solution for the system of two linear equations $3x + 4y = -8$ and $x - 2y = -1$ is $x = -a$ and $y = -b$.

Numerical Response

39. The value of $a + b$ to the nearest tenth is _____.

40. The total cost of printing summer catalogues for a particular department store is based on fixed setup costs plus a cost per book.

Line *A* represents the total cost of printing the catalogues last year. Line *B* represents the total cost of printing the catalogues this year. The equation for line *A* is written as $C = an + b$, and the equation for line *B* is written as $C = cn + d$.

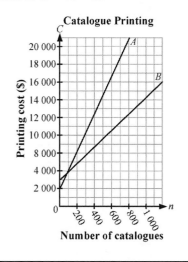

Catalogue Printing

Use the following information to answer the next multipart question.

a) Which of the following statements is **true**?

    A. The fixed setup cost for printing catalogues this year is lower than the fixed setup cost for printing catalogues last year.

    B. The cost per catalogue for printing last year was more than the cost per catalogue for printing this year.

    C. The cost per catalogue for printing this year is more than the cost per catalogue for printing last year.

    D. The fixed setup costs for printing catalogues last year and this year are the same.

b) Which of the following statements about the relationship between values *a* and *c* and values *b* and *d* is **true**?

    A. Value *a* is greater than *c*, and value *b* is greater than *d*.

    B. Value *a* is greater than *c*, and value *b* is less than *d*.

    C. Value *a* is less than *c*, and value *b* is greater than *d*.

    D. Value *a* is less than *c*, and value *b* is less than *d*.

Use the following information to answer the next multipart question.

41. A fitness club charges a one-time membership fee of $200 and a weekly fee of $18.50.

Written Response

a) Use the following table to show the total cost of the membership for the number of weeks given.

Number of Weeks at the Fitness Club	Total Cost ($)
2	237
4	
6	
8	
10	

b) Determine the equation that represents the linear relationship between the total cost, *C*, and the number of weeks, *n*, that an individual is enrolled at the fitness club.

c) How many weeks could Ron be enrolled at the fitness club for a total cost of $607?

c) Find the measure of angle D, to the nearest degree.

Use the following information to answer the next multipart question.

42. A sheet metal worker designs a piece of metal to be used for a special 3-D structure. Some of the dimensions are illustrated in the given diagram.

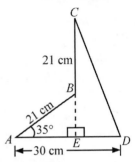

To complete the design, the worker needs to find the measure of angle D.

Written Response

a) To find the measure of $\angle D$, the measures of two sides of $\triangle CDE$ need to be determined. What two sides of $\triangle CDE$ could be determined if all the dimensions of $\triangle ABE$ were given? Explain your answer.

b) Determine the lengths of the two sides of $\triangle CDE$, to the nearest tenth of a centimetre.

PRACTICE TEST 2

1. Written in prime-factorized form, which of the following numbers is also a perfect cube?

   A. $2 \times 2 \times 3 \times 3 \times 5 \times 5$

   B. $3 \times 3 \times 3 \times 3 \times 3 \times 3 \times 3 \times 3$

   C. $2 \times 2 \times 2 \times 3 \times 3 \times 3 \times 7 \times 7 \times 7$

   D. $2 \times 2 \times 2 \times 3 \times 3 \times 3 \times 5 \times 7 \times 11$

2. Which of the following irrational numbers has the largest value?

   A. $-9\sqrt[3]{2}$ B. $-4\sqrt[3]{22}$

   C. $\sqrt[3]{-1\ 300}$ D. $\sqrt[3]{-1\ 600}$

3. The simplest form of the radical $\sqrt{512}$ is

   A. $2\sqrt{256}$ B. $4\sqrt{128}$

   C. $8\sqrt{8}$ D. $16\sqrt{2}$

4. In order for $\dfrac{\sqrt[3]{(-6)^a} \times (-6)^{\frac{7}{3}}}{(-6)^{\frac{4}{3}}} = \sqrt[3]{-6}$, to

   what must the value of a be equal?

   A. -2 B. $-\dfrac{2}{3}$

   C. $\dfrac{4}{3}$ D. 4

   Use the following information to answer the next question.

   > A family bought a painting worth \$9 000. The value of the painting increases at a constant rate of 3.56% per year.
   > The exponential growth model for the value of the painting is calculated using the formula $V_t = V_0(1 + r)^t$, where V_t is the estimated value in t years, V_0 is the original value, and r is the growth rate expressed as a decimal.

5. To the nearest dollar, the value of the painting in 13 years will be

   A. \$9 120   B. \$9 320

   C. \$10 184   D. \$14 182

Numerical Response

6. When the expression $\left(\dfrac{\frac{1}{2}}{6^{-\frac{2}{3}}}\right)^{\frac{2}{3}}$ is

   simplified and converted to the radical form $\sqrt[n]{6^m}$, the sum of $n + m$ is _____.

7. If $-2(3x + 5)^2 = ax^2 + bx + c$, then the value of $a + c$ is

   A. -34 B. -68

   C. -78 D. -110

8. Which of the following diagrams represents the expression $(3x - 2)(x + 5)$?

   A.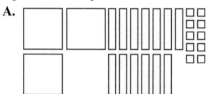

   B.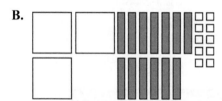

   C.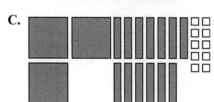

   D.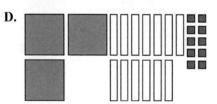

*Use the following information to
answer the next question.*

> A square with a side length of $(2x + 3)$ m
> is mounted along the width of a rectangle
> whose length is $(4x + 1)$ m. The width of
> the rectangle is equal to the side length of
> the square.

Written Response

9. What is the combined area of the square
and the rectangle?

Show your work.

10. The expression $36x^2 - 49$ can be written
in factor form as
A. $(6x - 7)(6x - 7)$
B. $(6x - 7)(6x + 7)$
C. $(7x - 6)(7x - 6)$
D. $(7x - 6)(7x + 6)$

11. If $5x + k$ is a factor of $10x^2 + 19x + 6$,
then what is the value of k?
A. 1   B. 2
C. 3   D. 6

Numerical Response

12. When the polynomial
$104x^3 - 32x^2 + 40x$ is factored to the
form $Ax(Bx^2 + Cx + D)$, the value of the
sum of $A + B + C + D$ is _____.

*Use the following information to
answer the next question.*

> Amanda built her own trundle wheel using
> the lid of an ice-cream pail. The diameter
> of the lid was a good referent for 1 ft.
> She used it to measure the distance from
> point *A* to point *B*.

13. If her trundle wheel made exactly $12\frac{3}{4}$
revolutions from point *A* to point *B*, then
the length of the curve, to the nearest
foot, is
A. 20 ft   B. 26 ft
C. 40 ft   D. 52 ft

*Use the following information to
answer the next question.*

> Four students used different measuring
> instruments to determine the height of a
> stack of 635 CDs.
> • Megan's measure: 56.15 cm
> • Ryan's measure: $\frac{5}{8}$ yd
> • Arianna's measure: 1 ft 11 in
> • Gary's measure: $22\frac{1}{2}$ in

14. If the thickness of one CD is 0.90 mm, how
many students correctly measured the
height of the stack?
A. 1   B. 2
C. 3   D. 4

Use the following information to answer the next question.

Zoe unfolds her right rectangular pyramid to form its corresponding two-dimensional net.

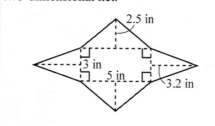

Numerical Response

15. To the nearest tenth square inch, the total surface area of the right rectangular pyramid is _____.

Use the following information to answer the next question.

A particular toy figure has a cylindrical bottom and a conical top, as shown.

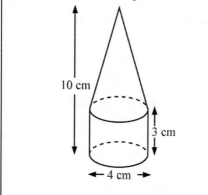

16. To the nearest tenth of a cubic centimetre, what is the volume of the toy figure?
A. 67.0 cm^3 B. 79.6 cm^3
C. 268.1 cm^3 D. 318.3 cm^3

Use the following information to answer the next question.

A gold sphere with a diameter of 120 mm is melted and then cast into a right rectangular prism with a base that is 95 mm long and 85 mm wide.

17. To the nearest millimetre, the height of the right rectangular prism is
A. 112 mm   B. 224 mm
C. 322 mm   D. 896 mm

Use the following information to answer the next question.

A cylindrical gasoline storage tank that is 4.8 m in diameter and 12 m in height is to be covered with a protective paint. The protective paint, which can only be purchased in whole cans, costs $48.50 per can including tax, and each can will cover an average of 34 m^2.

Written Response

18. What is the cost to cover the entire surface of the gasoline storage tank with one coat of paint?

Use the following information to answer the next question.

A labeled right triangle is shown.

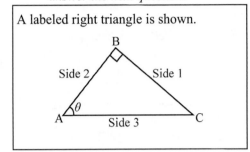

19. With respect to the given right triangle, which of the following statements is **false**?

   A. The hypotenuse is side 3.

   B. The adjacent side is side 2.

   C. The ratio sin θ is equal to side 1 divided by side 3.

   D. The ratio tan θ is equal to side 2 divided by side 1.

Use the following information to answer the next question.

A diagram of a triangle and a supplementary angle is given.

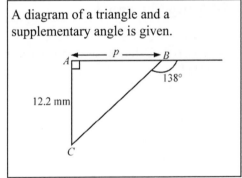

20. What is the length of side p?

   A. 8.2 mm   **B.** 9.1 mm

   C. 11.0 mm   **D.** 13.5 mm

Use the following information to answer the next question.

Two buildings are 40 m apart, as illustrated in the given diagram. From a point at the top of the shorter building, the angle of elevation to the top of the taller building is 37°. From the same point, the angle of depression to the foot of the taller building is 26°.

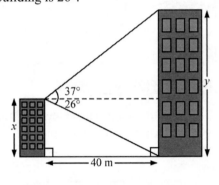

21. Rounded to the nearest tenth of a metre, the height y of the taller building is

   A. 52.8 m   **B.** 51.4 m

   C. 49.7 m   **D.** 27.1 m

Use the following information to answer the next question.

A surveyor wants to calculate the width of a river. He locates a point A, and then moves his transit 75 m along the shore to point B. From there, he determines that the angle to point C on the other side of the river is 37°.

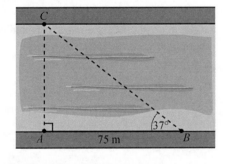

Numerical Response

22. The width of the river, line AC, to the nearest tenth of a metre, is _____ m.

A tour boat will leave its port and make a total of three stops. Two stops allow the passengers to go snorkeling and one stop is at an island village for lunch. The boat will then return to port.

23. Which of the following graphs **best** represents the distance that the tour boat is from port versus the time of day?

A.

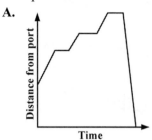

B.

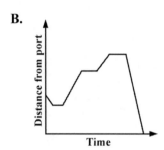

C.

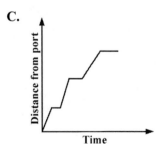

D.

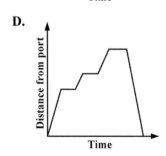

The captain of a small yacht fires a rescue flare into the air. The given table shows the height of the flare in relation to the time elapsed after the flare is fired.

Time (s)	Height of Flare (m)
0	0
1	150
2	240
3	270
4	240
5	150
6	0

24. Which of the following graphs **best** represents the information in the given table?

A.

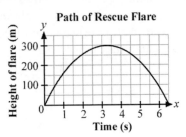

Path of Rescue Flare

B.

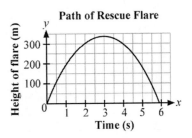

Path of Rescue Flare

C.

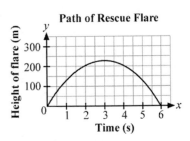

Path of Rescue Flare

D.

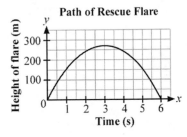

Path of Rescue Flare

25. Which of the following graphs could be the graph of a linear relation that has a slope of −1?

A.

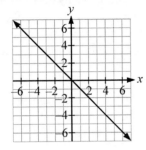

B.

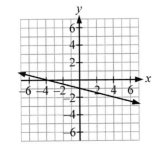

C.

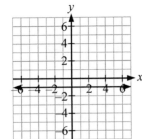

D.

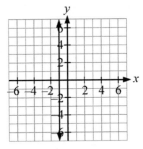

A local high school is hosting an athletic banquet at a community centre. The graph below shows how the total cost relates to the number of tickets sold.

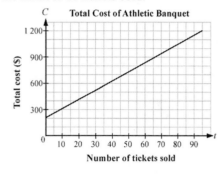

26. The slope of this graph represents the
    A. cost of food
    B. cost per ticket
    C. profit per ticket
    D. banquet hall cost

Line	Slope
I	3
II	−1
III	−3
IV	$-\dfrac{1}{3}$

27. Which two of the given lines are perpendicular?
    A. I and II   B. I and IV
    C. II and III   D. II and IV

Jeremy collected data describing the relationship between the unit price of a T-shirt, C, in dollars, and the total number ordered at one time, n. His data is recorded in the given table of values.

Number Ordered	Unit Price ($)
200	20.00
400	19.00
600	17.50
800	15.50
1 000	13.00
1 200	10.00

28. If this data is plotted as a scatter plot with points (n, C), the points move
    A. linearly upward from the left to the right of the graph
    B. linearly downward from the left to the right of the graph
    C. in an upward curve from the left to the right of the graph
    D. in a downward curve from the left to the right of the graph

As a tool salesman, Jacy earns $66 per day plus $6.50 for every set of tools, n, he sells.

29. Which of the following statements about Jacy's daily salary, S, is **true**?
    A. $S = 66 + 6.50n$, and the constant rate of change is 66.
    B. $S = 6.50 + 66n$, and the constant rate of change is 66.
    C. $S = 6.50 + 66n$, and the constant rate of change is 6.50.
    D. $S = 66 + 6.50n$, and the constant rate of change is 6.50.

30. The equation of the line $3x = 0$ has

    A. infinite y-intercepts

    B. infinite x-intercepts

    C. only one x-intercept

    D. only one y-intercept

Use the following information to answer the next question.

A contractor has building materials delivered from a lumberyard to various construction sites. The delivery cost, C, is based on a fixed amount plus a per-kilometer cost. The delivery cost and the distance, d, of the construction sites from the lumberyard are illustrated in the diagram shown.

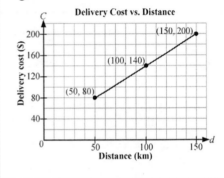

Numerical Response

31. To the nearest dollar, the fixed delivery cost (y-intercept) is $\$\underline{\hspace{2cm}}$.

32. Which of the following graphs represents the line $8x - 7y - 28 = 0$?

    A.

    B.

    C.

    D.

33. What is the equation of a line passing through the origin with a slope of 12?

    A. $x + y = 12$ **B.** $12x + y = 0$

    C. $x - 12y = 0$ **D.** $12x - y = 0$

34. What is the equation of the line that passes through the point $(-2, 8)$ and is perpendicular to the line $x = 5$?

    A. $x = 2$ **B.** $y = 8$

    C. $x = -2$ **D.** $y = -8$

Use the following information to answer the next question.

A line runs parallel to the line defined by the equation $3x + 4y + 5 = 0$. It has the same x-intercept as the line defined by the equation $4x + 5y - 6 = 0$.

35. What is the equation of the parallel line in general form?

    A. $-6x - 8y - 9 = 0$

    B. $-6x + 8y + 9 = 0$

    C. $6x + 8y - 9 = 0$

    D. $6x + 8y + 9 = 0$

Use the following information to answer the next question.

At Hidden Valley Golf course, Stacey pays an annual membership fee of $800 plus $23 for each round of golf she plays. The function $C(n) = 23n + 800$ represents the relationship between Stacey's total annual cost, $C(n)$, in dollars, and the number of rounds of golf, n, she plays in a year.

36. If her total annual cost, $C(n)$, was $1 352, how many rounds of golf did Stacey play at Hidden Valley in a given year?

    A. 24   **B.** 35

    C. 59   **D.** 94

Numerical Response

37. If two linear functions are defined as $f(x) = -2x - 11$ and $g(x) = 6x + 18$, the sum of $f(-4)$ and $g(10)$ is _____.

Use the following information to answer the next question.

To make a special blend of two teas, a store owner wants to mix Orange Blossom tea, selling at $6.40 per kilogram, with Red Dragon tea, selling at $7.20 per kilogram. He will sell 10 kg of the blended tea at $6.72 per kilogram. If he lets x represent the number of kilograms of Orange Blossom tea and y represent the number of kilograms of Red Dragon tea, he will be able to find out how much of each type of tea he needs for the blend.

38. The system of linear equations that can be solved to determine the amounts of tea needed to make the blended tea is

    A. $x + y = 10$
        $6.40x + 7.20y = 6.72$

    B. $6.40x + 7.20y = 10$
        $x + y = 6.72$

    C. $x + y = 10$
        $6.40x + 7.20y = 67.20$

    D. $6.40x + 7.20y = 10$
        $6.40x + 7.20 = 67.20$

Use the following information to answer the next question.

Rebecca is given a system of linear equations.

$$x + y = 365$$
$$3x + 2y = 925$$

39. In verifying the solution to this system of linear equations, Rebecca must replace x with

    A. 170 and y with 195 in both equations

    B. 195 and y with 170 in both equations

    C. 170 in the first equation and y with 195 in the second equation

    D. 195 in the first equation and y with 170 in the second equation

Use the following information to
answer the next question.

Two hikers are initially at two different
locations with respect to base camp.
Each hiker walks away from base camp
toward the top of a mountain at a
constant rate.

Line A represents the total distance, *d*, in
kilometres from base camp with respect to
the time, *t*, in hours of hiker A.

Line B represents the total distance, *d*, in
kilometres from base camp with respect to
the time, *t*, in hours of hiker B.

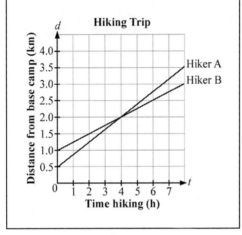

40. Which of the following statements
correctly interprets the graph?

A. Hiker A travels faster than hiker B
and will reach the top of the mountain
first.

B. Hiker B travels faster than hiker A
and will reach the top of the mountain
first.

C. Hiker A starts farther from the base
camp than hiker B, and he travels
faster than hiker B.

D. Hiker B starts farther from the base
camp than hiker A, and he travels
faster than hiker A.

Numerical Response

41. If $5x + y = 93$ and $2x + y = 48$, what is
the value of *y* in the solution to this system
of equations? _____

Use the following information to
answer the next multipart question.

42. Jackie's house is 600 m from the hardware
store, and David's house is 500 m from the
hardware store, as illustrated.

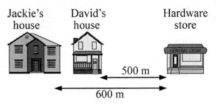

Not to scale.

Jackie and David leave their houses at the
same time to bike to the hardware store.
David bikes at a speed of 4 m/s. The line
showing David's distance, *d*, in metres
from the store over time, *t*, in seconds is
shown in the given graph. Jackie bikes at
a speed of 5 m/s.

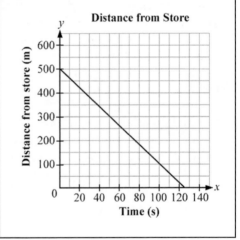

Written Response

a) Plot points at 10-second intervals
indicating Jackie's distance, *d*, in metres
from the store over time, *t*, in seconds, and
then draw a line through these points.

b) Find the point of intersection of the lines showing David's and Jackie's progress toward the hardware store, and explain what the point represents.

ANSWERS AND SOLUTIONS—PRACTICE TEST 1

1. C	11. B	21. 6	31. D	40. b) B
2. D	12. B	22. B	32. 13.5	41. WR
3. C	13. B	23. D	33. B	42. WR
4. B	14. 4231	24. C	34. B	
5. B	15. C	25. A	35. D	
6. 55.3	16. B	26. A	36. B	
7. WR	17. A	27. B	37. D	
8. B	18. 1440	28. B	38. C	
9. B	19. A	29. D	39. 2.5	
10. 8	20. D	30. C	40. a) B	

1. C

Step 1

Determine which of the given alternatives contains a number that is not divisible by 14.

Since 14 does not divide evenly into 40, the number 14 cannot be a factor of 40.

Therefore, the set 40, 84, and 280 is incorrect.

Step 2

Determine which of the given alternatives contains a number that does not divide evenly into 840. Since 126 does not divide evenly into 840, the number 840 cannot be a multiple of 126.

Therefore, the set 126, 210, and 420 is incorrect. To determine which of the remaining sets of numbers have a GCF of 14 and an LCM of 840, you need to list the multiples and factors of the numbers in each set.

Step 3

Determine the least common multiple of the sets of numbers 84, 140, 280, and 84, 210, 280 by listing the multiples of each number.

- Multiples of 84: 84168, 252, 336, 420, 504, 588, 672, 756, **840**, …
- Multiples of 140: 140, 280, 420, 560, 700, **840**, …
- Multiples of 210: 210, 420, 630, **840**, …
- Multiples of 280: 280, 560, **840**, …

The LCM of 84, 140, and 280 is 840 and of 84, 210, and 280 is also 840.

Step 4

Determine the greatest common factor of the sets of numbers 84, 140, 280 and 84, 210, 280 by listing the factors of each number.

x	Factors of x
84	1, 2, 4, 6, 7, 12, **14**, **28**, 42, 84
140	1, 2, 4, 5, 7, 10, **14**, 20, **28**, 35, 70, 140
210	1, 2, 3, 5, 6, 7, 10, **14**, 15, 21, 30, 35, 42, 70, 105, 210
280	1, 2, 4, 5, 7, 8, 10, **14**, 20, **28**, 35, 40, 56, 70, 140, 280

The GCF of 84, 140, and 280 is 28, and the GCF of 84, 210, and 280 is 14. Therefore, the set of numbers with a GCF of 14 and an LCM of 840 is 84, 210, and 280.

2. D

Step 1

Rewrite −1.5 as the cube root of −1.5 cubed.

$$-1.5 = \sqrt[3]{(-1.5)^3}$$

Step 2

$$\sqrt[3]{(-1.5)^3} \times \sqrt[3]{160}$$
$$= \sqrt[3]{-3.375} \times \sqrt[3]{160}$$
$$= \sqrt[3]{-3.375 \times 160}$$
$$= \sqrt[3]{-540}$$

3. C

Step 1

Determine if Kevin's statement is correct.

$\sqrt{1.7424} = 1.32$ is a rational number, since 1.7424 is a perfect square. Also, the resulting value is a terminating decimal.

Kevin's statement is correct.

Step 2

Determine whether Nicole's statement is correct.

$11^4 = (11 \times 11 \times 11 \times 11)$
$ = 14\ 641$

Since 14 641 is a perfect fourth power, Nicole's statement is correct.

Step 3

Determine if Tanner's statement is correct.

The expression $\sqrt[4]{-16}$ does not simplify to -2, since $(-2)^4 = 16$. $\sqrt[4]{-16}$ is undefined. Only even roots of positive radicands are possible (i.e.,

$\sqrt{24}, \sqrt[4]{36}, \sqrt[6]{48}\ldots$).

Tanner's statement is incorrect.

Step 4

Determine if Chelsea's statement is correct.

To compare the values $3\sqrt[3]{3}$ and $\sqrt[3]{80}$, convert $3\sqrt[3]{3}$ into entire radical form.

$3\sqrt[3]{3} = \sqrt[3]{3^3} \times \sqrt[3]{3}$
$\phantom{3\sqrt[3]{3}} = \sqrt[3]{27} \times \sqrt[3]{3}$
$\phantom{3\sqrt[3]{3}} = \sqrt[3]{27 \times 3}$
$\phantom{3\sqrt[3]{3}} = \sqrt[3]{81}$

Since the radicand 81 in $\sqrt[3]{81}$ is larger than the radicand 80 in $\sqrt[3]{80}$, $3\sqrt[3]{3}$ must be larger than $\sqrt[3]{80}$. Chelsea's statement is correct.

Therefore, Tanner made an incorrect statement.

4. B

Step 1

Use the negative exponent principle to convert each power into a power with a positive exponent.

$$\frac{(-2x^{-3})^{-3}}{(-2x^{-2})^{-4}} = \frac{(-2x^{-2})^4}{(-2x^{-3})^3}$$

Step 2

Apply the power of a product law to the powers in the numerator and denominator.

$$\frac{(-2x^{-2})^4}{(-2x^{-3})^3} = \frac{(-2)^4 x^{-2\times4}}{(-2)^3 x^{-3\times3}}$$
$$= \frac{(-2)^4 x^{-8}}{(-2)^3 x^{-9}}$$

Step 3

Apply the quotient of powers law to simplify the expression.

$$\frac{(-2)^4 x^{-8}}{(-2)^3 x^{-9}} = (-2)^{4-3} x^{-8-(-9)}$$
$$= (-2)^1 x^1$$
$$= -2x$$

The simplified form of the given expression is $-2x$.

5. B

Step 1

Convert each radical into a power with a rational exponent.

$$\frac{\sqrt[4]{a^{11}}}{\sqrt[4]{a^{-5}}} = \frac{a^{\frac{11}{4}}}{a^{-\frac{5}{4}}}$$

Step 2

Apply the quotient of powers law to simplify the expression to a^n.

$$\frac{a^{\frac{11}{4}}}{a^{-\frac{5}{4}}} = a^{\frac{11}{4}-\left(-\frac{5}{4}\right)}$$
$$= a^{\frac{16}{4}}$$
$$= a^4$$

The value of n in the simplified expression a^n is 4.

6. 55.3

Step 1

Use the negative exponent principle to convert the power into a power with a positive exponent.

$$\left(-\frac{3}{10}\right)^{-\frac{10}{3}} = \left(-\frac{10}{3}\right)^{\frac{10}{3}}$$

Step 2

Use your graphing calculator to evaluate the expression to the nearest tenth.

$$\left(-\frac{10}{3}\right)^{\frac{10}{3}} \approx 55.325\ 98$$
$$\approx 55.3$$

7. WR

Method 1

Substitute 50 000 for P_t and 27 for t. Solve for P_0.

$$P_t = P_0(3)^{\frac{t}{5}}$$

$$50\ 000 = P_0(3)^{\frac{27}{5}}$$

$$50\ 000 \approx P_0(377.0985)$$

$$\frac{50\ 000}{377.0985} \approx P_0$$

$$P_0 \approx 132.59$$

$$P_0 \approx 132$$

Notice that 132.59 is rounded down because there cannot be a fraction of a bacterium.

Method 2

Substitute 50 000 for P_O and -27 for t (since it is 27 min earlier). Solve for P_t.

$$P_t = P_o(3)^{\frac{t}{5}}$$

$$= 50\ 000(3)^{-\frac{27}{5}}$$

$$\approx 50\ 000(0.002\ 651\ 8272)$$

$$\approx 132.59$$

$$\approx 132$$

The population at 4:00 P.M was approximately 132.

8. B

Use the FOIL strategy, and multiply each term within the first set of brackets by each term within the second set of brackets.

$$3x(4x) + 3x(-1) - 4(4x) - 4(-1)$$

$$= 12x^2 - 3x - 16x + 4$$

Collect like terms.

$$12x^2 - 3x - 16x + 4$$

$$= 12x^2 - 19x + 4$$

Compare the expression $12x^2 - 19x + 4$ to the expression $12x^2 + bx + 4$. In order for the expressions to be equal, b must equal -19.

9. B

Use the distributive property to distribute the x and -3 through the second set of brackets. Then, collect like terms and simplify.

$$(x - 3)(x^2 + 2x - 4)$$

$$= \left(\begin{array}{l} x(x^2) + x(2x) + x(-4) + (-3)(x^2) \\ + (-3)(2x) + (-3)(-4) \end{array} \right)$$

$$= x^3 + 2x^2 - 4x - 3x^2 - 6x + 12$$

$$= x^3 - x^2 - 10x + 12$$

10. 8

Both the terms $9x^2$ and 25 are perfect squares. Thus, the given expression is a difference between two perfect squares.

Apply the difference of squares formula:

$$a^2 - b^2 = (a - b)(a + b)$$

$$9x^2 - 25 = (3x)^2 - (5)^2$$

$$= (3x - 5)(3x + 5)$$

$A = 3$ and $B = 5$, therefore the value of $A + B$ is $3 + 5 = 8$.

11. B

For the expression $x^2 + x - 30$, find two numbers, such that their product is -30 and their sum is 1.

The number -30 can be factored as $6 \times (-5)$ and the sum of 6 and -5 is 1.

Thus, the expression $x^2 + x - 30$ can be factored as $(x + 6)(x - 5)$

Since $(x - 5)$ is a factor of $x^2 + x - 30$, the value of k is 5.

12. B

Step 1

Since this is a trinomial of the form $ax^2 + bx + c$, find two numbers that have a product of $(a \times c)$ and a sum of b.

$$(a \times c) = (2 \times -28)$$

$$= -56$$

The factors of -56 are $\pm(1)(56)$, $\pm(2)(28)$, $\pm(4)(14)$, and $\pm(7)(8)$. The required factors must have a sum of b, or 1.

The required factors are $(-7)(8)$, since $-7 + 8 = 1$. Let $h = 8$ and $k = -7$.

Step 2

Rewrite the expression by replacing the middle term with the terms (hx) and (kx).

$$2x^2 + x - 28 = 2x^2 + 8x - 7x - 28$$

Step 3

Group using brackets.

$$2x^2 + 8x - 7x - 28$$

$$= (2x^2 + 8x) + (-7x - 28)$$

Step 4

Remove the GCF from each group.

$$(2x^2 + 8x) + (-7x - 28)$$

$$= 2x(x + 4) - 7(x + 4)$$

Step 5

Factor out the common binomial.
$2x(x + 4) - 7(x + 4)$
$= (x + 4)(2x - 7)$
The expression $2x - 7$ is a factor of the trinomial $2x^2 + x - 28$.

13. B

The inch is too small to measure the height of the flag pole. The yard and mile are too large. Therefore, the most appropriate unit is the foot.

14. 4231

To compare the linear measures, convert them into one common unit. In this case, use meters.

Step 1

Convert the measures of pipes 1, 3, and 4 into meters using proportions.
First, convert the length of pipe 1 into meters.
Convert 153 in. into meters.
$$\left(\frac{100 \text{ cm}}{1 \text{ m}} \times \frac{1 \text{ in.}}{2.54 \text{ cm}}\right) = \frac{153 \text{ in.}}{x}$$
$$x = \frac{153(2.54)}{100}$$
$$x = 3.8862 \text{ m}$$
Next, convert the length of pipe 3 into meters.
Convert 4 yd to meters.
$$\frac{1 \text{ yd}}{0.9144 \text{ m}} = \frac{4 \text{ yd}}{x}$$
$$x = 4(0.9144)$$
$$x = 3.6576 \text{ m}$$
Then, convert the length of pipe 4 into meters.
Convert 3 000 mm to meters.
$$\frac{1\ 000 \text{ mm}}{1 \text{ m}} = \frac{3\ 000 \text{ mm}}{x}$$
$$1\ 000x = 3\ 000$$
$$x = \frac{3\ 000}{1\ 000}$$
$$x = 3 \text{ m}$$

Step 2

Place the lengths of the pipes in ascending order.
$3 < 3.6 < 3.6576 < 3.8862$
The order of pipes from shortest to longest is 4, 2, 3, and 1, or 4 231.

15. C

Step 1

Draw a labelled diagram representing the right cone. Let s equal the length of the slant side of the right cone.

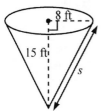

Step 2

Determine the length of the slant side, s, using the Pythagorean theorem, $a^2 + b^2 = c^2$.
Substitute s for c, 8 for a, and 15 for b.
$$a^2 + b^2 = c^2$$
$$s^2 = 8^2 + 15^2$$
$$s^2 = 64 + 225$$
$$s^2 = 289$$
$$s = \sqrt{289}$$
$$s = 17$$
The length of the slant side is 17 ft.

Step 3

Determine the surface area of the lateral face of the right cone.
The formula for the surface area of a right cone is $SA_{\text{cone}} = \pi r^2 + \pi r s$, where r is the radius.
The surface area of the lateral side is $\pi r s$.
$$SA_{\text{lateral side}} = \pi r s$$
$$= \pi(8)(17)$$
$$= 136\pi \text{ ft}^2$$

16. B

Step 1

Calculate the volume of the prism container using the formula $V_{\text{prism}} = A_{\text{base}} \times h$.
$$V_{\text{prism}} = A_{\text{base}} \times h$$
$$= (lw) \times h$$
$$= (12 \times 9) \times 20$$
$$= 2\ 160 \text{ cm}^3$$

Step 2

Calculate the volume of the cylinder container using the formula $V_{cylinder} = \pi r^2 h$, where $r = \dfrac{d}{2}$.

$$V_{cylinder} = \pi\left(\frac{d}{2}\right)^2 h$$
$$= \pi\left(\frac{12}{2}\right)^2(20)$$
$$= \pi(6)^2(20)$$
$$= \pi(36)(20)$$
$$\approx 2\ 262\ cm^3$$

Step 3

Determine which container has a larger volume.

$2\ 262\ cm^3 > 2\ 160\ cm^3$

Therefore, the cylindrical container holds more peanuts, since it has a greater volume of $2\ 262\ cm^3$.

17. A

Step 1

Calculate the radius of the cylinder and hemisphere using the formula $r = \dfrac{d}{2}$, where d is the diameter.

$$r = \frac{d}{2}$$
$$= \frac{50}{2}$$
$$= 25\ cm$$

Step 2

Calculate the volume of the cylinder using the formula $V_{cylinder} = \pi r^2 h$, where r is the radius and h is the height of the cylinder.

$$V_{cylinder} = \pi r^2 h$$
$$= \pi(25)^2(80)$$
$$\approx 157\ 079.6\ cm^3$$

The volume of a hemisphere is one-half the volume of a sphere.

Step 3

Calculate the volume of the hemisphere using the formula $V_{hemisphere} = \dfrac{V_{sphere}}{2}$, which can be rewritten as $V_{hemisphere} = \dfrac{\frac{4\pi r^3}{3}}{2}$.

$$V_{hemisphere} = \frac{V_{sphere}}{2}$$
$$= \frac{\frac{4\pi r^3}{3}}{2}$$
$$= \frac{\frac{4\pi(25)^3}{3}}{2}$$
$$\approx \frac{65\ 449.847}{2}$$
$$\approx 32\ 724.9\ cm^3$$

Step 4

Determine the total volume of the garbage bin.

$157\ 079.6\ cm^3 + 32\ 724.9\ cm^3 = 189\ 804.5\ cm^3$

To the nearest whole number, the volume of garbage the bin can hold if it is completely full is $189\ 805\ cm^3$.

18. 1440

In a right square pyramid, there are four congruent triangular faces and one square base.

Step 1

Calculate the area of the bottom square base.

$$A = s \times s$$
$$= 20 \times 20$$
$$= 400\ in^2$$

Step 2

Calculate the area of one of the triangular faces.

$$A = \frac{bh}{2}$$
$$= \frac{20 \times 26}{2}$$
$$= 260\ in^2$$

Step 3

Since there are four congruent triangular faces, multiply by 4.

$$A = 260 \times 4$$
$$= 1\ 040\ in^2$$

Step 4

Calculate the total surface area.

The total surface area is the sum of the area of the square base and the area of the four triangular faces.

$SA = 400 + 1\ 040$

$= 1\ 440\ \text{in}^2$

Therefore, the surface area of the right square pyramid is $1\ 440\ \text{in}^2$.

19. A

Step 1

Using the information in the diagram, apply the tangent ratio to find the measure of angle A.

$\tan \angle A = \dfrac{\text{opposite}}{\text{adjacent}}$

$= \dfrac{2}{5}$

$= 0.4$

Step 2

Use the $\boxed{\tan^{-1}}$ or $\boxed{\text{inv}}\ \boxed{\tan}$ key to find the measure of $\angle A$.

$\angle A = \tan^{-1}(0.4)$

$= 21.8°$

Rounded to the nearest tenth of a degree, the measure of $\angle A$ is $21.8°$.

20. D

Draw a labelled diagram to represent the situation. Remember that the angle of depression from the jet to the target is the same as the angle of elevation from the target to the jet.

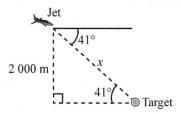

Since the opposite side of the angle (41°) is $2\ 000$ and x is the hypotenuse, the correct ratio to use is the sine ratio.

$\sin 41° = \dfrac{\text{opposite}}{\text{hypotenuse}} = \dfrac{2\ 000}{x}$

21. 6

First use the Pythagorean Theorem to obtain the length of the vertical beam, h.

$h^2 + 4^2 = 5^2$

$h^2 = 25 - 16$

$h^2 = 9$

$h = 3$

Next, use the sine ratio to find the length x.

$\sin 30° = \dfrac{3}{x}$

$x(\sin 30°) = 3$

$x = \dfrac{3}{\sin 30°}$

$x = 6$

Therefore, the length of side x, to the nearest foot is 6 ft.

22. B

Step 1

Determine the domain of the relation.

The domain of a relation is defined by all values of x for which x is defined. This relation has no values for which x is undefined, meaning that x is defined for all values for x. The domain of the relation is $x \in \mathbb{R}$.

Step 2

Determine the range of the relation.

The range of a relation is defined by all values of y for which y is defined.

The relation has a minimum y-value of -2, and y is also defined for all values greater than -2. Therefore, the y-values are defined for all values greater than or equal to -2. The range of the relation is $y \geq -2$.

23. D

The graph portrays the relationship between the number of hours of daylight in a day and the time of year in Ottawa. The left side of the graph shows that in January, there are fewer hours of daylight per day, as illustrated by the y-intercept. The number of hours of daylight per day increases from January until the end of June, located at the top of curve. From the end of June until the end of December, the number of hours of daylight per day decreases, located on the right side of the graph.

24. C

For a relation to also be a function, any x-value can have only one corresponding y-value, or the graph must pass the vertical line test in which any vertical line drawn through the graph cannot pass through more than one point.

In relation I, all the x-values are different, and each one has only one corresponding y-value. Thus, this relation is also a function.

Relation II is an equation of a linear function in the form of $Ax + By + C = 0$. Since the equation of the line does not describe a vertical line ($Ax + C = 0$), the graph of the line would pass the vertical line test. Thus, this relation is also a function.

In relation III, the x-value of -1 has two corresponding y-values of 5 and 2. Thus, this relation is not a function.

The graph of relation IV passes the vertical line test. Any vertical line through the graph would pass through only one point. Thus, this relation is also a function.

Based on these observations, three of the given relations are also functions.

25. A

Let the two points be (x_1, y_1) and (x_2, y_2).

$(x_1, y_1) = (4, 6)$
$(x_2, y_2) = (2, 12)$
slope $= m$

$$= \frac{y_2 - y_1}{x_2 - x_1}$$
$$= \frac{12 - 6}{2 - 4}$$
$$= \frac{6}{-2}$$
$$= -3$$

26. A

Let p represent the population and t the time.
Constant rate of change
$$= \frac{\Delta p}{\Delta t}$$
$$= \frac{340 - 150}{25 - 0}$$
$$= \frac{190}{25}$$
$$= 7.6 \text{ flies/day}$$

27. B

Parallel lines have the same slope but different y-intercepts.

Alternatives A and D have a positive and negative slope. The lines would intersect.

Alternative B has equivalent slopes.
$$\frac{10}{25} = \frac{10 \div 5}{25 \div 5} = \frac{2}{5}$$
$$\frac{2}{5} = \frac{2}{5}$$

Alternative C has two different slopes; the first being steeper than the second.

28. B

By definition, slope $= \dfrac{\text{rise}}{\text{run}}$.

Given that the slope is $\dfrac{-2}{3}$, the line falls 2 units for every 3 units to the right. You are given that the y-intercept is 2. This means that the value of y, when $x = 0$, is 2 [i.e., the point $(0, 2)$ is on the line]. Looking at the four alternatives, the only graph that contains point $(0, 2)$ and falls to the right (i.e., negative slope) is alternative B.

29. D

Determine the first differences of the areas.

$$0 \xrightarrow{+1} 1 \xrightarrow{+3} 4$$
$$\xrightarrow{+5} 9 \xrightarrow{+7} 16$$
$$\xrightarrow{+9} 25 \xrightarrow{+11} 36$$

Since the first differences are not constant, the area increases non-linearly as the side length increases.

Therefore, the statement, "The area, A, increases non-linearly as s increases, since the first differences are not constant" is true.

30. C

A linear relation has the form $Ax + By + C = 0$, where A, B, and C are real numbers. The degree of each term must be either 0 or 1.

There are four equations that can be expressed in the form $Ax + By + C = 0$ and which have terms with degrees of either 1 or 0. These are $3x - 2y + 7 = 0$, $y = -5x + 2$, $x = -2$, and $y = 3(x - 2)$.

The other three equations do not represent linear relations:

- The equation $y = \dfrac{x}{y}$ is equivalent to $y^2 = x$.

  The term y^2 has a degree of 2.

- The equation $4x^2 - 3y + 6 = 0$ contains the term $4x^2$, which has a degree of 2.

- The equation $y = x(x + 3)$ is equivalent to $y = x^2 + 3x$. The term x^2 has a degree of 2.

31. D

This graph shows the only line that does not have a range of $y \in \mathbb{R}$.

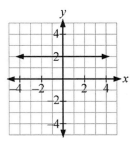

The line is horizontal and passes through the y-axis at $(0, 2)$. Therefore, every point on the line will have a y-value of 2. Therefore, the range of this line is $y = 2$.

32. 13.5

Step 1
Determine the x-intercept.
Inspecting the point where the line crosses the x-axis, the x-intercept is $(9, 0)$ or 9.

Step 2
Calculate the slope of the line.
Choose two points that are on the line, such as $(9, 0)$ and $(5, 2)$, and substitute them into the slope formula, $m = \dfrac{y_2 - y_1}{x_2 - x_1}$.

$$m = \frac{y_2 - y_1}{x_2 - x_1}$$
$$= \frac{2 - 0}{5 - 9}$$
$$= \frac{2}{-4}$$
$$= -\frac{1}{2}$$

Step 3
Substitute the values of one point, such as $(9, 0)$, and the value of the slope into the slope formula,
$m = \dfrac{y_2 - y_1}{x_2 - x_1}$, again to find the y-intercept, b, at the point $(0, b)$.

$$m = \frac{y_2 - y_1}{x_2 - x_1}$$
$$-\frac{1}{2} = \frac{b - 0}{0 - 9}$$
$$-\frac{1}{2} = \frac{b}{-9}$$
$$-9(-1) = 2(b)$$
$$9 = 2b$$
$$\frac{9}{2} = b$$
$$b = 4.5$$

The y-intercept is 4.5.

Step 4
Calculate the sum of the x-intercept and y-intercept.
The sum of the x-intercept and y-intercept is
$9 + 4.5 = 13.5$.

33. B

Isolate y in the given equation.
$4y - 2x - 6 = 0$

Add $2x$ and 6 to both sides of the equation (inverse operations).
$4y - 2x + 2x - 6 + 6 = 0 + 2x + 6$
$\qquad\qquad 4y = 2x + 6$

Divide both sides of the equation by 4 to isolate y.
$$\frac{4y}{4} = \frac{2x}{4} + \frac{6}{4}$$
$$y = \frac{x}{2} + \frac{3}{2}$$

34. B

A horizontal line has the equation $y = c$, where c is the y-coordinate of every point on the line. Since the line passes through the point $(3, 1)$, the equation of the line is $y = 1$.

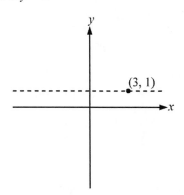

35. D

The slope of the line is $-\dfrac{4}{5}$, and a point on the line is $(2, -1)$.

Substitute these values into the point-slope form of the equation of a line, and rewrite the equation in the general form $Ax + By + C = 0$.

$$y - y_1 = m(x - x_1)$$
$$y - (-1) = -\frac{4}{5}(x - 2)$$
$$y + 1 = \frac{-4x}{5} + \frac{8}{5}$$
$$5(y + 1) = 5\left[\frac{-4x}{5} + \frac{8}{5}\right]$$
$$5y + 5 = -4x + 8$$
$$5y + 5 + 4x - 8 = 0$$
$$4x + 5y - 3 = 0$$

The equation of the given line is $4x + 5y - 3 = 0$.

36. B

Step 1

Since $f(1) = 2$, substitute 1 for x and 2 for $f(x)$.

$$f(x) = \frac{ax}{4} + \frac{11}{4}$$
$$2 = \frac{a(1)}{4} + \frac{11}{4}$$
$$2 = \frac{a}{4} + \frac{11}{4}$$

Step 2

Solve for a.

$$2 = \frac{a}{4} + \frac{11}{4}$$
$$4(2) = 4\left(\frac{a}{4}\right) + 4\left(\frac{11}{4}\right)$$
$$8 = a + 11$$
$$-3 = a$$

37. D

Step 1

Solve the relation $4x - 5y + 20 = 0$ for y.

$$4x - 5y + 20 + 5y = 0 + 5y$$
$$4x + 20 = 5y$$
$$\frac{4x + 20}{5} = \frac{5y}{5}$$
$$\frac{4}{5}x + 4 = y$$

Step 2

Replace y with $f(x)$, and exchange sides.

$$\frac{4}{5}x + 4 = f(x)$$
$$f(x) = \frac{4}{5}x + 4$$

38. C

Let the bags of wheat be W and the bags of flour be F. According to the question,

① $\quad\quad W + F = 13$
② $\quad 52.5F + 43.25W = 590$

Multiply equation 1 by 43.25.

③ $43.25F + 43.25W = 562.25$

Subtract equation 3 from equation 2.

$$52.5F + 43.25W = 590$$
$$43.25F + 43.25W = 562.25$$
$$9.25F = 27.75$$
$$F = 3$$

Substituting 3 for F into equation 1 gives:

$$W + (3) = 13$$
$$W = 10$$

There are 3 bags of flour and 10 bags of wheat.

39. 2.5

① $3x + 4y = -8$
② $\quad x - 2y = -1$

Rewrite equation 2 to solve for x.

$$x = 2y - 1 \text{③}$$

Substituting the value of x as $2y - 1$ in equation 1:

$$3x + 4y = -8$$
$$3(2y - 1) + 4y = -8$$
$$6y - 3 + 4y = -8$$
$$10y - 3 = -8$$
$$10y = -8 + 3$$
$$10y = -5$$
$$y = -\frac{5}{10}$$
$$y = -\frac{1}{2}$$

Substituting $-\dfrac{1}{2}$ for y in equation 3:

$$x = 2 \times \left(-\frac{1}{2}\right) - 1$$
$$= -1 - 1$$
$$= -2$$

$$\therefore x = -2 \text{ and } y = -\frac{1}{2}$$

To verify this result, substitute the values of x and y in the left hand side of both equations. If the left hand side of the equations equals their right hand sides, then the obtained solution is correct.

Substituting $x = -2$ and $y = -\dfrac{1}{2}$ in the left hand side of the equation $3x + 4y = -8$:

Left Hand Side $= 3x + 4y$

$= 3 \times (-2) + 4 \times \left(\dfrac{1}{2} \right)$

$= -6 - 2$

$= -8 = $ Right Hand Side

Substituting $x = -2$ and $y = -\dfrac{1}{2}$ in the left hand side of the equation $x - 2y = -1$:

Left Hand Side $= x - 2y$

$= -2 - 2 \times \left(\dfrac{1}{2} \right)$

$= -2 + 1$

$= -1 = $ Right Hand Side

The solution $x = -2$ and $y = -\dfrac{1}{2}$ of the given system of linear equations is verified. The value of $a + b$ to the nearest tenth is

$2 + \dfrac{1}{2} = 2.5$.

40. a) B

The fixed setup costs shown on the graph are given by the initial value, or vertical intercept, C, of each line. The fixed setup cost shown by line B (this year's catalogues) is greater than the fixed setup cost shown by line A (last year's catalogues).

Examine the positioning of each line. The steeper the line, the more each catalogue costs. Line A is steeper than line B, which means that the cost per catalogue for printing last year was more than the cost per catalogue for printing this year.

b) B

The constant rate of change $\dfrac{\text{rise}}{\text{run}}$ of line A is greater than the constant rate of change of line B because line A is steeper than line B. The numerical coefficient a in the equation representing line A is greater than the numerical coefficient c in the equation representing line B.

The initial value, or vertical intercept, of line A is less than the initial value, or vertical intercept, of line B. Value b in the equation representing line A is less than value d in the equation representing line B.

Therefore, a is greater than c, and b is less than d.

41. a) WR

Step 1

Create an equation that can be used to determine the total cost of the membership.

Since the weekly fee is constant at $18.50, it represents the constant rate of change. For every one week that the membership is extended, the cost increases by $18.50. For every two weeks, the cost increase is $2(18.50) = \$37.00$.

The equation is $C = 200 + 18.50n$, where n is the number of weeks at the fitness club and C is the total cost.

Step 2

Use the equation to calculate the different total costs.

$200 + 4(18.50) = 274$

$200 + 6(18.50) = 311$

$200 + 8(18.50) = 348$

$200 + 10(18.50) = 385$

Step 3

Complete the table.

This table shows the total cost of membership for the number of weeks shown.

Number of Weeks at the Fitness Club	Total Cost ($)
2	237
4	274
6	311
8	348
10	385

b) WR

The fixed amount is $200 (the initial membership fee or y-intercept), and the constant rate of change or slope is $18.50 per week. The equation in the form $y = mx + b$ that represents the linear relationship between the total cost, C, and the number of weeks, n, that an individual is enrolled at the fitness club is $C = 200 + 18.50n$.

c) WR

The total cost, C, is $607. Solve for the number of weeks, n, by using the equation $C = 200 + 18.50n$. Substitute 607 for C.

$607 = 200 + 18.50n$

$607 - 200 = 18.50n$

$407 = 18.50n$

$\dfrac{407}{18.50} = n$

$22 = n$

Ron could be enrolled at the fitness club for 22 weeks for a total cost of $607.

42. a) WR

If the length of side AE of $\triangle ABE$ was known, you could find the missing length of DE of $\triangle CDE$ as follows: $DE = 30\text{cm} - AE$

If the length of side BE of $\triangle ABE$ was known, you could find the missing length of CE of $\triangle CDE$ as follows: $CE = 21\text{cm} + BE$.

b) WR

To find the length of DE, find the length of AE in $\triangle ABE$.

$$\cos 35° = \frac{AE}{21}$$
$$21(\cos 35°) = AE$$
$$AE = 17.202\ 192\ 93$$

Therefore, the length of DE, to the nearest tenth of a centimetre, is $30 - 17.20219293 \approx 12.8$ cm.

To find the length of CE, find the length of BE in $\triangle ABE$.

$$\sin 35° = \frac{BE}{21}$$
$$21(\sin 35°) = BE$$
$$BE = 12.045\ 105\ 16$$

Therefore, the length of CE, to the nearest tenth of a centimetre, is $21 + 12.04510516 \approx 33.0$ cm.

c) WR

To find the measure of angle D use the tangent ratio.

$$\tan D = \frac{CE}{DE} = \frac{33.0}{12.8}$$
$$\angle D = \tan^{-1}\left(\frac{33.0}{12.8}\right)$$
$$\angle D = 68.799\ 783\ 34°$$

The measure of angle D, to the nearest degree, is $69°$.

ANSWERS AND SOLUTIONS—PRACTICE TEST 2

1. C	10. B	19. D	28. D	37. 75
2. C	11. B	20. D	29. D	38. C
3. D	12. 22	21. C	30. A	39. B
4. A	13. C	22. 56.5	31. 20	40. A
5. D	14. B	23. D	32. D	41. 18
6. 13	15. 37.1	24. D	33. D	42. WR
7. B	16. A	25. A	34. B	
8. C	17. A	26. B	35. C	
9. WR	18. WR	27. B	36. A	

1. C

A number is a perfect cube when its prime factorization can be grouped into three matching sets of prime factors. The prime factorization given in alternative C represents a perfect cube because it can be grouped into three matching sets.

$2 \times 2 \times 2 \times 3 \times 3 \times 3 \times 7 \times 7 \times 7$
$= (2 \times 3 \times 7) \times (2 \times 3 \times 7) \times (2 \times 3 \times 7)$
$= (2 \times 3 \times 7)3$

2. C

Step 1

Convert the mixed radical $-9\sqrt[3]{2}$ to its entire form.

$-9\sqrt[3]{2} = \sqrt[3]{(-9)^3} \times \sqrt[3]{2}$
$= \sqrt[3]{-729} \times \sqrt[3]{2}$
$= \sqrt[3]{-1\,458}$

Step 2

Convert the mixed radical $-4\sqrt[3]{22}$ to its entire form.

$-4\sqrt[3]{22} = \sqrt[3]{(-4)^3} \times \sqrt[3]{22}$
$= \sqrt[3]{-64} \times \sqrt[3]{22}$
$= \sqrt[3]{-1\,408}$

Step 3

Determine which value is the largest irrational number. The cube root with the smallest negative radicand will have the largest value. Determine the value of each irrational number by converting them all into decimal form.

$\sqrt[3]{-1\,300} = -10.913\,928\,83$
$\sqrt[3]{-1\,408} = -11.208\,157\,32$
$\sqrt[3]{-1\,458} = -11.339\,289\,45$
$\sqrt[3]{-1\,600} = -11.696\,070\,95$

The irrational number with the largest value is $\sqrt[3]{-1\,300}$.

3. D

One method of simplifying a radical is to choose the greatest set of equal factors of the prime factorization of the radicand.

Step 1

Determine the prime factorization of 512.
$512 = 2 \times 2 \times 2 \times 2 \times 2 \times 2 \times 2 \times 2 \times 2$

Step 2

Determine the greatest grouping of two equal factors.

$512 = \left(\begin{array}{c} (2 \times 2 \times 2 \times 2) \\ \times (2 \times 2 \times 2 \times 2) \times 2 \end{array} \right)$
$= 16 \times 16 \times 2$
$= 16^2 \times 2$

Step 3

Simplify the entire radical.

$\sqrt{512} = \sqrt{16^2 \times 2}$
$= \sqrt{16^2} \times \sqrt{2}$
$= 16 \times \sqrt{2}$
$= 16\sqrt{2}$

The simplest form of the radical $\sqrt{512}$ is $= 16\sqrt{2}$.

4. A

Step 1

Convert each radical into a power with a rational exponent.

$\dfrac{\sqrt[3]{(-6)^a} \times (-6)^{\frac{7}{3}}}{(-6)^{\frac{4}{3}}} = \sqrt[3]{-6}$

$\dfrac{(-6)^{\frac{a}{3}} \times (-6)^{\frac{7}{3}}}{(-6)^{\frac{4}{3}}} = (-6)^{\frac{1}{3}}$

Step 2

Simplify the left side of the equation by applying the product and quotient of powers laws.

$$\frac{(-6)^{\frac{a}{3}} \times (-6)^{\frac{7}{3}}}{(-6)^{\frac{4}{3}}} = (-6)^{\frac{1}{3}}$$

$$(-6)^{\frac{a}{3}+\frac{7}{3}-\frac{4}{3}} = (-6)^{\frac{1}{3}}$$

$$(-6)^{\frac{a+7-4}{3}} = (-6)^{\frac{1}{3}}$$

$$(-6)^{\frac{a+3}{3}} = (-6)^{\frac{1}{3}}$$

Step 3

Since the bases on both sides of the equation are the same, the exponents must be the same. Equate the exponents, and solve for a.

$$\frac{a+3}{3} = \frac{1}{3}$$

$$a + 3 = 1$$

$$a = 1 - 3$$

$$a = -2$$

5. **D**

Substitute 9 000 into the equation for V_0, 0.0356 for r, and 13 for t.

$$V_t = V_0(1+r)^t$$

$$= 9\ 000(1 + 0.0356)^{13}$$

$$= 9\ 000(1.0356)^{13}$$

$$\approx 9\ 000(1.575\ 783\ 48)$$

$$\approx 14\ 182.05$$

To the nearest dollar, the value of the painting in 13 years will be \$14 182.

6. **13**

Step 1

Use the negative exponent principle to convert the power in the brackets into a power with a positive exponent.

$$\left(\frac{1}{6^{-\frac{2}{3}}}\right)^{\frac{2}{3}} = \left(\frac{6^{\frac{2}{3}}}{1}\right)^{\frac{2}{3}}$$

$$= \left(6^{\frac{2}{3}}\right)^{\frac{2}{3}}$$

Step 2

Apply the power of a power law to simplify the expression.

$$\left(6^{\frac{2}{3}}\right)^{\frac{2}{3}} = 6^{\frac{2}{3} \times \frac{2}{3}}$$

$$= 6^{\frac{4}{9}}$$

Step 3

Convert the power into a radical.

$$6^{\frac{4}{9}} = \sqrt[9]{6^4}$$

Step 4

For the expression $\sqrt[9]{6^4}$, which is in the form $\sqrt[n]{6^m}$, calculate the sum of n and m.

$$n + m = 9 + 4$$
$$= 13$$

The sum of n and m is 13.

7. **B**

Step 1

Rewrite the squared binomial as a product, and then use the FOIL method to expand it.

$$-2(3x + 5)^2$$
$$= -2(3x + 5)(3x + 5)$$
$$= -2\binom{(3x)(3x) + (3x)(5)}{+ (3x)(5) + (5)(5)}$$
$$= -2(9x^2 + 15x + 15x + 25)$$
$$= -2(9x^2 + 30x + 25)$$

Step 2

Apply the distributive property to distribute -2 to all terms in the brackets.

$$-2(9x^2 + 30x + 25)$$
$$= -2(9x^2) - 2(30x) - 2(25)$$
$$= -18x^2 - 60x - 50$$

According to the expression given in the form of $ax^2 + bx + c$, $a = -18$ and $c = -50$.

Therefore, the value of $a + c = -18 + -50 = -68$.

8. **C**

Step 1

Expand and simplify the given expression. Apply the distributive property, or FOIL.

$$(3x - 2)(x + 5)$$
$$= 3x(x) + 3x(5) - 2(x) - 2(5)$$
$$= 3x^2 + 15x - 2x - 10$$
$$= 3x^2 + 13x - 10$$

Step 2

Represent the result using algebra tiles.

Modelling the resulting expression with algebra tiles requires 3 shaded x^2-tiles, 13 shaded x-tiles, and 10 unshaded unit tiles.

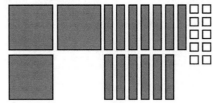

9. WR

$$s_{\text{square}} = (2x + 3) \text{ m}$$

Total area

$$A_{\text{square}} = (2x + 3)(2x + 3) \text{ m}^2$$
$$l_{\text{rectangle}} = (4x + 1) \text{ m}$$

Width of the rectangle

$$w_{\text{rectangle}} = s_{\text{square}} = (2x + 3) \text{ m}$$
$$A_{\text{rectangle}} = [(2x + 3)(4x + 1)] \text{ m}^2$$
$$A_{\text{total}} = \begin{bmatrix} (2x + 3)(2x + 3) \\ +(2x + 3)(4x + 1) \end{bmatrix} \text{ m}^2$$

Use the FOIL strategy to expand the polynomials.

$$= \begin{pmatrix} 4x^2 + 6x + 6x + 9 \\ +8x^2 + 2x + 12x + 3 \end{pmatrix} \text{ m}^2$$
$$= \begin{pmatrix} 4x^2 + 12x + 9 \\ +8x^2 + 14x + 3 \end{pmatrix} \text{ m}^2$$

Collect like terms and simplify.

$$= (12x^2 + 26x + 12) \text{ m}^2$$

10. B

The terms $36x^2$ and 49 are both perfect squares.

Thus, the given expression is a difference between two perfect squares.

Apply the difference of squares formula:

$$a^2 - b^2 = (a - b)(a + b)$$
$$36x^2 - 49 = (6x)^2 - (7)^2$$
$$= (6x - 7)(6x + 7)$$

11. B

Step 1

In order to factor $10x^2 + 19x + 6$, find two numbers with a product of $60 (a \times c)$ and a sum of 19 (the value of b).
In this case, the numbers are 15 and 4.

Step 2

Rewrite the expression by replacing the term $19x$ with $15x + 4x$.

$$10x^2 + 19x + 6$$
$$= 10x^2 + 15x + 4x + 6$$

Step 3

Group using brackets.

$$10x^2 + 15x + 4x + 6$$
$$= (10x^2 + 15x) + (4x + 6)$$

Step 4

Remove the GCF from each group.

$$(10x^2 + 15x) + (4x + 6)$$
$$= 5x(2x + 3) + 2(2x + 3)$$

Step 5

Factor out the common binomial.

$$5x(2x + 3) + 2(2x + 3)$$
$$= (5x + 2)(2x + 3)$$

Since $5x + 2$ is one factor, $k = 2$.

12. 22

Step 1

Factor the greatest common factor (GCF) out of each term of the polynomial $104x^3 - 32x^2 + 40x$.

Method 1—Division List
Determine all the factors of each term, and then select the GCF.

Term	Factors
$104x^3$	1, 2, 4, 8, 13, 26, 52, 104, x, x^2, x^3
$32x^2$	1, 2, 4, 8, 16, 32, x, x^2
$40x$	1, 2, 4, 5, 8, 10, 20, 40, x

The GCF is $8x$.

Method 2—Prime Factorization
Determine the prime factors of each term, and select the maximum shared prime factors.

$$104x^3 = \mathbf{2} \times \mathbf{2} \times \mathbf{2} \times 13 \times \mathbf{x} \times x \times x$$
$$32x^2 = \mathbf{2} \times \mathbf{2} \times \mathbf{2} \times 2 \times 2 \times \mathbf{x} \times x$$
$$40x = \mathbf{2} \times \mathbf{2} \times \mathbf{2} \times 5 \times \mathbf{x}$$

The GCF is $2 \times 2 \times 2 \times x = 8x$.

Step 2

Divide each term by the GCF.

$$104x^3 - 32x^2 + 40x = 8x(13x^2 - 4x + 5).$$

Step 3

Calculate the sum of $A + B + C + D$ for the expression $8x(13x^2 - 4x + 5)$, which is in the form $Ax(Bx^2 + Cx + D)$.

$$A + B + C + D = 8 + 13 + (-4) + 5$$
$$= 8 + 13 - 4 + 5$$
$$= 22$$

13. C

Determine the distance from point *A* to point *B* along the curve.

Step 1

Using the formula for the circumference of a circle, $c = \pi d$, where *c* is the circumference and d is the diameter, determine the distance covered by one revolution of the trundle wheel.

Remember that the diameter of the trundle wheel is a referent for 1 ft.

$$C = \pi d$$
$$= \pi(1)$$
$$\approx 3.1416 \text{ ft}$$

Step 2

Determine the distance, *d*, from point *A* to point *B*.

$$d = 12\frac{3}{4} \times 1 \text{ revolution}$$
$$\approx 12.75 \times 3.1416$$
$$\approx 40.0554 \text{ ft}$$

The distance from point *A* to point *B*, to the nearest foot, is 40 ft.

14. B

Step 1

Determine the height, *h*, of the stack of CDs.
$$h = 635 \times 0.90$$
$$= 571.5 \text{ mm}$$

Step 2

Convert 571.5 mm to centimetres and then to inches by using appropriate proportions, where *x* is in centimetres and *y* is in inches.

$$\frac{10 \text{ mm}}{1 \text{ cm}} = \frac{571.5 \text{ mm}}{x}$$
$$10x = 571.5$$
$$x = 57.15 \text{ cm}$$
$$\frac{2.54 \text{ cm}}{1 \text{ in.}} = \frac{57.15 \text{ cm}}{y}$$
$$2.54y = 57.15$$
$$y = 22.5 \text{ in}$$

Step 3

Convert Ryan's measure of $\frac{5}{8}$ yd to inches by using an appropriate proportion, where *x* is in inches.

$$\frac{1 \text{ yd}}{36 \text{ in.}} = \frac{\left(\frac{5}{8}\right) \text{yd}}{x}$$
$$x = \frac{5}{8} \times 36$$
$$x = 22.5 \text{ in}$$

Step 4

Convert Arianna's measure of 1 ft11 in. to inches.
$$1 \times 12 + 11 = 23 \text{ in}$$

Step 5

Compare the four students' measures to the actual height of 57.15 cm or 22.5 in.

Megan's measure of 56.15 cm ≠ 57.15 cm. Therefore, her measure is incorrect.

- Ryan's converted measure of $\frac{5}{8}$ yd = 22.5 in.

  Therefore, his measure is correct.

- Arianna's converted measure of 1 ft 11 in. = 23 in. is incorrect.

- Gary's measure of $22\frac{1}{2}$ in. = 22.5 in. Therefore, his measure is correct.

Two students correctly measured the height of the stack.

15. 37.1

The total surface area of the right rectangular pyramid is equal to the sum of the areas of the five regions of the 2-D net. Also, the top triangle and the bottom triangle have the same dimensions, and the right triangle and left triangle have the same dimensions. Therefore, finding the surface area can be broken up into three separate area calculations.

Step 1

Calculate the area of the top triangle and bottom triangle.

$$A_{\text{triangle 1}} = \frac{1}{2}bh$$
$$= \frac{1}{2}(5)(2.5)$$
$$= 6.25 \text{ in}^2$$

Step 2

Calculate the area of the left and right triangle.

$$A_{\text{triangle 2}} = \frac{1}{2}bh$$
$$= \frac{1}{2}(3)(3.2)$$
$$= 4.8 \text{ in}^2$$

Step 3

Calculate the area of the base.

$$A_{\text{base}} = lw$$
$$= (5)(3)$$
$$= 15\text{in}^2$$

Step 4

Calculate the total surface area.

$$SA_{\text{prism}}$$
$$= 2\left(A_{\text{triangle 1}}\right) + 2\left(A_{\text{triangle 2}}\right) + A_{\text{base}}$$
$$= 2(6.25) + 2(4.8) + 15$$
$$= 12.5 + 9.6 + 15$$
$$= 37.1 \text{ in}^2$$

16. A

Step 1

Determine the dimensions of the cone and cylinder.
Find the radius of the cone and cylinder.

$$r = \frac{d}{2}$$
$$= \frac{4}{2}$$
$$= 2 \text{ cm}$$

The height of the cone is 10 cm – 3 cm = 7 cm.

Step 2

Calculate the volume of the cone using the formula
$V_{\text{cone}} = \frac{\pi r^2 h}{3}$.

$$V_{\text{cone}} = \frac{\pi r^2 h}{3}$$
$$= \frac{\pi (2)^2 (7)}{3}$$
$$= 29.3 \text{ cm}^3$$

Step 3

Calculate the volume of the cylinder using the
formula $V_{\text{cylinder}} = \pi r^2 h$.

$$V_{\text{cylinder}} = \pi r^2 h$$
$$= \pi (2)^2 (3)$$
$$= 37.7 \text{ cm}^3$$

Step 4

Calculate the total volume by adding the volumes
together.
29.3 cm³ + 37.7 cm³ = 67.0 cm³

The total volume of the figure is 67.0 cm³.

17. A

Step 1

Find the radius, r, of the sphere.

$$r = \frac{1}{2} \text{diameter}$$
$$= \frac{1}{2}(120)$$
$$= 60 \text{ mm}$$

Step 2

Determine the volume of the gold sphere using the
formula $V = \frac{4\pi r^3}{3}$.

$$V_{\text{sphere}} = \frac{4\pi r^3}{3}$$
$$= \frac{4\pi (60)^3}{3}$$
$$= \frac{4\pi (2160)}{3}$$
$$\approx 904778.6842 \text{ mm}^2$$

Step 3

Determine the height of the right rectangular
prism, h, by using the formula of the volume of a
right prism, $V_{\text{prism}} = A_{\text{base}} \times h$.

$$V_{\text{prism}} = A_{\text{base}} \times h$$
$$904778.6842 = (l \times w) \times h$$
$$904778.6842 = (95 \times 85)h$$
$$904778.6842 = 8\ 075h$$
$$\frac{904\ 778.6842}{8\ 075} = h$$
$$112.046\ 8959 \text{ mm} \approx h$$

To the nearest millimetre, the height of the right
rectangular prism is 112 mm.

18. WR

The surface area, SA, of the cylindrical gasoline
storage tank can be determined by applying the
formula $SA = 2\pi r^2 + 2\pi rh$, where r = the radius
and h = the height, as follows.

$$SA = 2\pi r^2 + 2\pi rh$$

Substitute $\frac{4.8}{2} = 2.4$ for r, 12 for h, and use the π
button on your calculator.

$$SA = 2\pi (2.4)^2 + 2\pi (2.4)(12)$$
$$SA \approx 36.191 + 180.956$$
$$SA \approx 217.147 \text{ m}^2$$

Each can of protective paint can cover an average of
34 m²; therefore, $\frac{217.147}{34} \approx 6.4$ cans of paint would
be required. However, since the protective paint
only comes in whole cans, 7 cans of protective paint
must be purchased. Thus, the cost to cover the entire
surface area of the cylindrical gasoline storage tank
with one coat of protective paint would be
$48.50 × 7 = $339.50.

19. D

The definitions and trigonometric ratios of a right
triangle can be applied to the triangle $\triangle ABC$.

- The hypotenuse is the longest side, and it is across
  from the 90° angle, namely side 3.
- The opposite side is the side across from the given
  angle, θ, namely side 1.
- The adjacent side is the side next to the given
  angle, θ, namely side 2.

Determine the trigonometric ratios for $\triangle ABC$.

$$\sin \theta = \frac{\text{opp}}{\text{hyp}}$$
$$= \frac{\text{side1}}{\text{side3}}$$
$$\cos \theta = \frac{\text{adj}}{\text{hyp}}$$
$$= \frac{\text{side 2}}{\text{side 3}}$$
$$\tan \theta = \frac{\text{opp}}{\text{adj}}$$
$$= \frac{\text{side 1}}{\text{side 2}}$$

For $\triangle ABC$, the statement "the ratio $\tan \theta$ is equal to side 2 divided by side 1" is false.

20. D

Step 1

Calculate the angle inside the triangle at B.

The $138°$ angle is a supplementary angle to $\angle B$ inside the triangle.
$$\angle B = 180° - 138°$$
$$= 42°$$

Step 2

Calculate the length of p using the tangent ratio.

$$\tan \angle B = \frac{\text{opposite}}{\text{adjacent}}$$
$$\tan 42° = \frac{12.2}{p}$$
$$p = \frac{12.2}{\tan 42°}$$
$$p = 13.5 \text{ mm}$$

The length of side p is 13.5 mm.

21. C

Let the distance from the top of the shorter building to the top of the taller building be w. Thus, $y = w + x$.

Step 1

Apply the tangent ratio to solve for x.

$$\tan \theta = \frac{\text{opposite}}{\text{adjacent}}$$
$$\tan 26° = \frac{x}{40}$$
$$x = 40(\tan 26°)$$
$$x \approx 19.509 \text{ m}$$

Step 2

Apply the tangent ratio to solve for w.

$$\tan \theta = \frac{\text{opposite}}{\text{adjacent}}$$
$$\tan 37° = \frac{w}{40}$$
$$w = 40(\tan 37°)$$
$$w \approx 30.142 \text{ m}$$

Step 3

Substitute the values for x and w into the equation $y = w + x$, and solve for y.
$$y \approx 19.509 + 30.142$$
$$y \approx 49.651 \text{ m}$$

Rounded to the nearest tenth of a metre, the height of the taller building is 49.7 m.

22. 56.5

Draw a labelled diagram of the situation, letting $x = $ the distance across the river from A to C.

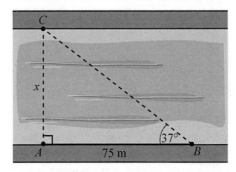

The ratio that includes the opposite and adjacent sides is the tangent ratio.

$$\tan 37° = \frac{x}{75}$$

Multiply both sides by 75
$$75(\tan 37°) = x$$
$$75(0.753\ 554\ 0501) \approx x$$
$$56.5 \approx x$$
$$x \approx 56.5$$

The width of the river, to the nearest tenth of a metre, is 56.5 m.

23. D

The trip starts at port, so the graph must start at (0, 0). Alternatives A and B are eliminated.

There are three stops, so there must be three plateaus where the distance does not increase. Alternatives C and D indicate this. Finally, the boat must return to port where the distance will once again have a y-value of zero. Alternative C is eliminated as it does not show the boat returning to port.

24. D

Label the specified ordered pairs in the graph

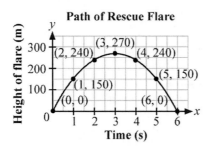

Therefore, graph D is the graph that best represents the information in the table.

25. A

A line falling from left to right has a negative slope. Alternatives C and D can be eliminated.

Since the slope is -1, for every rise of -1 (fall of 1 unit), there should be a run of 1. Only the graph of alternative A displays this slope.

26. B

Slope is given by the $\dfrac{\text{rise}}{\text{run}}$, where rise is represents the total cost and the run represents the number of tickets sold. So, the slope represents the cost per ticket.

27. B

Recall that two lines are perpendicular if their slopes are negative reciprocals; that is, the product of their slopes is -1.
When the slopes of equations I and IV are multiplied, they have a product of -1.

$$3 \times -\frac{1}{3} = -1$$

28. D

To find the constant rate of change of the graph, look at the first differences of the y-values in the table.

n	C
200	
400	$19 - 20 = -1.0$
600	$17.5 - 19 = -1.5$
800	$15.5 - 17.5 = -2.0$
1 000	$13 - 15.5 = -2.5$
1 200	$10 - 13 = -3.0$

Since the first differences are not constant, this relation is non-linear. Also, since the values of the rate of change are negative, the non-linear curve of the graph moves downward from the left to the right of the graph.

29. D

Jacy's daily salary is given by the equation $S = 66 + 6.50n$. The number 6.50 represents the constant rate of change. The correct numerical coefficient of n is 6.50 because every time n increases by 1, the value of S increases by 6.50. Therefore, Jacy's daily salary is given by the equation $S = 66 + 6.50n$, and the constant rate of change is 6.50.

30. A

The equation $3x = 0$, or $x = 0$, represents the y-axis, a vertical line running through an x-intercept of 0. Since this line lies on the y-axis, it has infinite y-intercepts.

31. 20

Step 1
Choose any two points on the graph in order to determine the constant rate of change.
One possible choice is $P(50,\ 80)$ and $Q(100,\ 140)$.

Step 2
Substitute the values of these points into the slope formula, $m = \dfrac{y_2 - y_1}{x_2 - x_1}$, where m is the slope.

$$
\begin{aligned}
m &= \frac{y_2 - y_1}{x_2 - x_1} \\
&= \frac{140 - 80}{100 - 50} \\
&= \frac{60}{50} \\
&= \frac{6}{5}
\end{aligned}
$$

Step 3

Substitute the values of one point and the value of the slope into the slope formula, $m = \dfrac{y_2 - y_1}{x_2 - x_1}$, to find the fixed delivery cost (y-intercept), C, of the point $(0, C)$.

One option is to use the point $(50, 80)$.

$$m = \frac{y_2 - y_1}{x_2 - x_1}$$

$$\frac{6}{5} = \frac{C - 80}{0 - 50}$$

$$\frac{6}{5} = \frac{C - 80}{-50}$$

$$6(-50) = 5(C - 80)$$

$$-300 = 5C - 400$$

$$100 = 5C$$

$$\frac{100}{5} = C$$

$$C = 20$$

To the nearest dollar, the fixed delivery cost (y-intercept) is \$20.

32. D

Step 1

Convert the equation of the given line into the slope-intercept form $y = mx + b$.

$$8x - 7y - 28 = 0$$

$$-7y = 28 - 8x$$

$$y = \frac{28}{-7} - \frac{8x}{-7}$$

$$y = -4 + \frac{8}{7}x$$

$$y = \frac{8}{7}x - 4$$

Step 2

Use the values of the y-intercept and the slope to graph the line.

The slope $\dfrac{8}{7}$ is positive with a y-intercept at -4.

Therefore, graph D represents the line $8x - 7y - 28 = 0$.

33. D

Step 1

Determine the value of m when the equation of the line is written in the form $y = mx + b$.

Since the slope is 12, $m = 12$.

Step 2

Determine the value of b when the equation of the line is written in the form $y = mx + b$.

Since the line passes through the origin, $b = 0$.

Step 3

Write the equation into the form $y = mx + b$.

$y = 12x + 0$, or $y = 12x$

Step 4

Write the equation in general form.

$$y = 12x$$
$$12x - y = 0$$

34. B

The line $x = 5$ is a vertical line passing through the x-axis at $(5, 0)$. A line perpendicular to this line would be a horizontal line of the form $y = b$, where b is the y-coordinate of every point on the line. Since $(-2, 8)$ is on this line, the equation is $y = 8$.

35. C

Step 1

Determine the slope of the parallel line.

Since the required line is parallel to the line defined by the equation $3x + 4y + 5 = 0$, both lines have the same slope.

Rewrite the equation in the form $y = mx + b$ to find the slope of the line defined by the equation $3x + 4y + 5 = 0$.

$$3x + 4y + 5 = 0$$

$$4y = -3x - 5$$

$$y = \frac{-3x}{4} - \frac{5}{4}$$

$$y = -\frac{3}{4}x - \frac{5}{4}$$

The slope of the parallel line is $-\dfrac{3}{4}$.

Step 2

Determine the x-intercept of the line defined by the equation $4x + 5y - 6 = 0$.

Substitute 0 for y in the equation $4x + 5y - 6 = 0$, and solve for x.

$$4x + 5y - 6 = 0$$

$$4x + 5(0) - 6 = 0$$

$$4x - 6 = 0$$

$$4x = 6$$

$$\frac{4x}{4} = \frac{6}{4}$$

$$x = \frac{3}{2}$$

$$x = 1.5$$

Step 3

Determine the equation of the parallel line.

The parallel line passes through the point (1.5, 0). Substitute the values of the x-intercept and slope into the slope-point form of the equation of a line, and convert it to general form.

$$y - y_1 = m(x - x_1)$$
$$y - 0 = -\frac{3}{4}(x - 1.5)$$
$$y = \frac{-3x}{4} + \frac{4.5}{4}$$
$$8(y) = 8\left[\frac{-3x}{4} + \frac{4.5}{4}\right]$$
$$8y = -6x + 9$$
$$6x + 8y - 9 = 0$$

The equation of the parallel line is $6x + 8y - 9 = 0$.

36. A

Step 1

Substitute $1 352, the total annual cost, into the function for $C(n)$.
$$C(n) = 23n + 800$$
$$1\ 352 = 23n + 800$$

Step 2

Solve for n.
$$1\ 352 = 23n + 800$$
$$552 = 23n$$
$$24 = n$$

Stacey played 24 rounds of golf at Hidden Valley Golf Course in the given year.

37. 75

Step 1

Substitute -4 for x in the function
$f(x) = -2x - 11$.
$$f(x) = -2x - 11$$
$$f(-4) = -2(-4) - 11$$

Step 2

Evaluate $f(-4)$.
$$f(-4) = -2(-4) - 11$$
$$= 8 - 11$$
$$= -3$$

Step 3

Substitute 10 for x in the function $g(x) = 6x + 18$.
$$g(x) = 6x + 18$$
$$g(10) = 6(10) + 18$$

Step 4

Evaluate $g(10)$.
$$g(10) = 6(10) + 18$$
$$= 60 + 18$$
$$= 78$$

Step 5

Calculate the sum of $f(-4)$ and $g(10)$.
$$f(-4) + g(10) = -3 + 78$$
$$= 75$$

38. C

Step 1

Create an equation for the total weight of the two blends.

① $x + y = 10$

Step 2

Create an equation for the total amount of sales.

- Let $6.40x$ be the amount made on the Orange Blossom tea.
- Let $7.20y$ be the amount made on the Red Dragon tea.
- The amount made on the blended tea is $67.20 ($6.72 \times 10 = 67.20$).

② $6.40x + 7.20y = 67.20$

This system of linear equations can be solved to determine the amounts of tea needed.
① $\qquad x + y = 10$
② $6.40x + 7.20y = 67.20$

39. B

Step 1

Label the equations.
① $\quad x + y = 365$
② $\quad 3x + 2y = 925$

Step 2

Multiply both sides of equation (1) by 2.
$2 \times$ ① $2x + 2y = 730$
$\qquad$ ② $3x + 2y = 925$

Step 3

Subtract the two equations, and solve for x.
$$2x + 2y = 730$$
$$\underline{3x + 2y = 925}$$
$$-x + 0y = -195$$
$$x = 195$$

Step 4

Substitute 195 for x in one of the equations. In this case, use equation (1).
$$x + y = 365$$
$$195 + y = 365$$

Step 5

Solve for y.
$$195 + y = 365$$
$$y = 170$$

Rebecca must replace x with 195 and y with 170 in both equations.

40. A

After hiking for 7 h, hiker A is farther away (3.2 km) from the base camp than hiker B (2.8 km). Since the lines are linear, the lines will not intersect after more than 4 h have gone by. Therefore, hiker A will reach the top of the mountain first, making the statement "Hiker A travels faster then hiker B and will reach the top of the mountain first" correct.

Hiker A travels up the mountain at a faster rate than hiker B. This is visible on the graph as the steeper line representing hiker A, compared to the line representing hiker B. This makes the statements "Hiker B travels faster than hiker A and will reach the top of the mountain first" and "Hiker B starts farther from the base camp than hiker A, and he travels faster than hiker A" incorrect.

Looking at the graph, hiker B starts farther from the base camp than hiker B. This makes the statement "Hiker A starts farther from the base camp than hiker B, and he travels faster than hiker B" incorrect.

41. 18

Step 1
Label the equations.
① $5x + y = 93$
② $2x + y = 48$

Step 2
Solve the system by elimination. Subtract equation ② from equation ① .

$$\begin{array}{r} ① \quad 5x + y = 93 \\ ② \quad 2x + y = 48 \\ \hline 3x + 0 = 45 \end{array}$$

$$x = \frac{45}{3}$$
$$x = 15$$

Step 3
To find y, substitute 15 for x in one of the equations. In this case, use equation ② .

$$2x + y = 48$$
$$2(15) + y = 48$$
$$30 + y = 48$$
$$y = 48 - 30$$
$$y = 18$$

The value of y is 18.

42. a) WR

Step 1
Determine Jackie's initial distance from the hardware store.
Jackie lives 600 m from the hardware store. Therefore, the initial value is 600.

Step 2
Determine the constant rate of change of the line. Jackie bikes at a speed of 5 m/s. Calculate the distance she covers in 10 s.
The value is negative because she is getting closer to the hardware store.

$$\frac{-5 \times 10\text{m}}{1 \times 10\text{s}} = -50\text{m}/10\text{s}$$

Step 3
Build a table of values.
Calculate the values by subtracting 50 m for every 10-second interval. The following table is a partial table of the values.

Time (s)	Distance from Store (m)
0	600
10	600 − 50 = 550
20	550 − 50 = 500
30	500 − 50 = 450

Step 4
Use the table of values and plot the points on the graph. Draw a line through the points.
The given graph shows the line of Jackie's progress toward the hardware store.

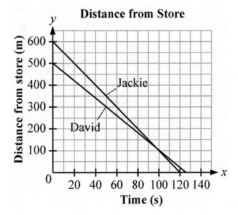

b) WR

This graph shows David's and Jackie's progress.

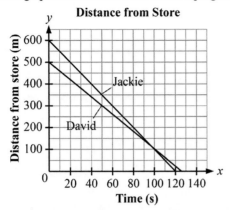

The point of intersection is at (100, 100).
The x-coordinate represents the time both Jackie and David pedalled ($t = 100$s). The y-coordinate represents the distance from the store ($d = 100$m).

This point of intersection represents the time and the distance from the store where Jackie catches up to David.

NOTES

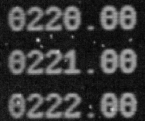

0211.00
0212.00
0213.00
0214.00
0215.00
0216.00
0217.00
0218.00
0219:00
0220.00
0221.00
0222:00
0223.00
0224:00

FORMULA SHEET

MEASUREMENT

Right Triangles

Pythagorean theorem: $\qquad\qquad\qquad c^2 = a^2 + b^2$

Primary trigonometric ratios:

Sine ratio: $\sin A = \dfrac{\text{opposite}}{\text{hypotenuse}}$

Cosine ratio: $\cos A = \dfrac{\text{adjacent}}{\text{hypotenuse}}$

Tangent ratio: $\tan A = \dfrac{\text{opposite}}{\text{adjacent}}$

ALGEBRA AND NUMBER

Exponent Laws

Product of powers law: $\qquad x^m \times x^n = x^{m+n}$

Quotient of powers law: $\qquad x^m \div x^n = x^{m-n},\ x \neq 0$

Power of powers law: $\qquad (xy)^m = x^m y^m$

Power of quotient law: $\qquad \left(\dfrac{x}{y}\right)^m = \dfrac{x^m}{y^m},\ y \neq 0$

Powers with zero exponent: $\qquad x^0 = 1,\ x \neq 0$

Powers with negative exponent: $\qquad x^{-n} = \left(\dfrac{1}{x}\right)^n \text{ or } \dfrac{1}{x^n},\ x \neq 0$

Powers with rational exponent: $\qquad x^{\frac{m}{n}} = \sqrt[n]{x^m} \text{ or } \left(\sqrt[n]{x}\right)^m$

Radicals

Multiplication property: $\qquad \sqrt[n]{xy} = \sqrt[n]{x} \times \sqrt[n]{y}$

Division property: $\qquad \sqrt[n]{\dfrac{x}{y}} = \dfrac{\sqrt[n]{x}}{\sqrt[n]{y}},\ y \neq 0$

Expanding Polynomials

Distributive property: $\qquad a(x + y) = ax + ay$

Factoring polynomials

Perfect square trinomials:
$$a^2 + 2ab + b^2 = (a+b)(a+b)$$
$$a^2 - 2ab + b^2 = (a-b)(a-b)$$

Difference of squares: $\qquad a^2 - b^2 = (a-b)(a+b)$

RELATIONS AND FUNCTIONS

Slope of Line(s)

Slope formula:

$$m = \frac{\text{rise}}{\text{run}}$$
$$= \frac{y_2 - y_1}{x_2 - x_1}$$

Horizontal line: $\quad m = 0$

Vertical line: $\quad m = \text{undefined}$

Parallel lines: $\quad m_1 = m_2$

Perpendicular lines: $\quad m_2 = -\dfrac{1}{m_1}$

Equation of a line

Slope-intercept form: $\quad y = mx + b$

Slope-point form: $\quad y - y_1 = m(x - x_1)$

General form: $\quad Ax + By + C = 0$

FORMULAS—GEOMETRICAL SHAPES

2-D Shape	Perimeter (circumference)	Area
Rectangle	$P_{rectangle} = 2(l + w)$	$A_{rectangle} = lw$
Parallelogram	$P_{parallelogram} = 2(a + b)$	$A_{parallelogram} = bh$
Triangle	$P_{triangle} = a + b + c$	$A_{triangle} = \dfrac{bh}{2}$
Trapezoid	$P_{trapezoid} = a + b + c + d$	$A_{trapezoid} = \dfrac{(a + b)h}{2}$
Circle	$C_{circle} = 2\pi r$ or πd	$A_{circle} = \pi r^2$

3-D Shape	Surface Area	Volume
Right Prism Base (polygon), Lateral face, h	$SA_{prism} = A_{bases} + A_{lateral\ face}$ $= 2(A_{base}) + hP_{base}$, where $P =$ perimeter	$V_{prism} = (A_{base})h$
Right Cylinder Base (circle), Lateral face, h, r	$SA_{cylinder} = A_{bases} + A_{lateral\ face}$ $= 2\pi r^2 + 2\pi rh$	$V_{cylinder} = (A_{base})h$ $= \pi r^2 h$
Right Pyramid Triangular face, Base (polygon), h, s, b	$SA_{pyramid} = A_{base} + A_{triangular\ faces}$ $= A_{base} + n\left(\dfrac{bs}{2}\right)$, where $n =$ number of faces	$V_{pyramid} = \dfrac{(A_{base})h}{3}$
Right Cone Lateral face, Base (circle), s, r	$SA_{cone} = A_{base} + A_{lateral\ face}$ $= \pi r^2 + \pi rs$	$V_{cone} = \dfrac{(A_{base})h}{3}$ $= \dfrac{\pi r^2 h}{3}$
Sphere Face, r	$SA_{sphere} = A_{face}$ $= 4\pi r^2$	$V_{sphere} = \dfrac{4\pi r^3}{3}$

Unit Conversions – Length

SI Unit Conversions	
Unit	**Multiplier**
Kilometre (km)	1 000
Hectometre (hm)	100
Decametre (dam)	10
Metre (m)	1
Decimetre (dm)	0.1
Centimetre (cm)	0.01
Millimetre (mm)	0.001

Imperial Unit Conversions
1 mile (mi) = 1 760 yd = 5 280 ft
1 yard (yd) = 3 ft = 36 in
1 foot (ft) = 12 in

Conversions Between SI and Imperial Units	
Imperial to SI	**SI to Imperial**
1 in = 2.54 cm	1 cm ≈ 0.3937 in
1 ft = 0.3048 m	1 m ≈ 3.28084 ft ≈ 1.0936 yd
1 yd = 0.9144 m	
1 mi = 1.609344 km	1 km ≈ 0.62137 mi

Number Lines

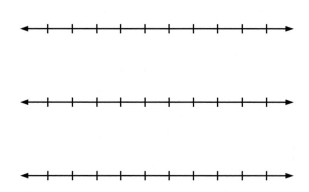

RIGHT SQUARE-BASED PYRAMID

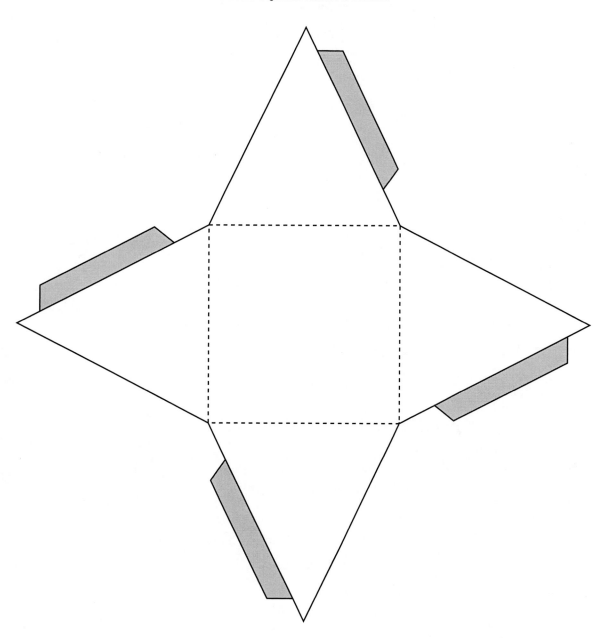

RIGHT CYLINDER

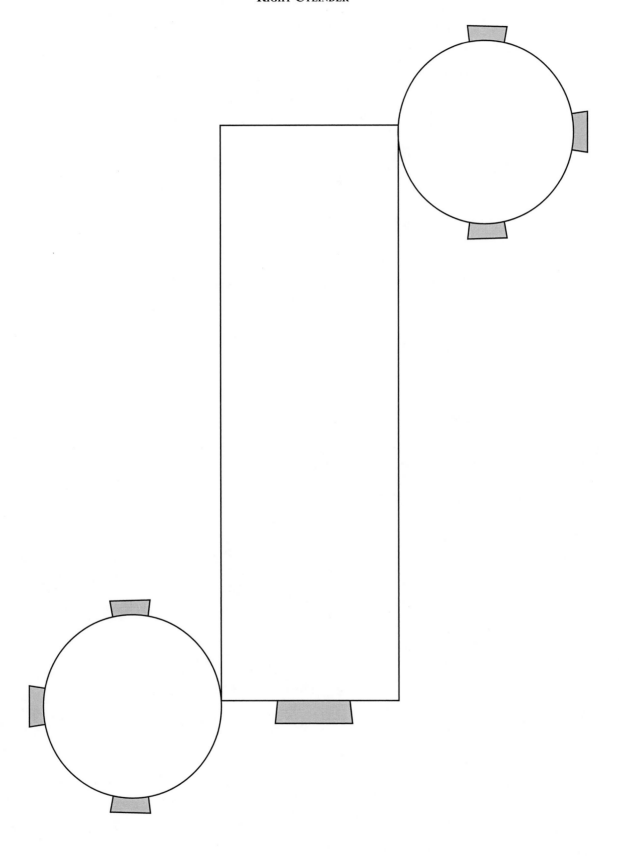

ALGEBRA TILES

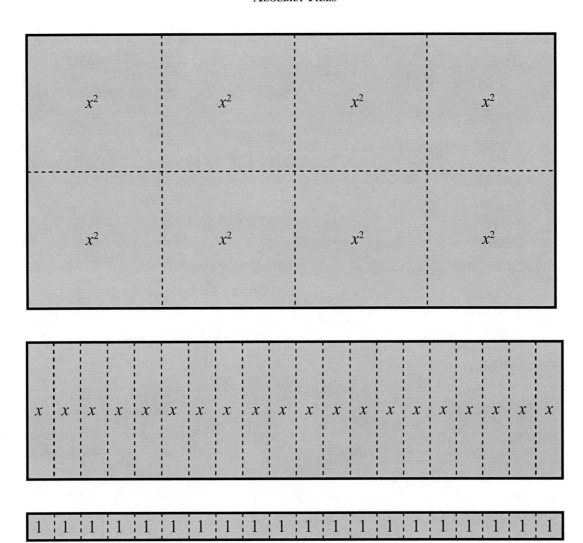

ALGEBRA TILES

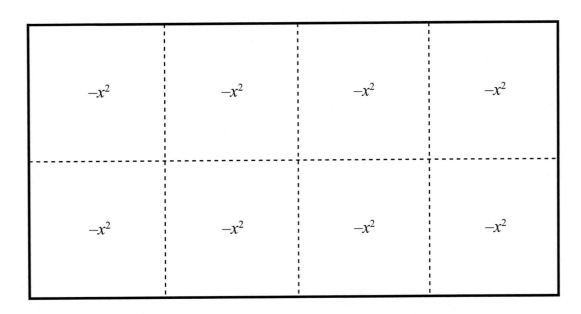

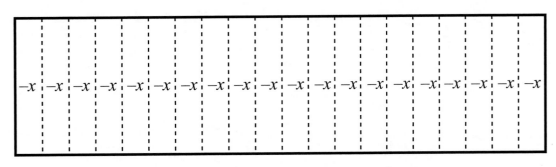

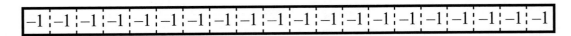

16 × 16 Grids

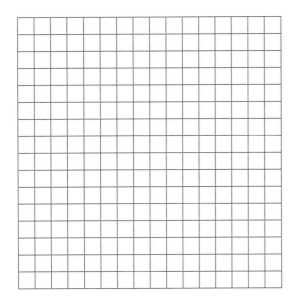

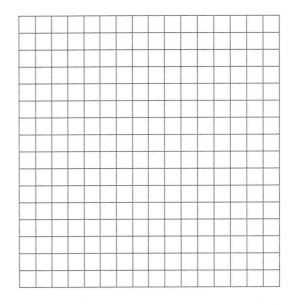

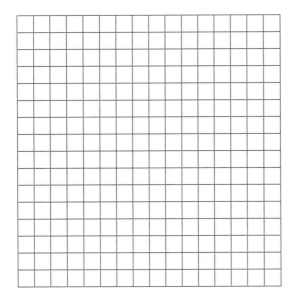

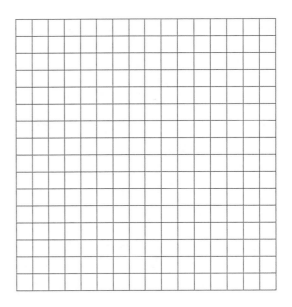

16 × 16 Grids

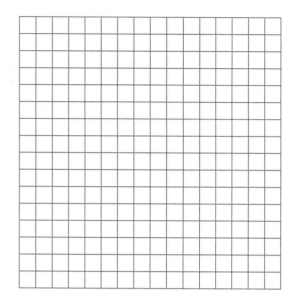

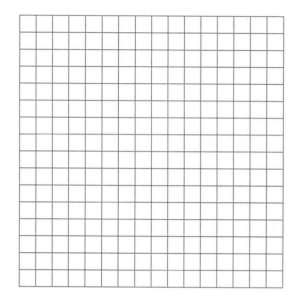

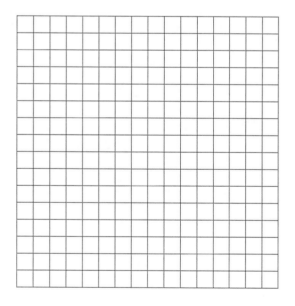

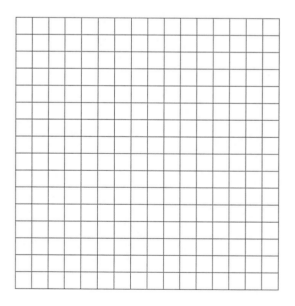

NOTES

NOTES

NOTES

NOTES

NOTES

NOTES